ORIENTATION
TO
LANGUAGE
AND
LEARNING
DISORDERS

ORIENTATION
TO
LANGUAGE
AND
LEARNING
DISORDERS

Edited by

MITCHELL R. BURKOWSKY, Ph.D.

Associate Professor of Education
State University of New York College
at Fredonia

WARREN H. GREEN, INC.

St. Louis, Missouri, U.S.A.

Published by

WARREN H. GREEN, INC.
10 South Brentwood Blvd.
St. Louis, Missouri 63105, U.S.A.

Library of Congress Catalog Card No. 75-176182

Printed in the United States of America
208

THE AUTHORS

Frank W. Broadbent, Ed. D., is presently Associate Professor in Elementary Education at Syracuse University. His varied educational experiences include classroom teaching in the intermediate grades, development of a teacher training program in problems of teaching, supervision of student teaching, college and university teaching, and direction of a Title III project for low achievers in mathematics.

Mitchell R. Burkowsky, Ph. D., formerly of the Division of Special Education and Rehabilitation at Syracuse University, is Associate Professor of Education, State University of New York College at Fredonia. He has been an elementary school speech correctionist, teacher and administrator in an Army education center, Director of the University of North Dakota Speech and Hearing Clinic, and has worked extensively with foreign students, deaf, autistic, mentally retarded and emotionally disturbed children in addition to conducting several workshops for in-service teachers, administrators and parents of children with learning problems. He has also held a post-doctoral fellowship in Communicative Disorders at the University of Florida.

Jane L. Clarke, A. B., is Director of a special project in dyslexia for the Children's Aid Society of Erie County, and heads a private program for children with learning disabilities in Buffalo—CAC Tutorial Systems. Her previous experiences include being a reconstructive language teacher in the South Wales, N.Y., school system and Head of the Reading Department in the Niagara Falls, N.Y., school system.

W. Scott Curtis, Ph. D., formerly Administrator, Speech Pathology program at Syracuse University, is presently Professor and Chairman of Audiology and Speech Pathology at the University of Georgia in Athens, Georgia. For the past several years, he has been especially concerned with problems of multiply handicapped deaf-blind children, and with Dr. Donlon, has deeply investigated needs in the areas of diagnosis and habilitation for such children.

Theodore Di Buono, M. D., is Deputy Director of the Syracuse State School, Director of Community Services for Syracuse State School (New York State Division of Mental Hygiene), Clinical Assistant Professor in the Department of Pediatrics at the State University of New York Upstate Medical Center, and Lecturer, Division of Special Education, Syracuse University. He has served as: Director, Birth Defects Clinic, Syracuse Memorial—Crouse Irving Hospital; Director, Pediatric Referral Center, State University of New York Upstate Medical Center, and Director, Special Evaluation Clinic for Children with Learning Disabilities, State University of New York Upstate Medical Center. A diplomate of the National Board of Examiners and of the American Board of Pediatrics, he also held a fellowship in the Children's Psychiatric Service at Johns Hopkins Hospital.

Edward T. Donlon, Ed. D., served for several years as Co-ordinator of the program for the Deaf-Blind and Multiply Handicapped at Syracuse University. In addition to having been an elementary school teacher and principal, he is a certified school psychologist, was a clinical psychologist in the Children's Division of Syracuse Psychiatric Hospital, and has been consultant to several agencies concerned with blind, deaf-blind and multiply handicapped children. He and Dr. Curtis have collaborated on several studies in the area of multiply handicapped deaf-blind children. He is President of Limerick Enterprises, a private educational rehabilitation firm.

Pamela Ferraro, M. A., has recently moved from Syracuse to Charlotte, North Carolina. She has taught History and Remedial Reading in the public schools, and has also been a school psychologist. She served in dual reading and psychological roles with the Special Evaluation Clinic for Children with Learning Disabilities at the State University of New York Upstate Medical Center and was Senior Reading Clinician at the Syracuse University Reading Clinic. She has published in the area of interdisciplinary approaches to reading difficulties, and has taught in the Reading department of Syracuse University. Presently, she is a developmental specialist with the Charlotte Pediatric Clinic and an Instructor in Reading at the University of North Carolina at Charlotte.

Ruth R. Gossett, A. C. S. W., is Assistant Professor of Social Work and Associate Director of Field Instruction at Syracuse University. She has worked extensively as a social worker in urban areas, interacting with an astounding variety of community agencies. In addition to her other duties, she supervises the social work components of the Syracuse University Psychoeducational Teaching Laboratory.

Elizabeth A. Lawrence, Ph. D., is Associate Professor of Special Education at Western Michigan University. She is a former teacher of cerebral palsied children in Westchester County, New York, and was a demonstration teacher with brain-injured children and Lecturer at Illinois State Normal University at Normal, Illinois. Dr. Lawrence has also served on the faculty of the Exceptional Children Education Division, State University College at Buffalo. Prior to her present position, she taught at Syracuse University.

D. Roger Meehan, Ed. D., is Director, EDPA Project, Maryland State Education Department. He was formerly Supervisor of Special Classes, Butler County, Pennsylvania, and for six years was a public school teacher of the mentally retarded.

Daniel D. Sage, Ed. D., is Associate Professor of Special Education and Co-ordinator, Special Education Administration Training Program, School of Education, Syracuse University. He was formerly a school psychologist and administrator of special education programs in Hayword, California, and has been a classroom teacher in elementary, secondary and special education in the public schools.

Sandra L. Smith, Ph. D., was a clinician in the Syracuse University Learning Center, a psychologist in Head Start programs in Syracuse, and School Psychologist in the Liverpool, New York, School District. Currently, she is Psychologist for the United Cerebral Palsy and Handicapped Children's Association, Inc., in Syracuse.

James F. Winschel, Ed. D., is Associate Professor of Special Education, Division of Special Education and Rehabilitation, Syracuse University. He served as a teacher of mentally retarded and disadvantaged children for more than ten years with the Pittsburgh, Pennsylvania, public schools, and was formerly on the faculty of the Exceptional Children Education Division, State University College at Buffalo.

PREFACE

The authors of the chapters in this book were selected in terms of one primary consideration: they have all been on the "front lines" working either with children who have learning and adjustment problems or with teachers and ancillary personnel who deal with such children. The major guideline for writing was: "write your chapter in the style that is most comfortable for you!" Therefore the writing styles vary somewhat from chapter to chapter and even within chapters.

You, the reader, are encouraged to compare your experiences and thoughts with those of the chapter authors, to disagree with us if you think we are wrong, and to realize that *no* authority figure knows the entire and objective truth about any area of specialization. In other words, any person intelligent enough to read this book is probably intelligent enough to become a specialist or "authority" in these or similar areas. It is not difficult to help children prepare to learn better. It is more difficult to convince yourself that *you* have the ability to do so. Please realize that you, even before you read the rest of this book, have many skills and insights that may be used to help many children learn. Don't be afraid to try!

ACKNOWLEDGMENTS

Many people have contributed directly or indirectly to this book—too many for all to be listed by name. Administrators who facilitated activities and concept formation include David Krathwohl, James Manwaring and Burton Blatt of the Syracuse University School of Education, and Julius Richmond, formerly Dean of the State University of New York Upstate Medical Center. Among other friends whose input is appreciated are Bill Anderson, Ellen Barnes, Heather Campbell, Dale Chadwick, Linda Chaput, Charlotte Church, Anne Cooney, Raymond Domenico, Byron Egeland, Emily Goldman, Suzanne Grant, Frank Greene, Carol Jennison, Peter Knoblock, Barbara Newton, Peter Rynders, David Shepard, Sally Timberlake, Ken Winer and Eva Woolfolk.

Refinements of concepts in Chapter Eight reflect the influences of workshop groups on the Syracuse University campus and at off-campus centers at Camillus, Elmira, Fairport, Geneva and Utica, New York. Other workshop groups met in Johnson City and New Hartford, New York, the latter under the auspices of the Mohawk Valley Learning Disabilities Association.

My wife, Diane, has been unfailing in her patient support and consideration during the two years this project has been in progress. Without her encouragement it might not have been completed. Without the influence of Frank Greene (presently of McGill University) it would never have been started. I am especially grateful to my daughter, Ruth, who helped me with the indexing to the detriment of her vacation.

Mitchell R. Burkowsky
Fredonia, New York

CONTENTS

xiii

ORIENTATION
TO
LANGUAGE
AND
LEARNING
DISORDERS

Chapter I

LEARNING DISABILITIES: A CRITICAL EXPOSURE

JAMES F. WINSCHEL
and
ELIZABETH A. LAWRENCE

INTRODUCTION

This movement, as in so many other professional areas, has more sound than fury, more unanswered questions than solutions, more ambiguity than direction, more clinical "guestimates" than researched postulates, more room for growth and development than self-righteousness and complacency, and undoubtedly more inappropriate than appropriate services.

Maietta (1969)

Learning disability is only a label; yet debates in the fields of medicine, psychology and education question its meaning and challenge its implications. *Learning disability* is largely an unknown; yet into this void the professional press spews praise and contempt alike, largely without direction, meaning or accomplishment. *Learning disability* may be an educational nightmare and a professional fraud or merely an expedient joke upon a status-hungry teaching profession. *Learning disability* may benefit some —the professional educator indulging his genius, teachers excluding difficult pupils, companies producing expensive gadgetry— but less often has it benefited the very children in whose behalf we have pursued our selfish interests. It is this ultimate paradox which has spurred the debates and fanned the controversies. It is this dilemma which we must face, and for which answers must be found.

In the history of education, we have successively resorted to

3

excluding, or at least stigmatizing, the blind and the deaf, the crippled and retarded, the poor and the black. The inclusiveness of the *learning disability* label suggests that we are as much broadening our attack upon the dignity of the learner as we are coming to grips with the difficult problems of instruction. Labeling — never a process of bringing us together — has consistently fragmented instruction into categories of fortunate and unfortunate, can do and can't do, normal and abnormal. One suspects that an old breed of bigot is again loose in our schools working a new magic, with *learning disabilities* as its guise and children as its victims.

Nevertheless, one must acknowledge that some children do have demonstrable learning disorders not easily explained by ordinary models, nor easily dealt with through typical instructional practices. It is for these children that the *learning disabilities* movement with its concern for diagnosis and remediation holds the most promise, not as a new label but rather as a new approach to instruction which is not only tolerant of diversity, but genuinely welcomes differences in learning style. The *learning disabilities* concept offers us a rare chance to examine our educational conscience, and an even rarer opportunity for creative action. As Barsch (1968) wrote:

> To pursue a course of defining a category to be fitted among other existing categories constitutes an entrapment in traditional thought. To treat learning disabilities as a concept instead of a category represents an opportunity to consider an entirely new set of dimensions and parameters. It is an exciting opportunity for creative thought in education and should not be ignored. (p. 14)

"The chief strength of the emphasis on learning disabilities," wrote Ernest Siegel (1968), "would seem to be that it makes a renewed plea for good teaching, i.e., teaching based on an understanding of the child's needs as well as an awareness of what the specific task entails and a recognition of its sequential components" (p. 437). It is not that one doubts that children with learning disorders are present in our schools — most certainly they are — but rather that among the diverse reasons for the learning difficulties such children manifest is the instructional system itself.

Labeling, segregating, excusing, ignoring, along with poor teaching, all contribute.

This introduction is not intended as an assault upon education and teachers, but rather a defense of children (who are so often victimized by labels). The *concept* of learning disabilities is undoubtedly useful. But we need to pause, if ever so briefly, before clasping it to ourselves as solace for the shortcomings of a sometimes weary and outmoded educational enterprise.

FOCUS ON HISTORY

The child with a learning disability is a child of history. He is only of this time because man is of this time—but he is not new.
Barsch (1968)

Scripture has it that in the beginning was the word, and the word was made flesh; but in *learning disorders* we have reversed the biblical adage. That is, in the beginning was the flesh, and the flesh was made word. Children with disorders in learning have always been with us, and likely man's ascent to civilization was slowed by their presence in the populations of prehistory. Yet it is with an air of discovery that we have identified children with rather unglamorous patterns of failure, and with a note of triumph have characterized them as *learning disabilities*. Naming, after all, has always won acceptance when explanation was not easily available.

Prior to the twentieth century, individual differences in ability to learn were little heeded by the educational establishment; survival of the fittest ruled the classroom, and exclusion was the price one paid for academic inaptitude or clumsiness. The advent of the child labor laws and compulsory school attendance brought an influx of new students, and forced schools to confront the deviant learner. The mental testing movement, nourished by the contributions of Binet and others, was education's expedient response. Its purpose was to maintain the purity of the educational enterprise through the efficient elimination—not of the grossly unfit who were always easy to identify—but rather of those marginally manageable learners who were not easily molded to the methodology of their times. It was inevitable, perhaps, that in the normal course of history we have since come to view the child as defective, rather than the method.

While many children were classified, excluded, or otherwise shunted aside, it was not until the publication of *Aftereffects of Brain Injuries in War,* in 1942, that Kurt Goldstein inadvertently laid the groundwork for a challenge to the inviolate nature of educational pedagogy, and heralded the emergence of the learning disabilities movement almost two decades later. As he studied soldiers who had sustained head injuries, Goldstein noted that even when physical recovery from brain damage appeared complete, such individuals continued to manifest disorders of behavior which included perceptual disturbances, emotional lability, and distractibility. Shortly thereafter, Alfred Strauss reported similar disorders of behavior which appeared characteristic of certain retarded children at the Cove Schools. These behaviors were presumed to be the result of brain damage etiologically implicated in their retardation.

With the publication in 1947 of the Strauss and Lehtinen classic, *Psychopathology and Education of the Brain Injured Child,* a seemingly new breed of learner made his debut on the educational stage where he held the attention of significant portions of the medical, education, and psychological professions for the next twenty years. The rapid and overwhelming acceptance of the "brain injured" child as reality rather than a pragmatically useful, but theoretical, concept was undoubtedly enhanced by the extensive instructional techniques which were supplied by the above authors, and devoured voraciously by a teaching profession eager for the "final solution" to a host of instructional quandaries. However, as it became apparent that brain injury was too often an organically unsubstantiated assumption and, as many children failed to respond to the new methodology, the professions (as always, equal to the task of coining new and terrifying terms) have largely substituted the child with *learning disabilities* for the *brain injured child.* It would seem that we had once again sought to solve a problem by giving it a name. As stated by McCarthy and McCarthy (1969):

> The term *learning disabilities* began appearing with regularity in the early 1960's largely as a substitute for *brain-*

injured. By referring to behavior rather than etiology, the term *learning disability* circumvented objections. . . . However, the logical inconsistencies associated with the concept of the brain injured child were not dissipated by the act of providing it a new name (p. 3).

Let there be no doubt; we believe that the child with learning disabilities is with us, in concept if not in reality, and he must be confronted by the educators of our day. As a child of history, he may be reinterpreted, and the chronology of his being reordered, but as a child of our times he cannot be denied. Socrates knew him; he was probably the first to fail the Socratic method. Jesus must have met him for he is surely a lesson in divine patience, tolerance, and love. And Columbus must have been aware of his presence—a speck of mankind constantly afoul of the rigging. Only the Phonecians, those ancient inventors of the alphabet, and Gutenberg who capitalized on the invention seemed unaware of his presence, else they would not have perpetrated a monstrous symbolism upon an imperfect species. Today, the ever increasing tempo of the presses, and the accelerated use of abstract symbols, as in the new math or the language of computers, has made us still more aware of learning disabilities at all levels of social endeavor. Education in particular has been perturbed by the child at odds with routine diagnosis and instruction; troubled by an organism unknowingly in search of something unique in education and stubborn in its resistance to the usual. In similar vein, Maietta (1969) has written:

> Although many professional organizations prefer to wink at the learning disabilities movement, anticipate its rapid decay or decline, or simply dismiss the existence of children identified by various labels implying brain dysfunction, the unalterable fact faces society that too many children in and out of schools have ways of learning that do not respond to the usual methods utilized in most current educational settings (p. 245).

History has always had its learners who have appeared marginal or disordered, but only in our age have we begun to focus on the nature of the problem, and only now do we see the outline of a developing picture. It suggests not so much a different method for a defective child, but rather a different child, the victim of defective method. History gives us but a brief chance to change that picture; tomorrow we will have moved on.

FOCUS ON DEFINITION

> More often than not labels conceal more of the nature and the treatment needs of a human being than they reveal. Although they may be accurate and informative, they are less often helpful.
>
> Blatt (1969)

Attempts to define *learning disabilities* have probably consumed more of the intellectual energies of interested professionals than have all other aspects of the problem combined. Typically, the multiplicity of definitions are prefixed by apologetic qualifiers indicating the opinion-level status of the definition and its personal-pragmatic usage. "Compounding the problem," wrote Maietta (1969), "are the vested interests of many professional groups anticipating loss of power or prestige if their causes and definitions are not constantly kept before the eyes of the public and those with special influence" (p. 246). And one could add that the personal bias of individual professionals against the labeling process seldom inhibits the enthusiasm with which they define the label once it has become attached to children.

As one probes the labyrinth of definitions that pervade the professional literature, it becomes apparent that *learning disability* is variously defined to suit the research and funding needs, convictions, or whimsey of individual authors. The attempt to develop a single definition, engaged in publicly midst an aura of sincerity and cooperation, runs contrary to the promotion of individual professional reputations and is, therefore, unlikely to succeed. Fortunately, a single definition, codified by general consensus, is not necessary if one understands that all definitions have reference to a discrepancy between anticipated and perceived achievement in a child who is not easily categorized by the more standard classifications of exceptionality. The presumption is made that this disparity reflects the child's deficiency in one or more of the essential learning processes of perception, integration, and expression, and that the identification and remediation of same will accrue to the overall benefit of the child. This latter assumption is both challenging and challengable, and needs to be debated in greater detail than has been evident to this time.

The problem with definition lies in its peculiar ability to add sting to terms which might otherwise remain understandable and relatively harmless. "Dumb" kids are largely accepted by other children; the mentally retarded are shunned, ridiculed, and tormented. Smart children may be envied a mite, but the gifted are cause for hostility and disdain. In like manner, the stutterer is a child whose speech at one time was merely "funny" or at worst a trifle odd. The essential difference between the commonly understood terms and the more professionally accepted labels lies in the capacity of the latter to hurt and stigmatize by severing the child from an ordinarily accepted range of normality. Only the naive would suggest that the majority of children so defined have been better off for our definitions. So it may be with *learning disabilities;* a term with the potential to cover an almost unlimited range of real or imagined problems of learning is bound to find these problems in abundance in children so defined.

The negative effect of identification and definition and the social implications of the labeling process as it pertains to learning disabilities can hardly be overemphasized. As Towne and Joiner (1968) stated:

> ... The meaning of the label "learning disabled" (or of "cerebral dysfunction," "Neurological handicap," "brain injury," or whatever other terms may be applied) will expand beyond the set of diagnostic behaviors that define the category so that the child is now thought of as being generally personally defective rather than as a child deficient in specific learning skills.
>
> Thus, whatever the label means to others, regardless of its accuracy or connection with the child's immediate behavior, each person's expectations and interpretations of the child's behavior will be affected by his definition of what this kind of person is supposed to be like (p. 219).

That people see what they expect to see is a well documented psychological phenomenon, and almost any trial lawyer can testify that witnesses often remember—vividly—what they think they *ought* to remember. Unfortunately, these processes of self-delusion often occur in schools to the detriment of children. In the minds of teachers and others, a child identified as having a specific problem is immediately recognized as having a host of concomitant problems typically associated with the original. This spread effect can and does take place in the total absence of the associated deficits.

The scenario for the above charade is as deceptively reasonable in tone as it is vicious in application: a child of supposed normal intelligence is experiencing difficulty in maintaining grade level progress in reading. He is not known to have physical, emotional, or motivational difficulties which could account for the problem. As a matter of fact, efforts to diagnose such deficiencies prove negative. The adequacy of instruction is not contested as most children in his class are progressing as expected. Further observation of the child suggests some deficiency in auditory memory span, although one notes that this observation is first made after the search for an explanation to the reading problem has begun. Additional testing seems to confirm the auditory deficiency and, in the absence of other indications of deviance, a tentative diagnosis of specific learning disability is made.

The preliminary diagnosis seems to generate its own support. Teachers now seem to recall that the child manifested other behaviors which at the time seemed quite normal but which on reflection take on the mystic air of abnormality. Natural exuberance becomes hyperactivity; normal aggression becomes emotional lability; occasional inattention, distractibility; and childhood clumsiness, general incoordination. And woe to the student who was, on occasion, impulsive, for impulsivity is but another indication of learning disorders.

It should be obvious to the reader that most children with learning disabilities are not born; they are manufactured by a well-meaning education industry. More often than not a learning disability is, in reality, a deficiency of the educational enterprise; it is above all a failure of the school rather than a deficit of the child. In common terms it is the inability of personnel responsible for diagnosis and evaluation to harmonize their estimate of a child's ability with their assessment of achievement following the child's exposure to a regimen of ordinary instruction. Education, psychology, and to a lesser extent medicine—often at loggerheads over the problems of diagnosis and pedagogy—have joined forces to exceptionalize large numbers of children who might otherwise progress through our schools as normal, even if sometimes haltingly and unsure. It is a paradox of the greatest significance that in our attempt to help the child we make exceptions out of the rules, find problems that don't exist, deprive children of their valued anonymity, and destroy the confidence of teachers in their ability to deal normally with the outposts of normal variation.

FOCUS ON DIAGNOSIS

> We take it for granted that society assigns roles in a reasonable way and that those who fail to fulfill roles have something wrong with them. I think we have grounds for questioning this assumption.
>
> McCarthy & McCarthy (1969)

Jean Marc Itard is dead! Pinel is gone, as are Esquirol and Seguin. Few remember their names, and none mourn their passing. Montessori and Binet are household words, but they, too, have long since passed away. We admit that our sense of loss is more romantic than real, more wistful than relevant. Yet these were clinicians of the first magnitude, and one rather believes that diagnosis was, to them, more a sacred undertaking than a task to be performed. The human quality these clinicians personified has been largely lost, for today technology runs unrestrained through education and psychology, and those with the potential for greatness have taken up residence in the market place where they hawk their wares in mockery of the diagnostic tradition they had so amply inherited.

The apparent demise of the diagnostic tradition as a human relationship between clinician and client was exposed by Engel (1969) when she wrote:

> Diagnosis has become synonymous with testing, and this is part of many contemporary shifts away from substance to

technology: in this shift the "how" defines the "what" and tools define the questions to be asked of nature, as though the technology of science has pre-existed to science itself and is not really born of it. Thus the typical student in search of a thesis is not out of place if he begins with a test—a statistical or a clinical test—at any event he begins with a tool—then scouts for a question that can be asked with that tool. Were we to rewrite the history of science in this vein, we would have a Galileo with telescope in hand, anxious to find something to look at, and at his advisor's suggestion, finding the sky a likely means by which to demonstrate the utility of his tool (p. 231).

In spite of the present state of the art, the commitment to the diagnostic process remains strong, and comprehensive diagnosis is generally acknowledged as the precursor of adequate remediation.

While the efficacy of remediation based on diagnostically established deficits remains stubbornly resistant to proof (Bateman, 1966), it is widely assumed that amelioration must eventually proceed along this path. Adequate diagnosis is seen, therefore, as a crucial aspect of the habilitation process, and the commitment to assessment as necessary as the more obvious obligation to remediation. Emerging from the work of Cruickshank *et al.* (1961), McCarthy and McCarthy (1969), and others, is a new respect for diagnosis as an integral part of educational intervention. Fortunately, this awakening to the need for specific and individualized programs of remediation based on comprehensive assessments of ability and disability comes about at a time when improved scientific techniques and materials are becoming more widely available at the school and classroom level. We do not disparage the continuing need for the *Menschenkenners,* the great men with whom diagnosis was conducted with an almost innate intuitive instinct but, rather, we support the notion that the adequate diagnosis of children seeming to have those difficult-to-define problems of learning is becoming increasingly within the capability of teachers and others with direct responsibility for the child's education.

Regardless of one's commitment to the principle of diagnosis, both student and practitioner need be aware of significant philosophical and procedural problems that permeate a diagnosis of learning disability. What is the effect of diagnosis on the child?

Can the process cause problems as well as identify them? Has the discrepancy principle been applied erroneously? How do we justify disparities in diagnosis resulting from differences in theory? As diagnosis leads to classification, is it inevitably harmful? More doubts could be raised; it is perhaps fortunate that man has always had more of an instinct for questions than for answers. Nevertheless, the few we have raised will serve to illustrate the need to approach diagnosis with both caution and humility.

Even when precisely stated, the diagnosis which confirms a generalized or even a specific learning disability is rather like knowing the patient has a little touch of cancer; it really doesn't hurt too much, but simply in the knowing, its potential for mischief is unlimited. The person who has just been told he has cancer is likely thereafter to manifest dramatic changes in psycho-social behavior. While the knowledge might well mobilize his energies to combat the disease, few would be surprised if this knowledge also had negative effects, or even if the total impact of knowing was erosive of both physical and mental health. But the diagnosis of *learning disability* lacks the mortal consequences of cancer; indeed a learning disability is more often like having psoriasis— and somewhat more mysterious and frightening.

Years ago one of the present authors received just such a diagnosis from a physician—"psoriasis!" He was assured that there was no cause for worry, that the treatment would be painless, and that recovery was assured. In spite of these assurances, changes in his life style — now too embarrassing to mention — were the ordained result. It was not until weeks later that he realized that the perplexing disease was in reality a small patch of dry skin.

The above incident serves to illustrate the many dangers of diagnosis, and emphasizes the care required in the exercise of our educational prerogatives. Most problems of learning are anything but fatal, have only a marginal relationship to a happy and productive life, and are best left undetected, to be remediated or not in the normal course of a child's *normal* education. We propose that children need as much protection from their friends as from their occasional enemies in the educational establishment, and a "bill of rights" that protects children from well meaning problem hunters is long overdue. It takes a high level of sophistication to deal effectively with the more subtle problems of learning. Generally, it is a skill beyond the capabilities of parents, teachers, psychologists, and university professors alike, and in all circumstances it is a skill best used sparingly.

There are two major educational approaches to the diagnosis of learning disabilities; both are commonly utilized and neither is altogether adequate to the task. The first is the cumulative signs approach as defined by McCarthy and McCarthy (1969). It consists essentially of *a priori* assumptions about those signs which manifest brain injury (or learning disabilities), followed by the administration of a relatively large and varied battery of tests or test items. The relevant behaviors (diagnostic signs), i.e., perceptual-motor impairment, general coordination deficits, disorders of memory and thinking, etc., are pursued with vigor until such time as their accumulation suggests probable disability, or upon failure to accumulate, some alternate explanation is sought.

The second broad approach utilizes the concept of functional discrepancies. In brief, the examiner seeks to establish discrepancies in performance between two related tests, i.e., intelligence and achievement, or between facets of the same test. This approach is especially significant in that most definitions of learning disability assume discrepancies between estimated ability and actual achievement. The presumption of learning disability on the basis of discrepancies in performance within a single test is tenuous indeed. In summarizing a major work which sought to establish the link between symptoms and brain injury, McCarthy and McCarthy (1969) noted the flimsiness of the discrepancy argument when they stated, "The use of discrepancies between scores on sections of a single test is particularly suspect, because these sections tend to lack sufficient reliability" (p. 96).

More intriguing than the reliability problem are the questions which surround the practice of establishing discrepancies between tests, usually between a test of generalized learning ability (intelligence) and a specific or general test of achievement. In the first place, if one were to accept the Jastak (1949) concept whereby the potential to achieve is best indicated by the highest subtest score on tests of intelligence, 99% of the population would qualify as disabled learners as determined by present achievement. Perhaps we would do better to reverse the Jastak concept when making a diagnosis of possible learning disability. That is, the discrepancy between ability and achievement should be predicated on a disparity between the lowest subtest score and functional achievement. This practice would perhaps present a more realistic criterion measure against which achievement would be evaluated than does the customary average intellectual performance. Whether the lowest subtest performance or a median score or the average of those scores which fell below the mean or some other more realistic criterion were established, the effect would be a reduction of the number of children viewed as deficient while in no way interfering with appropriate instruction or the concept of the child as a normal learner. After all, the magnitude of the discrepancy between estimated capacity and performance which constitutes a learning disability has always been judgmental in nature. The procedure we advocate would reduce both the number of decisions and the range within which critical decisions are made.

The diagnosis of learning disabilities is not unlike the story of the blind men and the elephant; one's perception of the phenomenon is largely determined by where you take hold! Of course this happenstance is no more confined to education and psychology than it is to blind men and elephants. Psychiatrists don't agree on mental illness; architects on design; or baseball players on managers. Disagreement, then, is natural enough, and should not be derided simply because it occurs in education or even because the subject of our differences is children.

Dunn (1968) tells of a number of clinical teams operating in the same geographic area and servicing rather similar populations but, nevertheless, arriving at highly disparate diagnoses. The clinicians agreed that the differences in diagnoses could be attributed mainly to the different backgrounds and interests of the professionals involved in the diagnostic process. Michal-Smith and Morgenstern (1965) make a similar point when they state:

> The diagnosis of a learning disability depends to a large degree on the examiner's thinking and frame of reference. Clinical tools by themselves, no matter how refined or forceful, reveal no theory and shed no light without interpretation, and interpretation in turn, depends on the examiner's orienta-

tion. It is the examiner's views on learning, perception, feelings, and thinking and the inter-relationships among these
psychic processes that establish the diagnosis. Unless these
statements of orientation, simplified as they may be, are
emphasized, it is close to impossible to understand the possible differences of diagnoses among the disciplines or the fact
that diagnoses are not mutually inclusive (p. 172).

The examiner's "frame of reference" to which Michal-Smith
and Morgenstern refer is basically the product of that set of theory
which has permeated the clinician's training and practice. And
the important thing to remember about theory is this: theory is
only a substitute for knowing. In the area of learning disabilities
this is the lesson the student must learn above all; we do not yet
know what we are doing, and like the blind men we must examine
the phenomenon in greater detail.

There are a number of additional problems in the diagnosis of
learning disabilities about which the reader needs to be skeptical or
at least properly cautious. For instance, we note that the number
of seemingly confirmed cases of learning disability—of whatever
nature—increases with aplomb as programs become available.
School personnel have always been subject to the *horror vacui,* we
think, and are seldom at a loss in fashioning a learner to the speci-
fications of problem-oriented programs. And then there is the ever
present danger of confusing diagnosis with classification. It is
indeed unfortunate that diagnosis is often terminated at the point
where child or problem has been labeled. Blatt (1969) noted his
mistrust of the process when he wrote:

> I am distrustful because we seem to confuse activity—doing
> something—with progress. We seem to confuse passing new
> laws and creating new programs with progress. We seem to
> confuse labels with diagnosis and diagnosis with help (p. 237).

Lastly, we'd like to caution our readers against the assumption
that all symptoms of disorders in learning are associated with a
common cause simply because *a cause* has been identified. In
example, one recognizes that perceptual deficiencies and language
dysfunctions may both be associated with "minimal brain damage." But the possibility also exists that within any individual

there is no causative relationship between the two dysfunctions, and that one may yield to the most modest remedial techniques while the other repeatedly defies our concerted efforts. This is possible — even probable, we think — and must not be lost sight of in our efforts to shape a nicely neat diagnostic syndrome.

In this section we have focused on diagnosis. We do not deny its necessity; we only raise the questions and provide the warnings. The reader, in light of his own experiences, must now provide his own answers.

FOCUS ON REMEDIATION

Oftentimes, the mere act of such intercession affixes to the child a "problem" image; and he may live with that image long after he outgrows the nonconforming behavior.

Silberberg (1971)

It seems clear to us that the trouble with remediation in the area of learning disabilities is in the application of the remedy, and its consequent effect upon children and teachers alike. Remediation interferes with the concept of normalcy, leads to a dubious policy of "fix and return," and is predicated on altering the child rather than questioning the curriculum. Remediation may also restrict the focus of our efforts to the exclusion of other needed instruction, and lastly, in itself may constitute a self-fulfilling prophecy. The indictments are straightforward and supportable!

The question of normalcy is central to the issues we raise. How does it feel, in an educational setting, to be both a child and a "bluebird"? Obviously, the answer depends not only upon the status of children, but also upon the status of "bluebirds." Like the redbirds or the yellowbirds (we refer, of course, to the some-time habit of labeling instructional groups), "bluebirds" may be tall or short, fast or slow, good at arithmetic or confounded by the new math, and all the while understand, quite clearly, that their differences don't really make a difference. But the learning disability bird soon learns that his difference does indeed make a difference. He may sense it in the underlying frustrations of the teacher, in the repetition of diagnostic routines, or simply in the intensity with which the "remedy" is applied.

Remediation does not take place in a social or educational vacuum. As Towne and Joiner (1968) have noted, most discussions of remedial techniques are carried on "without acknowledging that these techniques are applied in social settings and that their effectiveness is influenced by social processes" (p. 220). Remediation inevitably conveys to the child an added sense of differentness in learning and behavior at the very time the teacher is seeking to eliminate such differences. If the child is perceptive — and we have never met one that was not — he is as much affected by the teacher's expectations of discongruity as by her desire for remediation. One may at least speculate that the teacher's recognition of hyperactivity in the child, by promoting both in herself and in the child expectations of hyperactive behavior, may outweigh in its negative effects those positive measures to reduce stimuli or otherwise remediate the symptom.

What is to be done if the negative effects of remediation are to be overcome? We reject the usual answer which proposes the careful and understanding application of diagnosis and remediation in a supportive educational milieu. The intent of this approach may be admirable enough, but it is, nevertheless, insufficient to the task. In the majority of children with significant difficulties in learning, remediation as both concept and practice must be recognized for what it is, an apology for defective education. In short, the limits of normality have been too narrowly drawn, and the techniques of a normal education too restrictively defined. The solution to the problem, then, rests on our willingness to expand the range of learning characteristics viewed as normal classroom behavior and to adapt our instructional techniques to accommodate that range.

While we have no scientific evidence to support our claim, we are reasonably convinced that success in teaching mentally retarded children is most evident in the presence of a monumental inability to think of children as "stupid." The field of learning disabilities could profit from just such an inability. It is not enough to treat the child *as if* he were normal, or *as if* he had the potential for normalcy; we must go beyond these *as if* behaviors. It is necessary to *believe* the child is normal because you *know* he's normal, and then to teach him accordingly, regardless of any specific learning characteristics.

In an historic sense, remediation in the areas of medicine, psychology, and education has implied a return to normalcy after some limited treatment period. As these allied disciplines were instrumental in the development of the learning disabilities field as a unique habilitation entity, the "fix and return" model was quite naturally accepted. This acceptance seemed particularly appropriate when one assumed that he was dealing with an essentially intact organism (McCarthy, 1969; Johnson and Myklebust, 1967) demonstrating a discrepancy presumed subject to remediation. The implication of these assumptions and philosophy for education was noted by Barsch (1968) when he wrote:

> The fundamental philosophy of "fix and return" may place the entire population of learning disability cases in a territory midway between the provincial boundaries of regular and special education. Where formerly a precise and well defined fence line separated the two provinces, a zone of overlap is now developing. As this neutral zone expands (an inevitable consequence of development) it is possible to conceive of a sufficiently wide band of territorial grayness as to promote the definition of a third major category in education (p. 17).

In spite of the wide ranging possiblities for the reorganization of education presented by the learning disabilities model, the "fix and return" concept has not been without its critics.

Silberberg and Silberberg (1969) reviewed significant research in remedial reading, almost all of which indicated that improvements recorded at the close of remediation "washed out." In these studies, children failed to maintain the advantage of their short term gains and most seemed to return to levels of achievement "commensurate with their preremedial experience (p. 211)." In commenting on similar findings, Bateman (1966) indicated the inadequacy of the "return to normalcy" model and proposed that it be superseded by the concept of "continued support." The latter model has the advantage of being in harmony with quality education for all children and, unless one is compulsively intent upon utilizing labels as a camouflage for inadequate instruction,

may be applied in the classroom without the need for special designation or euphemistic tommyrot. In our terms, school is a place
where diverse learners are *always* members of the "in" group, and
"continued support" is what education is all about.

Perhaps the gravest indictment of the philosophy of remediation
lies in the subtle presumption that we are most often dealing
with an operationally defective system. Only in the abstract do we
acknowledge our sins. In practice it is as Engelman (1969) suggested, "If children succeed, the program is responsible; if they
fail, the children are responsible (p. 194)." In the same vein,
Bruner (1967) proposes that almost any child can learn almost
anything if properly programmed. In application, however, faith
in this dictum is weak, and children are inescapably the victims
of our doubts. As Dunn (1968) has said, "Failures are program
and instructor failures, not pupil failures" (p. 13).

Instead of revising instructional techniques, we often engage in
activity designed to accentuate differences in learning style and to
further separate individuals—children and teachers alike—from the
mainstream of education. Too frequently our uncertain purpose
has been but to molify parents, salve the conscience of teachers,
and vindicate our system of education. Labels, diagnosis, and
remediation should be used sparingly, we think, and under no
circumstances should new programs substitute for improved
instruction or new monies for renewed effort.

In our uncertainty we also note that the remediation of learning
deficits provokes delightful excursions into esoterically devised
programs replete with pseudo-scientifically contrived machines
and materials. It is heady stuff—and on occasion it appears to
work. Deficits disappear, children learn, and an air of accomplishment pervades the educational arena. The arena is also enlivened,
one observes, by the newly discovered "educational" inventions
of former pinball manufacturers (surely), and by the garish prod-
ucts of printing presses gone mad. We are overwhelmed by costly
gadgets and inundated by a torrent of words neatly packaged and
attractively advertised. Fine (1970) described it so:

> The number of publishers and manufacturers of materials for
> remediation has quadrupled, bringing in a "Madison Ave-
> nue" marketing approach, replete with claims and assertions

—while the relative amount of empirical evidence supporting the use of these materials becomes progressively more limited (p. 133).

The effect of the materials explosion has been to distract us from the serious business of educating children. Time and energy may be so disproportionately devoted to their use in the amelioration of deficits peripheral to the main problem of learning, i.e., perceptual training as opposed to reading instruction, that many children, while demonstrating some improvement in the former, may evidence little if any progress in the latter. As one clinical group (Braum *et al.*, 1965) said, "unless it can be demonstrated that retraining in a specific function shows generalization to the child's performance in criterion areas, the training cannot be considered necessary and significant" (p. 17).

Indeed, the expenditure of our instructional resources on matters neither necessary or significant, has been the hallmark of remediation in the area of learning disabilities. It is the normal consequence of ignorance and good will, and, on balance, it has probably done more harm than good.

FOCUS ON THE FUTURE

The cause will not be helped by those who are fighting to defend this or that old or new system of . . . instruction. It will be helped only by those who recognize and appreciate the vast diversity of intellects, and who will seek to provide for each child the teaching experience which is appropriate to his way of learning.

Masland (1966)

There is much that is wrong with the field of learning disabilities, but much that is right as well. Though the state of the art is crude, it is each day more refined, more sharply honed by the theory, research, and practice of dedicated people. That we are ignorant is an evident fact, but that each day we learn more about children is also evident. In the long run it is immaterial whether learning disabilities as a unique field stands or falls. What matters is only that we shall have used our allotted time in the cause of better education for all children. And it is in this larger purpose that the concepts and practices of the field have most to offer.

Learning disabilities could become but another category in our litany of exceptional children; but if wisdom and experience prevail, it will become, instead, the means by which education is infused with a new flexibility, a flexibility, as Rice (1970) noted, "to deal more effectively with ever broadening individual differences and needs, while keeping the individual pupil within the main stream of educational life" (p. 194). The old categories of exceptionality, medically oriented and anachronistic in current educational theory, are now best abandoned to history. We need a bringing together of pedagogue and scientist, of teacher and clinician, of learner and learning style in a new pattern of education, sensitive to diversity and more aware of its responsibilities to children. If we are but imaginative, the concepts emanating from the field of learning disabilities can serve this purpose well.

It is not surprising that the new concepts of learning—and failure to learn—have been met by criticism and derision. What is being challenged is the content and practices of curriculum two hundred years old, designed for the children of privilege and privileged by design—privileged to select its clientele, privileged to brand the deviant and the non-conformer, and privileged above all to hold itself in perpetuity, unchanging, uncompromising, and unchallengeable. It is fortunate that the learning disabilities movement has come upon the scene not in a paroxysm of energy, soon to burn itself out, but rather as an inexorable force, sometimes inconsistent, always self-critical, and ever mindful of the continuing need for change. In recognition of that need, learning disabilities may yet prove a positive force.

Changes are already taking place in teacher training as Schools of Education gear themselves to the task of preparing clinically oriented teachers, steeped in the psycho-diagnostic tradition and trained in the theory of learning. Prescriptive teaching has become a schoolhouse cliche overnight, yet in its concern for individual differences in learning style, it offers the promise of a better education for all children. It is too early to tell how effective our clinical teachers will be or even the precise nature of their role. Nevertheless, the teacher so trained will have a greater appreciation of the infinite variety of conditions which interfere with learning, a greater tolerance for differences, and a greater willingness to expand the limits of normality.

Several years ago Ray Barsch (1968) wrote what we feel is a fitting conclusion to our discussion when he said:

> It is a time for debate and rebuttal—a time for daring innovation and sober compromise—a time for phantasy laden with promise of reality—a time for intrepid educational adventure sharpened by the wisdom of expereince . . . (p. 19).

We might only add that the opportunities for good or evil are ours. What we do with them will forever say more of us than of those we seek to instruct. In the lives of children, it is already tomorrow, and for some already too late.

REFERENCES

Barsch, R. H.: Perspectives on learning disabilities: The vectors of a new convergence. *Journal of Learning Disabilities, 1*:7–20, 1968.

Bateman, B.: Learning disorders. *Review of Educational Research, 36*:93–119, 1966.

Blatt, B.: Introduction. *Seminars in Psychiatry, 1*:237–239, 1969.

Braun, J. S., Rubin, E. Z., Beck, G. R., Llorens, L. A. Mottley, N., and Beall, C. D.: Cognitive-perceptual-motor functions in children—a suggested change in approach to psychological assessment. *Journal of School Psychology, 3*:13–17, 1965.

Bruner, J. S., Olver, R. R., and Greenfield, P. M.: *Studies in Cognitive Growth.* New York, Wiley, 1967.

Cruickshank, W. M., Bentzen, F. A., Ratzeburg, F. H., and Tannhauser, M. J.: *A Teaching Method for Brain-Injured and Hyperactive Children.* Syracuse, N. Y., Syracuse University Press, 1961.

Dunn, L. M.: Special education for the mildly retarded—Is much of it justifiable? *Exceptional Children, 35*:5–22, 1968.

Dunn, L. M.: Minimal brain dysfunction: A dilemma for education. In H. C. Haywood (Ed.), *Brain Damage in School Age Children.* Washington, D. C., The Council for Exceptional Children, 1968.

Engelman, S.: Teaching reading to children with low mental ages. *Education and Training of the Mentally Retarded, 2*:193–201, 1967.

Engel, M.: Dilemmas of classification. *The Journal of Special Education*, *3*:231–239, 1969.

Fine, M.: Considerations in educating children with cerebral dysfunction. *Journal of Learning Disabilities*, *3*:132–142, 1970.

Goldstein, K.: *Aftereffects of Brain Injuries in War*. New York, Grune & Stratton, 1942.

Jastak, J.: A rigorous criterion of feeblemindedness. *Journal of Abnormal and Social Psychology*, *44*:367–378, 1949.

Johnson, D. J., and Myklebust, H. R. *Learning Disabilities: Educational Principles and Practices*. New York, Grune & Stratton, 1967.

Maietta, D. F.: Current halloos confronting special learning disabilities. *Seminars in Psychiatry*, *1*:245–252, 1969.

Masland, R. L.: Forward to Thompson, L. J., *Reading Disability—Developmental Dyslexia*. Springfield, Ill., Thomas, 1966.

McCarthy, J. R.: Learning disabilities: where have we been? where are we going? *Seminars in Psychiatry*, *1*:354–361, 1969.

McCarthy, J. J., and McCarthy, J. F.: *Learning disabilities*. Boston, Allyn and Bacon, 1969.

Michal-Smith, H., and Morgenstern, M.: Learning disorders—an overview. *Learning Disorders*, *1*:170–196, 1965.

Rice, D.: Learning disabilities: an investigation in two parts. *Journal of Learning Disabilities*, *3*:193–199, 1970.

Siegel, E.: Learning disabilities: substance or shadow. *Exceptional Children*, *34*:433–438, 1968.

Silberberg, N. E.: Is there such a thing as a learning disabled child? *Journal of Learning Disabilities*, *4*:273-276, 1971.

Silberberg, N. E., and Silberberg, M. C.: Myths in remedial education. *Journal of Learning Disabilities*, *2*:209–217, 1969.

Strauss, A., and Lehtinen, L.: *Psychopathology and Education of the Brain Injured Child*. New York, Grune & Stratton, 1947.

Towne, R. C., and Joiner, L. M.: Some negative implications of special placement for children with learning disabilities. *The Journal of Special Education*, *2*:217–222, 1968.

Chapter II

ORGANIC DYSFUNCTION: THE LEAP OF FAITH

THEODORE Di BUONO

INTRODUCTION

Man's knowledge of his own physiologic functioning is new and very, very incomplete. We continually acquire data which brings greater understanding of our bodies, but this data is difficult to assimilate and new facts frequently convince us that what we thought we knew was not so at all. Our minds are a part of our body (with maybe a little something extra thrown in). But in terms of understanding what goes on in our own brains we are, in the words of Wilder Penfield: "like men at the foot of a mountain. We stand in the clearings we have made on the foothills, looking up at the mountain we hope to scale. But the pinnacle is hidden in eternal clouds and many believe it can never be conquered" (Penfield, 1960).

The "leap of faith" to which the title of this chapter refers is the leap from the foothills over the pinnacle of the unconquered mountain. Surprisingly enough, many of us make it daily — and with great self-assurance. That is, we make *inferences* and *conclusions* about the children with learning problems whom we are trying to help, even though we do not know enough to support those conclusions and, frequently, even before we have done the preliminary work of clearing the particular "foothills" of a specific case. We talk glibly of brain damage which we often infer from *behaviors* rather than specific neurophysiologic evidence, even though we know that many of those behaviors can be caused by non-permanent, non-organic disturbances. Or we speak, perhaps more politely, of dysfunction without knowing what the

25

range of normal functional variation is, or how it changes as the child grows older.

THE RELEVANCE OF ORGANIC FACTORS

In discussing the relevance of organic factors in learning problems of children, the following key issues continually suggest themselves:

1. What do we know about the normal physiologic functioning of the particular area of the central nervous system which we are questioning?
2. What specific signs or special criteria do we have for recognizing damage or dysfunction in that area? Can we discriminate from these signs whether an area is, in fact, damaged, or just not working as expected (dysfunctional)?
3. What is the acceptable normal variation of functioning at any one given age?
4. What developmental changes normally occur as one views children sequentially over the entire age range?
5. What factors *other* than the organic ones can affect, enhance, or even mimic organic dysfunction?
6. What specific therapies (medical, educational, or psychosocial) do we have at our disposal to correct a dysfunction once it has been identified? If true damage exists, can the functioning of that area be restored? abetted? circumvented?
7. What supports can we offer to enhance the specific therapies, or to maximize adaptation even when no specific therapy exists? What is the full range of therapeutic support that can be mustered to facilitate normal development?

These issues are of great clinical importance and should be raised with each child who is undergoing evaluation and planning in regard to his learning difficulty. The relevance of any organic factors which may be established in a specific case emerges only as one considers all the implications of these key issues. That is; the presence of contributory organic factors, even if established by the best available criteria, does not provide automatic solutions, but only bits of data in a complex whole. The traditional medical model which seeks to establish a causal relationship between a disease-producing agent or pathogenetic process and a given disease state does not produce great yield when applied to behavioral areas. To be sure, cause and effect relationships exist, but "behavior" represents a complex interaction of inputs which is not easily explained by either simplistic or global hypotheses. Very often in our approach to clinical situations, we make the mistake of focusing too sharply on single factors, or else we make blurred global observations. In either case, we are likely to err in our clinical hypotheses and miss the mark in our planning and programming.

THE MULTIFACTORIAL-ADAPTATIONAL MODEL

What is our goal for the children we serve? Our hope is that each child will reach his fullest potential, but what does that imply? That he develop and *use* all the internal and external resources available to him in order to make the most successful adaptations he can to the situations in which he is placed. Although the forces which shape the development of the child are complex and intimately related, one may attempt to conceptualize these interrelationships in a concise manner, using the following model (Fig. 1) (Richmond and Lustman, 1954; Richmond with DiBuono, 1971).

With this model in mind, development can be viewed as a complex adaptive phenomenon influenced by any or all of the factors outlined. Successful adaptation and optimum development are only possible when the homeostatic relationships among these factors are properly balanced. Quite obviously, each child has a unique genetic background and constitutional makeup which influences the way in which he responds. It is true that deficits or dysfunctions in his organic development will alter his performance, but so, too, will deficits in his environment and his psyche — the result being less than optimal adaptation. Any support which can be given in the social and psychological spheres, as well as the organic sphere, will help offset deficits and restore homeostatic balance toward optimal functioning. For example:

In the example given, even though specific therapy may fail to control attention span or immediately alter perceptual ability, progress is made through the structuring of the external environment and emotional support for the child and family. Many other

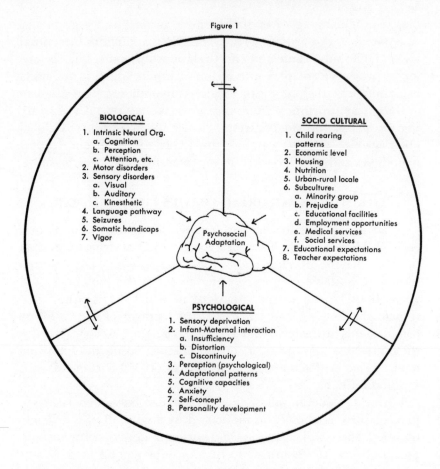

Figure 1. Multiple factors affecting psychosocial behavior.

examples could be used, illustrating the gamut of difficulties observed in children with problems in learning, but the principle is always the same. That is: a comprehensive approach to the problem, one which takes into account and seeks solutions in both internal and external environment is always necessary.

This raises the important question: Who is well enough trained and equipped to deal with problems in such a comprehensive way? Can the teacher or family doctor provide what is needed? Can school resource personnel or medical specialists do the job?

Figure 2. Adjustment to Learning Situation

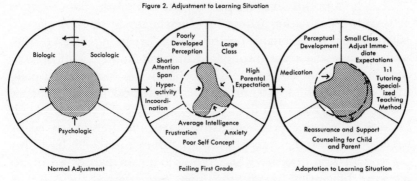

Figure 2. Adjustment to learning situation.

Perhaps in the future we can train individuals as learning special-ists and vest this responsibility in a single person, but for now, the best approach seems to lie in the multidisciplinary team.

THE MULTIDISCIPLINARY APPROACH

There is no evidence that a multidisciplinary approach to learn-ing disorders is to be preferred, or that it represents the most eco-nomical use of crucial personnel. However, at this stage in our knowledge regarding learning disorders, and given the restricted range of training experiences which most disciplines provide for their professional trainees, the multidisciplinary approach is the most sensible for the child and the most comforting for the staff.

If one reviews the conceptual model outlined above, it is easy to see the rationale for multidisciplinary involvement. Physician, social worker, psychologist, counselor, teacher, resource personnel, parents, and the child, himself, all have important contributions to make to the solution of the problems at hand. In addition, a widening circle of community backup services is essential when one considers the diverse resources necessary to stabilize the child's internal and external environments and facilitate healthy adaptation.

Basically, the four major strands of professional input include Medicine, Social work, Education, and Psychology, but these large categories must be viewed as broadly encompassing the full range of programs and personnel engaged in human service.

Elsewhere in this text (Chapter 8), Dr. Burkowsky has described a Learning Evaluation Clinic in which many of us have participated. Prior to the establishment of that program, children were seen in diverse settings throughout our community, with no concerted effort made to provide comprehensive evaluation and planning for each child. At our university medical center pediatric clinic, we saw many children who were referred by their schools because of learning problems. Most often, the question asked by the school personnel was the same: "Does this child have any organic medical disorder which can account for part or all of his learning difficulties?" Even though we were aware at the outset of the dangers of diagnostic labelling, our answer to this question was, of necessity, one of two alternatives: "Yes, he has organic findings which could relate to his learning difficulties" or "No, he does not!" In either case, the medical information which we supplied did little toward resolving the problem, and contributed little information of value in educational programming for the child. On the contrary, quite often the teacher was made ultimately to feel that she was powerless to deal with the child *because of* the medical findings! More specifically, if a teacher's impression that her pupil's short attention span or hyperactivity was due to organic dysfunction was confirmed, her likely conclusion would be that she rightly could not be expected to handle him. Deficits in her own training and undue expectancies from physicians often combine to lead the teacher (and other school personnel) to seek solutions outside the classroom. Sometimes this takes the form of a demand for medical treatment (i.e., behavior modifying drugs) before the child is reaccepted. Sometimes the solution resorted to is "placement" of the child in whatever "special" class exists. Often, expediency rather than sound educational programming determines where the child is placed. And, in many cases, where no appropriate "special" class exists, exclusion is the only readily apparent resort. Far too often, a sequence of panicked decisions ensues from the confirmation of organic factors, rather than a rational use of this information in programming for the child. This can be avoided via the multidisciplinary approach, where all data regarding the child are shared and the relevance of each strength and deficit which the child exhibits can be weighted and translated into a program for classroom action. However, multidisciplinary effectiveness hinges on the success with which such diverse data can be coalesced into a meaningful plan which the child's *teacher* helps to devise, understands, can accept, and is supported in.

EVALUATION OF THE ROLE OF THE PHYSICIAN

If the physician cannot be regarded as holding the solution to the problems of the learning disabled child, what are the specific contributions he can make toward remedying those problems? Table I indicates the functions which may properly be considered as areas for the physician's attention, always remembering that it is his participation with representatives of other disciplines which makes his contributions valuable.

TABLE I
The Role of the Physician in the Evaluation and Treatment of Learning Disorders

1. Liaison with family as unbiased advocate for the child.
2. Developmental assessment and diagnosis of specific developmental disorders or delays.
3. Comprehensive health assessment and preventive maintenance including screening for known possible handicapping disorders.
4. Specific examination for deficits related to learning.
   a. Adequacy of visual and auditory acuity.
   b. Deficits in visual or auditory discrimination.
   c. Competency of speech apparatus.
   d. Adequacy of kinesthetic (tactile) input systems.
   e. Deficits in coordination and balance.
   f. Assessment for hyperkinesis and/or disordered attention.
   g. Signs or symptoms suggesting seizure phenomena.
5. Referral to other medical or para-medical specialists (i.e., child neurologist, psychiatrist, psychologist, ophthalmologist, optometrist, orthopedist, audiologist, speech pathologist, physical therapist, etc.).
6. Interpretation of medical data to family, clinical associates,

and school personnel, and determination of relevancy of
any medical findings.

7. Coordination of general and specific medical treatment
plans.
   a. correction of disorders involving general health.
   b. supervision of correction for sensory deficits, i.e. glasses,
   hearing aids, etc.
   c. administration of drug therapy for seizures.
   d. administration of drug therapy for hyperkinesis.
   e. support management plans devised by other medical
   specialists.
   f. assure continuity of medical follow-up once therapies
   are in progress.

8. Reassurance to concerned individuals when an organically
intact child is so diagnosed and direction of investigation
into other spheres.

Quite obviously, not every physician has the required skills
which enable him to carry out all these functions (DiBuono,
1971). It is incumbent upon each medical person to set the limits
of his participation in such problems as his time, training and
interest allow. Generally speaking, however, there are individuals
within most medical communities who do possess the prerequisite
skills and inclinations necessary to involve themselves in such
work, even if on a limited basis. The clearer the physician's own
responsibilities are made, and the more the roles of the other participating professionals are defined, the easier is the job of each!

Some further discussion of the functions outlined in Table I is
required at this point. The physician, particularly the child's own
family physician or pediatrician, usually commands the respect
and trust of the family. Sometimes this is based on an unrealistic
appraisal of the physician's potency, but, nevertheless, he is often
regarded as a counselor and confidant, even in matters outside the
purely medical realm. Very often he is the first person the family
consults when a learning problem is determined, and it is his
advice that they are likely to accept when a course of action needs
to be determined. He is thus an important ally to enlist in determining the needs of the child and obtaining the cooperation of
the family. The physician who becomes involved in school issues,

however, must be careful to be aware of the biases presented by his closeness to the family, as well as his professional association with the child's school or other clinical colleagues. He should at all times remain the child's advocate and avoid the pitfall of taking sides with the parents against the school, or vice-versa. His judgments must be as objective as possible and based on the consideration of all available data. Whenever he is not equipped to aid in the determination of an issue, it is best to reserve judgment and urge clarification by another appropriate professional. Too often, the physician allows himself to be enlisted, either by the parents or school, in a cause of which he is uncertain and, thereby, lends powerful support by association, sometimes to the detriment of his patients.

Likewise, the physician who has a special interest in the area of learning disorders, or who functions as part of a multidisciplinary unit, must be careful to preserve the patient-physician relationship which families expect and trust, rather than attempt to confuse them in his role as medical expert. His job is to interpret and explain rather than to confound or convince, and he should observe this function in regard to colleagues as well as parents.

In regard to child development, physicians, particularly pediatricians, represent our largest manpower force of development observers and facilitators. The daily work of the physician is to follow the children in his care and to help assure their optimum growth and development. This charge is carried out via an organized health care program which begins at birth and extends through childhood into adulthood. Physicians who are providing such continuous care for their young patients come to know them intimately, particularly in regard to the manner in which each one's development has progressed. Observing large numbers of children over a continuous spectrum of time equips the physician to recognize the range of developmental norms and to be alert to children whose development is lagging. This is not always true of teachers, who are apt to become associated with a single age group. They may come to know development in this cross-sectional group well, but may lack experience with the complete developmental spectrum. In addition, their cross-sectional sample usually reflects classroom behavior rather than the full range of behaviors exhibited by children, and they may be quite uncertain, therefore, when confronted with a child who is performing atypically.

In recent years, the training of physicians, again particularly pediatricians, has emphasized the importance of developmental assessment and the early recognition of developmental abnormalities. Specific approaches to the monitoring of developmental progress and the assessment of developmental status have been made part of the pediatrician's training and are beginning to be reflected in general office practice. One example of this is the Denver Developmental Screening Test (Frankenburg and Dodds, 1969), an instrument which has good reliability in the detection of developmental lags and which is brief enough to be practical in an office situation. This same test is also in widespread use by lay persons in non-medical settings such as adoption agencies, nursery schools, and day-care programs, where developmental screening of young children is important. There also exist within the ranks of subspecialized physicians, certain individuals whose main interest is specifically in early childhood development. In numbers, such individuals are rare, and they are usually academically based, but frequently programs are facilitated by consultation and planning with such individuals. Many pediatricians feel that "development," per se, is the science upon which the practice of pediatrics is based (Richmond, 1967). Some foresee a major role for the pediatrician in developmental programs. However, the exigencies of practice often compromise the physician's inclination to move into these areas and, conversely, we have yet to explore the exciting possibilities of training non-medical manpower to fill roles as assessors and facilitators of development.

The general physician's skills come most sharply into focus, of course, in the area of comprehensive health assessment. When all is said and done, this is what most physicians have been trained to do and what we should basically look to the physician for. A comprehensive examination provides assurance to all concerned that the child is either intact or that the extent of his abnormality or disability has been defined. *Regular* examinations provide added insurance that emerging problems will be dealt with before they result in disability. This aspect of medical care is conveyed by the term "preventive maintenance," and is an indispensable ingredient in the provision of adequate care. Unfortunately, many of our children either have not had access to or have not utilized resources for the provision of regular care and have tragically suffered needless disability (Cochrane and DiBuono, 1970). It is probably safe to say that if there are organic factors interfering with a child's school progress, they are far more likely to be of an obvious (but neglected) nature than an exotic or subtle variety. Our greatest need is still to provide quality medical care to every child rather than to practice a finely focused art upon a few children who are pre-selected by either economic privilege *or* academic failure (Birch and Gussow, 1970).

Assuming that general care has been provided for a particular child, what are some of the specific areas which warrant further medical evaluation? Probably the most important part of a specialized assessment for the child with a learning disorder is the evaluation of his sensory apparatus (Lawson, 1968; Lloyd, 1970). To begin with, one must be absolutely sure that the child has normal visual and auditory acuity. If gross testing bears this out, such may be deemed adequate, but whenever suspicion exists, specialized resources (i.e., ophthalmologist, audiologist) must be called upon. Likewise, one must be assured that the child can discriminate and process visual and auditory stimuli. Here, the physician's skills are usually quite limited and the aid of others (psychologist, audiologist, speech pathologist, etc.) is usually sought. Increasingly, however, physicians interested in learning disorders have armed themselves for investigation of discriminatory functions and many evaluation "batteries" reflect this (Ozer, 1968; Koppitz, 1964; Frostig, 1963; Wepman, 1958; Denhoff, 1968; Kephart, 1960; Zedler, 1968; Conners, 1967).

The adequacy of the child's tactile abilities may also be ascertained by a variety of simple testing maneuvers which tell us whether a child can touch, feel, identify and discriminate stimuli with his fingers, hands, mouth, skin, and other body parts. This provides extremely important data as to the adequacy of various input systems and may give valuable clues as to preferred routes by which information may be channelled to the child (Cohn, 1964). Such data may be directly translated into teaching methods which immediately utilize the child's most adequate input systems while ongoing therapy is being aimed at the habilitation of less adequate input systems (Myklebust and Johnson, 1967; Fernald, 1943). Frequently, *no* deficit is found in any of the sensory apparati, and all sensory functions are pronounced normal. It is interesting how often this is met with mild dismay or disbelief, as if all concerned were disappointed that the child has no discernible deficit. A "clean bill of health," of course, suggests that the trouble lies elsewhere and often re-focuses scrutiny upon the interactions of the child with his parents, teachers and peers. Nevertheless, the most valuable contribution the physician can make is to assure everyone that the organically intact child *is* organically intact. *Only* the physician can do that! It is a role that is difficult for most physicians, as they are more accustomed to saying what is wrong with their patients rather than what is right with them. Nevertheless, as regards learning problems, conveying the assurance of organic adequacy is of the utmost importance. Such assurance should then be met with relief and renewed vigor in the search for the core of the child's difficulties.

The educational relevance of deficits in fine motor coordination and balance is not as readily appreciated as that of sensory deficits. There is consequently a large body of medical literature in which the wisdom of the physician's close scrutiny of these areas is debated. The essential question is: What difference can it make in the child's learning if he has minor motor handicaps? So minor, in fact, that they merit inclusion only in a newly described category referred to as "soft" neurological signs. There is no doubt that intact output systems for visual tracking, forming speech, manipulation, and locomotion are a clear asset to learning. And there are many who believe that motor activity programs can be devised which give the child a greater feeling of self-awareness and accomplishment through body mastery (Cratty, 1967). However, at this point, we really do not know what effect peripheral motoric activities have on improvement of integrative functions at cortical and sub-cortical levels in the brain.

On the other hand, the concept of fine motor incoordination and minor imbalance as *indicators* of poor neurologic integration may have real diagnostic validity (Birch, 1969). That is, the child who shows "soft" neurologic findings and who is learning poorly may be performing as he is because of faulty neurologic organization. Is this, then, the child with organic dysfunction? There are pitfalls in answering this question, and they relate mostly to the discussion at the opening of this chapter. One must be very sure that one has standardized developmental norms for all functions that are being examined. Objective normative data for many of the motor balance skills which are regularly tested have not been available and therefore subjective judgment as to a child's organic adequacy is too often tendered in place of a factual statement of the child's performance in regard to other children his age. Most often, this subjective judgment reflects not only the *perception,* but also the *professional bias* of the examiner, so that a neurologist, a pediatrician, a teacher, a physical education instructor, etc., might have very different conclusions upon simultaneous viewing of the performance of a particular child at a given set of tasks. The application of standardized tests with developmental norms, when available, will much improve this current chaos.

Another widely debated area into which the physician is regularly drawn is in regard to hyperkinesis (Werry, 1966). The community's expectation of the physician here is usually quite clear. Very often the physician's involvement in a case is sought in the form of a demand that he place the child on medication to control hyperactivity (Ladd, 1970). Sometimes the referral comes with the following admonition: "This child is excluded from school until you see him and start him on medication!" While it is flattering to be placed in a position of such authority, it is also frightening, intimidating, and grossly unfair. And the physician who responds to such demands is likewise being grossly unfair to his charge, the child. The plea for sanity in all such cases should take the form of a counter-request that careful observational data be provided, firsthand when possible, which will clarify the nature and extent of the hyperactivity. That is, just what the child is doing and under which circumstances must be first established before the remedy can be decided upon. The physician needs to review such data and to add his own judgment based on his examination of the child, but beyond this, it is also his responsibility to jointly consider alternate methods of behavior control with those who are dealing directly with the child. In this way, a system of priorities can be decided upon which gives assurance of an adequate time trial for each therapeutic intervention (medical or non-medical) rather than "blitzing" the child with a multi-disciplined attack or abandoning him solely to the vagaries of drug management, which is still a bit like Russian Roulette! There is no doubt that drug management is an important part of the available armamentarium for children with learning disorders (Millichap, 1967; Connors, 1966). And there is no doubt that the physician plays an important role as coordinator of therapeutic drug trials. However, he has much more than that to contribute, and should properly resist one-dimensional involvement in such a multi-dimensional area.

Little needs to be said regarding the role of the physician in treatment of seizure disorders. Anti-convulsant drug maintenance is altogether a separate issue from that of drug usage for modification of behavior. The physician is well-advised to solicit data from school personnel regarding the child's performance, attention and affect, but usually his judgment as to the best therapeutic management program is based on medical considerations for which there is solid validation in the literature and in practice. The type and dosage of anti-convulsant drug is carefully designed to control seizure activity and should not lightly be tampered with. School personnel are best advised to reserve judgments in regard to seizure-prone children and to refer their parents to physicians whenever problems arise.

The physician who assumes the role of the child's advocate should see himself as a coordinator of activities on the child's behalf. Much of his responsibility can and should be delegated to other specialists, both medical and non-medical, but he should not lose sight of either immediate or long range objectives for the child he serves, especially where medical problems exist. Continuity and coordination of care for the child with learning disorders are just as important as they are to the child with renal disease, cardiac disease, or any other chronic condition.

There is no magic in what the physician does. He has skills, but not powers. His *influence* may be power*ful,* but its effectiveness depends upon how he wields it. To the extent that he can share and interpret well-substantiated medical data with others, he can contribute meaningfully to an over-all understanding of the child's problems. His therapeutic assets may likewise prove important or even indispensable to the child's progress, but they should be seen as part of a concerted treatment effort.

PHYSIOLOGIC RESEARCH DIRECTIONS

If a person says "Mares eat oats and does eat oats" into his tape recorder and, on the playback, it comes out "Mairzy dotes and dozey dotes," there is a simple explanation somewhere. Perhaps he didn't say what he thought he said. Perhaps the microphone didn't pick it up correctly. Perhaps the tape speed was inaccurate. Perhaps the signal amplification is poor. Perhaps the instrument is not capable of more faithful reproduction. In any case, one has only to take it to the nearest authorized service outlet and a trained expert will look in the black box, tell you what went wrong, and, most likely, fix it with a pop-in circuit or transistor. If you still don't like the fidelity of the instrument, you can throw it away and buy a more deluxe model.

If a child garbles what is said to him or shown to him, if he runs at the wrong speed, if he fails to pick up or retain the input message, what options does one have? Who can he be taken to who can penetrate the black box in his head and tell us what is wrong? The physician can say whether end organs such as eyes, ears and fingers are adequate to receive stimuli. The psychologist can elicit responses to stimuli and can make "educated" assumptions as to why they came out the way they did. But no one can really trace for us exactly how the stimulus was processed on the way in, how and where it was received and stored, or how it was mediated and translated into a response. If something is wrong anywhere along this input-output chain, the child is dysfunctional (Chalfant and Scheffelin, 1969). And we simply do not have the technology to be able to say just why, where or how to fix it. And we cannot throw the child away!

Although much is known about the brain and its functions, much more is unknown. We do not even know what occurs neurophysiologically or neurochemically at the moment when learning takes place in the brain (Galambos and Morgan, 1960). On the other hand, there is beginning to be gathered a large and provocative neurophysiologic literature (Chalfant and Scheffelin, 1969; Hebb, 1949; Magoun, 1963; Eccles, 1960; Lashley, 1952; Laufer, Denhoff and Solomons, 1957; Penfield and Roberts, 1959; Kagan and Lewis, 1965; Hernandez-Peon, 1961; Gellhorn, 1967; Luria, 1966), and as this raw data becomes assimilated and applied by clinicians, we may begin to see some significant progress in the area of learning disorders. When we develop the technology that will enable us to trace stimulus input through response output with a clear understanding of all the inhibitory and facilitatory influences along the way, we will be freed from the guesswork which now passes for diagnostic evaluation. When we have adequately explored methods of measuring neurophysiologic responses (as are now being developed) (Lipton and Steinschneider, 1967; Lacey and Kagan, 1963; Venables and Martin, 1967), we will be able to say what the normal variation of a given response is and how this changes as children grow and develop. Conversely, such normative data will enable us to identify with authority the truly dysfunctional child and may restore some dignity to the concept of brain damage as a distinct entity rather than a faddish concordance which masks professional ineptitude. This seemingly harsh judgment regarding the current state of the science of learning disorders is not meant to reflect discredit upon the thousands of professionals from all disciplines who labor daily on behalf of children everywhere. However, if we are practitioners of an art, let us not call it a science. In so doing, we are forcing children to pay a double price. That is, they must both suffer their particular handicaps *and* endure the stigma of the names we devise to cover our knowledge gaps.

Children are different. They are different from adults. They are different from one another and they are different from themselves as they change and grow. We must have the courage to accept and the patience to explore these differences. It is knowledge which bridges the gap between supposing and being sure. As regards organic dysfunction, such knowledge may be nearly within our grasp. Not now, but someday soon, the "leap of faith" will require only a step. In the meantime, the well-being of the children we serve depends upon how rationally and responsibly we conduct ourselves as artful practitioners of a developing science.

REFERENCES

Birch, H., and Bortner, M.: Neurologic findings in children education-ally designated as "brain damaged." *American Journal of Ortho-psychiatry,* Vol. 39:437–447, April, 1969.

Birch, H. G., and Gussow, J. D.: *Disadvantaged Children: Health, Nutrition and School Failure.* New York, Grune and Stratton, 1970.

Chalfant, J. C., and Scheffelin, M. A.: *Central Processing Dysfunctions in Children: A Review of Research.* NINDS Monograph #9. U.S. Department of Health, Education and Welfare, Bethesda, Mary-land, 1969.

Cochrane, H. S., and Di Buono, T. J.: *Health Care of Children—A Challenge.* Syracuse, Syracuse University Press, 1970.

Cohn, R.: The neurological study of children with learning disabil-ities. *Exceptional Children,* 31:179, 1964.

Connors, C. K.: Drugs and learning in children. In Hellmuth (Ed.): *Learning Disorders,* Vol. 3. Seattle, Special Child Publications, 1966.

Connors, C. K.: The syndrome of minimal brain damage. *Pediatric Clinics of North America,* 14, 4:749–766, Nov., 1967.

Cratty, B.: *Motor Activity and the Education of the Retarded.* Phila-delphia, Lea and Feibiger, 1969.

Denhoff, E.: Developmental and predictive characteristics of items from the Meeting Street School Screening Test. *Developmental Medicine and Child Neurology,* 1968, 10:220–232.

Di Buono, T. J.: Training programs. In *Report of 61st Ross Confer-ence on Pediatric Research—Learning Disorders in Children.* Co-lumbus, Ohio, Ross Laboratories, 1971.

Eccles, J. C.: *The Neurophysiologic Bases of Mind.* New York, Ameri-can Phys. Soc., 3:1919, 1960.

Fernald, G. M.: *Remedial Techniques in Basic School Subjects.* New York, McGraw-Hill, 1943.

Frankenburg, W., and Dodds, J.: The Denver Developmental Screen-ing Test. *Journal of Pediatrics,* 71:181, 1967.

Frostig, M.: *Development Test of Visual Perception.* Palo Alto, Calif., Consulting Psychologists Press, 1963.

Galambos, R., and Morgan, C. T.: The neural basis of learning. In *Handbook of Physiology.* Sect. 1—Neurophysiology, Vol. III. Washington, D.C., American Physiological Society, 1960.

Gellhorn, E.: *Principles of Autonomic-Somatic Integration.* Minne-apolis, University of Minnesota Press, 1967.

Hebb, D. O.: *The Organization of Behavior*. London: Chapman and Hall, 1949.

Hernandez-Peon, P.: Reticular mechanisms of sensory control. In Rosenblith, W. A. (Ed.): *Sensory Communication*. New York, M.I.T. Press, John Wiley and Sons, 1961.

Kagan, J., and Lewis, M.: Studies of attention in the human infant. *Merrill-Palmer Quarterly*, 2, 2:95–127.

Kephart, N.: *The Slow Learner in the Classroom*. Columbus, Ohio, 1960.

Koppitz, E. M.: *The Bender-Gestalt Test for Young Children*. New York, Grune and Stratton, 1964.

Lacey, J., and Kagan, J.: The visceral level—situational determinants and behavioral correlates of autonomic response patterns. In Knapp, P. H. (Ed.): *Expression of the Emotions in Men*. International Universities Press, 1963.

Ladd, E. T.: Pills for classroom peace. *Saturday Review,* Nov. 21, 1970.

Lashley, K. S.: In Band, P. (Ed.): *Patterns of Organization in the C.N.S.* Baltimore, Williams and Wilkins, 1952.

Laufer, E., Denhoff, E., and Solomons, G.: Hyperkinetic impulse disorder in children's behavior problems. *Psychosomatic Medicine,* 19, *1*:38–49, 1957.

Lawson, L. J.: Ophthalmologic factors in learning disabilities. In Myklebust (Ed.): *Progress in Learning Disabilities,* Vol. 1. New York, Grune and Stratton, 1968.

Lipton, E., and Steinschneider, A.: Studies on the psychophysiology of infancy. In Brackbill, Y. and Thompson, G.: *Behavior in Infancy and Early Childhood*. New York, MacMillan, 1967.

Lloyd, L. L.: Audiologic aspects of mental retardation. In Ellis, N. (Ed.): *International Review of Research in Mental Retardation,* Vol. 4. New York, Academic Press, 1970.

Luria, A. R.: *Human Brain and Psychological Processes*. New York, Harper and Row, 1966.

Magoun, H. W.: *The Walking Brain,* 2nd Edition. Springfield, Ill., Thomas, 1963.

Millichap, G., and Fowler: Treatment of "minimal brain dysfunction" syndromes. *Pediatric Clinics of North America,* 14, *4*:767–779, Nov., 1967.

Myklebust, H., and Johnson, D.: *Learning Disabilities: Educational Principles and Practices*. New York, Grune and Stratton, 1967.

Ozer, M.: The neurological evaluation of children in Head Start. In

Hellmuth (Ed.): *The Disadvantaged Child,* Vol. 3. Seattle, Special Child Publications, 1968.

Penfield, W.: *Handbook of Neurophysiology.* Washington, D.C., American Physiological Society, Sec. 1, Vol. III, p. 1441, 1960.

Penfield, W., and Roberts, L.: *Speech and Brain Mechanisms.* Princeton, New Jersey, Princeton University Press, 1959.

Richmond, J. B.: Child Development: A basic science for pediatrics. *Pediatrics, 39*:360, May, 1967.

Richmond, J. B. (with Di Buono, T. J.): Epidemnology of learning disorders. In *Report of 61st Ross Conference on Pediatric Research—Learning Disorders in Children.* Columbus, Ohio, Ross Laboratories, 1971.

Richmond, J. B., and Lustman, S. L.: Total Health—A conceptual visual aid. *Journal of Medical Education,* May, 1954.

Venables, P. H., and Martin, J.: *A Manual of Psychophysiological Methods.* Amsterdam, North-Holland Publishing Co., 1967.

Wepman, J.: *Auditory Discrimination Test.* Chicago, Language Research Associates, 1958.

Werry, J. S.: The diagnosis, etiology, and treatment of hyperactivity in children. In Hellmuth (Ed.): *Learning Disorders,* Vol. 3. Seattle, Special Child Publications, 1966.

Zedler, E. Y.: Screening underachieving pupils for risk of neurological impairment. In Hellmuth (Ed.): *Learning Disorders,* Vol. 3. Seattle, Special Child Publications, 1968.

Chapter III

THE SOCIAL WORKER AND LEARNING DISABILITIES IN CHILDREN

RUTH R. GOSSETT

Smith (1968) suggests that the baffling, subtle and amorphous qualities of learning disabilities have varying impacts on the youngster as well as on others who have responsibility for his care and education. For the child, learning disabilities can be frustrating, chaotic and painful; for the teacher, exasperating; and for the parent, anxiety-building and guilt-provoking. Therein lie the social worker's directions in treatment of children with learning disabilities: the teacher, the child, and the parent. These roles and functions expand to include treatment of families and communities.

The social worker's goals are, therefore, the reduction of the level of frustration within the youngster, the elimination of much of the aggravation for the teacher, the elimination of much guilt for the parent, the development of acceptance within the family and the amelioration of conditions within the community which contribute to and perpetuate learning disabilities in children.

The social worker's contacts with children with learning disabilities traditionally have been initiated by schools, medical facilities and families, usually in that order. Many families are either unaware of or unable to accept retarded intellectual development in their children prior to the child becoming of school age, unless of course, the lack of development is so gross that it becomes readily observable or is combined with other areas of retarded development. In any case, the social worker's responsibility is clearly that of bringing all of the possible resources to bear for the enhancement of individual functioning. Basic to treatment, which includes the harnessing of resources, is the acquisition of a knowledge and skills base:

1. Knowledge of cause, treatment and prevention.
2. Knowledge of the relationship of disabilities to interpersonal relationships.
3. Knowledge of the relationship of learning disabilities to the total functioning of the family unit.
4. Knowledge of the impact of learning disabilities on the individual child and how they affect his relationship to his environment.
5. Skills in the provision of ancillary and referral services to the various constituents.
6. Skill in the development of a frame within which other professionals and constituents can "look at" the impact of family interaction, life style, culture and environment on children's ability to relate positively to academics.
7. Skills in positively affecting functional, attitudinal and behavioral change in individuals and social systems.

This chapter, therefore, will be devoted to an historical overview of the social worker and learning disabilities, the identification of the constituents of the learning disabilities (including those which lie outside the individual), and the nature of the social worker's role in treating each constituent.

HISTORICAL OVERVIEW

In researching the history of school social work, Costin (1969) found that prior to 1906 the social worker's contact with children in this category was primarily through private agencies and civic organizations. The impact therefore was limited to small numbers of children. These agencies and organizations served as advocates with school boards for the provision of social-work services to children within the school systems. New York City, Boston, Massachusetts, and Hartford, Connecticut, school boards accepted the value of social work and agreed to finance and administer it as an

integral part of the system in the school year 1906–07. This acceptance was influenced largely by:

1. Legislation concerning compulsory school attendance for
   children.
2. Developing awareness of the differences in individual needs
   and conditions for response.
3. Recognition of the importance of school and education and
   the pertinence of education to the child's present and future
   life (Costin, 1969).

The social worker's presence in the schools (public) at that
point was not related directly to learning or inability to learn, but
to irregular school attendance. Visits were made to the home for
determination of the reason for absence. During that period, child
labor laws were in the formative stages of legislative development
and children frequently left school at early ages to become gain-
fully employed. The conditions that the social worker found in
many of the homes often verified the need for additional family
income and the social worker had the responsibility of interpreting the value of education to parents and children alike.

As legislation expanded, the scope of compulsory school laws
was enlarged to provide for larger groups of children within a
wider age distribution and greater range of abilities and interest.
Within this group, the social worker's role was basically the same
with parents but took on another dimension with teachers and
administrators. That role was one of interpreting the impact of
forces outside the school on the child's ability to take advantage
of educational opportunities.

In the thirties, the depression retarded not only the growth of
school social work but also the growth of social services to children. Beginning with the forties, school social work began another
period of expansion and was accepted as an integral part of the
school system. The method was primarily *casework*. In 1955,
group work was introduced in direct service to children. The
focus was directed at helping individuals to use what the school
systems had to offer. Currently, social workers within the school
systems and outside of the school systems are providing an advocate's role, focusing on the total community as a means of helping

the schools use and develop more positively the basic resources the children bring to the school situation.

Although casework and group work continue to dominate the social worker's function with learning disabilities, the *team* approach and the *community organization* approach are growing as more viable means of treatment of children, families and community. Casework involves working with the individual child, his teacher and the parent. Group work involves peers, teachers, and parents, both on individual and group bases. The team approach is one of working in collaboration with the teacher, principal, and various other professional persons within the school. The community organization approach involves parents in schools and community groups that advocate change within the schools and other social systems. All of these methods have a role to play in the provision of comprehensive services, and must extend beyond the child to others who have responsibility for shaping the child's future.

IDENTIFICATION OF CONSTITUENTS

It is not possible to discuss learning disabilities without recognizing the children who represent the largest group of children labeled as non-learners. These are the deprived children of the poor—the children who lack the emotional stimulation and motivation because of the circumstances of their birth. Treatment of this group is most difficult because of failure of some parents, teachers, professionals, etc., to recognize the negative impact of unequal opportunities, services, and facilities on this group.

Smith (1968) points out that our basic concern for children with learning disabilities is because of the diversity and degrees of disability; some less handicapped youngsters can compensate more easily than others; some need longer periods of specialized care.

In being concerned for children, we view the child as a composite of his environment, an environment upon which he has some impact, an environment which has some impact on him. In spite of the fact that he is an integral part of this environment, he is an entity with a self. Treatment of the child must therefore deal with the total being—the being as a member of a family group, a peer group, a cultural group, a member of a community and of a larger society. These groupings comprise an environment with which the child can live in either harmony or conflict. The level of functioning and well-being of one or a combination of these groupings will determine how the child lives within them.

The concept of family, its responsibility and its interaction with the child should be fairly clear. Within the context of the family is included the extended family. Less clear might be the concept of community and its relationship to the individual and to the larger society. Within this context are included church, school, health, education and welfare agencies, and recreational facilities. The concept of society is being dealt with as a social order from which laws emanate. This concept indeed works both ways, and both affects and is affected by the quality and interaction of community, family, and individual life.

Children with learning disabilities are particularly vulnerable to the dysfunction of the groupings. Social workers' intervention with the child and one or more of the groupings on some level can transform a conflictual barren existence to one of harmony with enrichment.

When family life breaks down, less security and support are provided, protection is weakened, and basic needs often go unmet. When cultural groups fail to function adequately, a sense of belonging and continuity is lost, isolation occurs, and security suffers. When peer groups fail, socialization and identity suffer. When communities become dysfunctional, services become fragmented and inadequate. When society fails, rights and privileges are threatened. All of these components must be operational to provide comprehensive services to those who have problems with understanding basic realities of the universe which surrounds them.

THE NATURE OF
THE SOCIAL WORKER'S ROLE IN TREATMENT

An in-depth treatment plan for each constituency or component of a child who is a disabled learner will not be undertaken at this point. The focus will be directed to outlining treatment possibilities for the child as a unit, the parents and family as a unit, and the teacher and community as a unit (the unit thereby being identified as the client).

There are some generic principles which should be kept in mind which are of equal value in planning with each unit in the treatment milieu. These principles are:

1. Basic belief in the uniqueness of each individual.
2. Basic belief that each unit possesses basic common human needs.
3. Basic belief that behavior functions and attitudes are modifiable.
4. Basic belief that each individual possesses certain strengths.

In treatment, the most valuable tool is the self. In order to modify behavior, increase total functioning and alter attitudes, a healthy working relationship must be developed.

All children have similar developmental stages. However, continuity of development is more difficult for the handicapped.

Infancy is described by Schauer (1951) as being the developmental stage when there is complete dependence on the parent figure, usually the mother. During this period, the parent provides the model for identification and imitation, and healthy growth dictates that the infant have a warm feeling for this model. The learning disabled child is often deficient in his ability to identify with and imitate this model without external assistance. He is therefore retarded in his progression from infancy to childhood. At the very early stages of development, there is also the need for reality testing, at which time the child must differentiate between friendly and dangerous surroundings. Nemiah (1961) explains the process of early development as being complicated, taking place under the influence of 1) the innate thrust to maturation, which determines growth potential, and 2) the physical and human environment which, with external pressures, shapes and molds the child and determines whether and in what manner potential is achieved.

Within this context, then, the learning disabled child has little understanding of the pressures placed on him by external, physical and human environments, and his inner potential for development is in jeopardy. It is necessary for the social worker to recognize the complexity of the problem prior to instituting help in order to deliver comprehensive services.

Hirshberg (Smith, 1968) considers five aspects of learning disabilities: 1) psychological; 2) physical brain damage which affects psychological factors in learning; 3) sociological factors; 4) motivational factors, and 5) emotional factors.

These considerations sketch out a framework within which the social worker plans in terms of *needs-provision* and *problem-solving,* as each one or a combination of these factors has some bearing on the over-all problem.

Learning-disabled children, like their learning counterparts, need love, food, clothing, shelter, security, education and protection; any plan must necessarily build in these items. Therefore it is most important to also treat those whose responsibility it is to provide the above.

The worker, having prepared himself with the base of knowledge and skills, given the proper attention to the general principles and special considerations, must explore within himself his own fears, guilt, and pity which surround him when confronted in a helping relationship with those who are different. Having dealt with himself on these issues he is now ready to begin to plan and implement a treatment regime.

The social worker must determine which method or combination of methods will best serve his client. In many cases, casework and groupwork with the youngster might be appropriate. Both methods can be implemented by the same social worker. Timing is of the essence in determining the introduction of a new method into the treatment regime. In some instances, it might be decided that a casework situation is the most valuable at a given time with one of its objectives being integration into a group situation. In other cases, the group situation might come first, with one of its objectives being tolerance of a casework situation; or both could be used simultaneously, the objective being integration into a more structured, less homogeneous group situation.

In addition to method, in spite of the general principles, there are also some very specific treatment methodologies and goals for the child. Individual goals vary with the youngster; however, the basic goal for all the learning-disabled is better social adjustment.

To attain better social adjustment, there must be greater ego strength; the child must have successful and satisfying experiences on many levels, through various interpersonal relationships. A result of the development of greater ego strength is greater acceptance of self and individual limitations.

Many tools can be utilized in helping the disabled. These tools or materials must always be introduced and used purposefully, the social worker utilizing materials other than himself to communicate, to provide pleasure, to develop motor skills and to determine interests. Consultations with other professionals involved are also considered tools—tools utilized to enable the youngster to function at his maximum.

Consideration will now be given to some of the mechanics of how to reach the client. The social worker must become very involved in setting the focus of the interview and with those children whose language skills are retarded and who experience difficulty in understanding verbal communication will need to rely more heavily on non-verbal skills in conveying an attitude of personal interest and acceptance. The worker's use of skills in observation is helpful in determining stimuli, response, motivation and growth. According to Begab (1970), utilization of non-verbal communication skills and body movements in certain activities provides more assurance and support than repeated words. When language is used, the client's level of comprehension must be considered, and tone of voice is important in conveying understanding. In interviews with the learning-disabled, constant verbal reinforcement provides great carry-over from interview to interview.

Utilization of the formal interview with most children, especially those children who experience difficulty in relationships, is not always the most efficient and effective method of eliciting appropriate responses. The worker should therefore take advantage of community resources, utilizing various settings: parks, office, the child's home, recreation centers, etc., to help shorten the communication gap. Appointments should be consistent so that the youngster will know when to expect the worker, and what preparations must be made for the visit. The worker must be warm and accepting, yet able to be firm and set limits. Reward freely only when appropriate!

Although Begab (1970) believes that a basic principle in social work is the client's right to self-determination, he also believes that there are many constraints placed on this right when the client is incapable of making decisions in his own best interest. For the individual who is unable to exercise reason and judgement, it is unrealistic to stress such a right since reality includes the external environmental pressures and the capacity of the individual to choose between alternative courses of action. One whose reason and judgment are impaired has need of protection from his own imprudence. In spite of the fact that many children will be in need of continuous personal care, supervision and protection, they do have the right to participate in this care, supervision and protection—within their capabilities.

The social worker's role therefore includes the training of the child for participation in roles. A method that has proved to be helpful in the development of participation in roles has been group work. Once having decided that this will be an area of concentration, the social worker, with the aid of parents and other professionals involved in the treatment, can begin to help the child move toward a meaningful group experience.

THE CHILD IN THE GROUP

Once the decision is made for group participation, the selection of a proper group is far from an easy task. Consideration for group participation should be based on the value of the group for the development of socialization skills. The goals should include the child's ability to 1) interact appropriately with his peers, 2) develop positive attitudes toward authority figures, 3) experience problem-solving and decision-making within the group context, and 4) develop a more accepting attitude toward others while 5) providing a better perspective with which to view himself.

SUMMARY

This chapter has dealt primarily with the social worker's role in treating children with learning disabilities, stressing the theory that the child is a part of a larger society which affects his ability to function within normal limits.

The social worker's major goal is the child's "increased social and academic achievement."

Methods have been described as being those of casework, group work and community organization or a combination of the three, and the roles vary from situation to situation.

Early identification and treatment provides the proper nucleus for the amelioration of adverse conditions within communities which tend to make life extremely difficult for the learning disabled.

REFERENCES

Adamson, W., Ohrenstein, D., Hersh, A., and Lake, D.: Separation used to help parents promote growth of their retarded child. *Social Work, 9*:4, 1964.

Begab, M.: Adapting techniques, in *Social Work and Mental Retardation,* Schreiber, M. (ed). New York, John Day, 1970.

Cohen, P. C.: The impact of the handicapped child on the family. *Social Casework. 43*:3, 1962.

Costin, L. B.: A historical review of school social work. *Social Casework. 50*:8, 1969.

Mendelbaum, A., and Wheeler, M. E.: The meaning of a defective child to parents. *Social Casework. 51*:7, 1960.

Nemiah, J. M.: *Foundations of Psychopathology.* New York, Oxford University Press, 1961.

Schauer, G.: Motivation of attitudes toward blindness. *Outlook for the Blind and Teachers Forum. 45*:2, 1961.

Smith, B. K.: *Your Non-learning Child.* Boston, Hagg Foundation for Mental Health, Beacon Press, 1968.

Chapter IV

VERBAL AND NON-VERBAL
LEARNING DISABILITIES

JANE L. CLARKE

A learning disability may be defined as that which prevents an intellectually and physically normal child or human individual from achieving his native, inherent capacities for absorbing information, organizing experience, and expressing the synthesis in ideas and actions, at a level that comports with his true potential.

Learning may be generally categorized into two distinct and discrete areas—verbal (communicated by formal language) and non-verbal (communicated by other than formal language experience).

Education, using the term in its broadest sense, is most effective when the two categories are smoothly synchronized in a human individual, as for example, when academic learning is synchronized with non-academic experience. Verbal learning involves digital codification, most notably in the phonetic alphabet and in numerical systems. Nonverbal learning involves analogic codifications, or a series of symbols that in proportion and relation are similar to the thing, idea or event for which they stand. Both are experienced through the five hierarchies of learning; sensation, perception, imagery, symbolization, and conceptualization.

Individuals may experience learning disabilities in either or both verbal and nonverbal areas. Both types can be habilitated although considerably more experience has been built up in the verbal area. Up to now, little has been known or tried relative to nonverbal learning disabilities. This situation results naturally from the fact that formal education traditionally has been, and currently is, most concerned with verbal learning. Reading (in its broadest sense) is of course central.

My experience, although initially and for a considerable time aimed at habilitation techniques for verbal or specific language disabilities, has inexorably brought me face to face with the parallel importance of nonverbal disabilities. Habilitation techniques for nonverbal learning disabilities are even more in their infancy. The following discussion describes, first, experience with, research into, and habilitative methods for specific verbal disability, and secondly the resulting and similar experience with and developing habilitation for nonverbal learning disabilities.

SOME CAUSES – VERBAL LEARNING DISABILITIES

The traditional concepts of reading, writing and symbolic mathematics, are, and will be for the foreseeable future, the critical underpinnings of academic learning in spite of modern technology and media. In the past, these skills were not as difficult to acquire as they are today. In a simpler time, there was more concentration on the "3 R's." This concentration was not diluted with so many extraneous, and often conflicting, goals and philosophies. The increasing complexity of modern society has challenged education in ways that were totally unheard of a few years ago. The simple fact of the population explosion, as only one very obvious example, causes problems in all areas. Crowded cities, roads, and institutions are now a normal way of life. The overload in many systems causes breakdowns which were not present in the past and were unforeseen for the future. Swiftly moving environmental influences have been responsible in large measure for difficulties in the language continuum which are observed in Academe today. One example which has been little explored or scientifically documented, based on the thesis of the biological origins of language, is the influence of changed diet which has been witnessed in the last generation. Lenneberg (1969) states that diet may have a great influence on the apparent increase of language disability observed in the school population today. Dietary factors, combined with the complexity of the environment, combined with an overload of visual (e.g., television) stimulus on children whose systems are not adequately developed may result in overloading the capacity to achieve the basic skills of reading, writing, and arithmetic. Children whose ability to absorb and discriminate is not developed sufficiently to be able to adjust to the impact of television without some type of detrimental impact surely must suffer a certain amount of injurious effect.

TOWARD A SOLUTION OF PROBLEMS
IN VERBAL LEARNING DISABILITIES

Until there is a combination of the varied peripheral knowledge in the field of learning disabilities, it will become increasingly difficult to develop research toward an understanding of their causes, as well as the measures necessary to prevent these disabilities from developing in the first place. In the meantime, it is the responsibility of education to provide opportunity for individuals who are capable of great contributions to society if properly educated; individuals whose functioning is handicapped by one or more of the disabilities for which effective methods of compensation are now known. These methods unfortunately are not uniformly or universally understood.

Amidst all the confusion and talk about children in the school population who do not read adequately, it is important to keep foremost in mind the simple truth that all human beings differ; each is unique by virtue of being a human being. It is not possible for all students to learn how to read by the same method. Children who have adequate sight and hearing, adequate emotional adjustment, adequate motor coordination, and average or above average intelligence all differ, and each is unique. They all may be categorically summarized as normal, yet all normal children do not learn to read by the same method.

Each one of us has neurological idiosyncracies, most of which can be classified as normal. Thus far, this has prevented the development and acceptance of any one method of teaching reading as being uniformly most effective. It might be advisable to use the look-say method for Johnny, strict association between auditory and visual symbols (an enlarged synthesized phonetic method) for Billy, the tracing method for Dick, and the perceptual motor method for Harry. Possibly an answer to the whole problem with intellectually normal children is simply training teachers to understand all methods, and training them to understand in which cases the various methods are appropriate. If this is the case, then the solution lies in a different approach to elementary school teacher training. In addition to an understanding of the various methods of teaching reading, such training must include greater understanding of learning and reading disabilities, and greater in-depth understanding of the already-available methods of coping with them.

RATIONALE FOR PROBLEMS

Our nation's educators expect children to read their way to maturity. These children are entitled to a proper preparation for the long journey. A child with a reading disability from whatever cause is unable, within the normal school program, to develop the skills necessary for the educational growth of which he is inherently capable. Children with good intellectual capacity, currently unable to profit *fully* from a regular school program, deserve the opportunity to develop the skills that would be expected from their inheritance and background.

Some children have had repeated failures in their lives and have poor social skills because of a distorted self-concept. This distorted self-image can be the result of a learning disability. Until the learning disability is corrected and a better self-concept obtained, the basic insecurity will continue to exist. The desperate plight of the normal child with a reading disability is so very tragic because his minor impairments are so psychologically destructive. His neurological idiosyncracies which cause the reading disability may be no more severe than the neurological idiosyncracies which we all have as individuals.

A learning disability can be as crippling for an intellectually normal individual as polio, muscular dystrophy, or multiple sclerosis is for a physically able body. If we understand that a child with perfectly formed muscles and bones cannot walk due to a neurological impairment, it should not be difficult to understand that a child can have difficulty in reading, writing, and spelling due to neurological impairment. The striving and the struggling for achievement by children who instinctively know they are not stupid, mentally retarded, or emotionally disturbed, leave scars which can be irremedial unless the disability is identified and treated. The inner frustrations and distortion of self-concept often bring on behavioral overlays which are the *result* of the learning disability and *not the cause* of it.

CLASSIFICATION OF READING PROBLEMS

In dealing with the great number of intellectually normal children seen in a regular school classroom who have problems in learning, it must be recognized that world-wide research today indicates that from 15% to 25% of the world's population normally have some type of verbal or reading disability. The term "functionally illiterate" is one which former Commissioner James E. Allen, Jr. uses. Within this category there exists a wide range of problems in reading, writing, spelling, grammar, syntax, and symbolic logic (arithmetic). Compensatory methods thus far developed are generally referred to as either *remedial* or *corrective* or *reconstructive*. ("Developmental" methods are here considered to be those which have as their objective the achievement of more efficient and speedier reading, comprehension, organization and expressive skills on the part of the average or above-average student without a reading disability. They do not apply to this discussion of methods for habilitating individuals with learning disabilities. The term "developmental reading" and "remedial reading" unfortunately are widely used in loose and confusing ways.) *Remedial* methods are, or should be, aimed at providing abilities or skills which are not present in individuals because of the failure of that individual to acquire them early enough. There is a variety of reasons for this category of disabilities. Probably the most important reason is that the original training and reading methods were inappropriate for that individual. This category includes many students whose performance is not sufficiently consistent with grade standard to warrant the use of accelerated developmental techniques.

In addition to those language art handicaps for which developmental and remedial techniques are properly therapeutic, there is a group of problems which currently are being subjected to either developmental or remedial procedures but which belong in the category of those needing *corrective* help. Individuals who should be helped with habilitative teaching are usually those silent ones who fall by the wayside because their actual handicaps are unrecognized, unknown or undiagnosed by most educators. These individuals are capable, with the right help, of making solid, substantial contributions to society. This category includes those students with whom I have worked most exhaustively.

For these individuals, verbal learning disability designations include the following: dyslexia or specific language disability; perceptual handicap; psychoneurogenic learning disability; neurological handicap. *Dyslexia* used as the inclusive term designates a learning disability which prevents a child from reading adequately even though he is of average, or in many cases above-average intelligence, has adequate vision and hearing, adequate emotional adjustment, and adequate motor integration. I want to stress "reading adequately" because most dyslexics can read a little. The ones with mild or moderate impairment are the ones found in a regular school situation. A dyslexic who has an IQ of 140 may not read accurately enough to achieve a grade of more than 60 or 65 in his academic subjects. The difficulty in recognizing this student is largely due to group IQ testing which is dependent on the ability to read accurately and therefore does not give an accurate measure of inherent ability. This condition of faulty reading is thought to be a result of either heredity, or a maturational dysfunction. Professional estimates are that at least 15% of the male population of the world is afflicted with dyslexia in varying degrees, and at least 4% of the female population. Some authorities are convinced the percentages are much higher.

DEFINITION AND HISTORICAL BACKGROUND OF DYSLEXIA

Dyslexia (derivation—dys—bad, lexis—word, speech) is not limited to the English language. A great deal of relevant research has been done in other than English-speaking countries, for example at the Word Blind Institute in Copenhagen, Denmark, and in Czechoslovakia. In 1967, Dr. Zdenek Matejcek of Prague lectured at the Congress of the World Federation of Neurology in

Dallas, Texas, on the topic of Dyslexia and World Illiteracy. Authorities from English-speaking areas who, among many others, have made recent and important contributions to the field include Dr. MacDonald Critchley of the Neurological Institute, London, England; Dr. Ralph Rabinovitch, McGill University, Montreal, Canada; Dr. John Money at Johns Hopkins, Baltimore, Maryland; Dr. Lauretta Bender; and Dr. Katrine de Hirsch at Columbia University, New York.

Dramatic happenings have occurred in the field of dyslexia during the last twenty-five years. A great many of these have been offshoots of the Cortical Function Language Laboratory established at the Massachusetts General Hospital by Dr. Edwin Cole. In 1957 Dr. Roger Saunders, then a psychologist for the Board of Education of Baltimore County, Maryland, was dissatisfied with the program dealing with reading disabilities. He instituted Gillingham-oriented training measures as advocated by the Cortical Function Language Laboratory of Massachusetts General Hospital. From this beginning, much more research and effective retraining has resulted. Some states (Vermont, Connecticut, Massachusetts, Maryland, Texas, and Pennsylvania) allocate state funds for special habilitation for dyslexics. In February 1970, the New York State Legislature passed the 1969 Legislative Act for Specific Learning Disabilities.

In 1962, the Hockaday School in Dallas, Texas, and a group of civic-minded businessmen recognized that there was a problem among children who were intellectually superior, had the inheritance and background to presume reading ability, yet were unable to read. Dr. Lucium Waites directed a program with the Orton-Gillingham-Childs techniques, upon which he reported at the 1967 meeting of the Orton Society, Inc. The program was eminently successful. Dr. Waites humorously said that the subject of dyslexia was next to God and Motherhood in the state of Texas that year. The Language Training Unit of the Scottish Rites Crippled Children's Hospital in Dallas was established as a result. In addition, one of the first pieces of scientific research on training dyslexics came out of this program documented in the form of a doctoral dissertation by Clifton W. Wolfe (Wolfe, 1966).

In order to understand dyslexia, it is necessary to broaden one's superficial concept of "reading" to include not only the extraction of meaning in the orthodox sense but also the neurological organization involving the areas of language in the cortex of the brain. When you teach a child to read, write, or spell, you are teaching him a basic neurological function. An understanding of dyslexia therefore must be based on a knowledge of the neurological processes necessary for learning: one, the psychodynamic factors; two, the peripheral nervous system functions; and three, the central nervous system functions. *Psychodynamic factors* are the emotional-psychic processes consisting of first, identification, second, imitation, and third, internalization (Johnson and Myklebust 1967). Identification occurs when an infant hears the sound of his first babbling. Babbling is the first expressive human act. This requires auditory feedback, or imitation to be meaningful. The baby makes a sound, hears himself make the sound (identification), duplicates the same sound (imitation), and assigns meaning to it (internalization). Internalization can be defined as the assimilation of the surrounding environment. The *Peripheral Nervous System* includes all the sensory modalities. The *Central Nervous System* is the area in which the neurology of learning in dyslexics is disturbed. The condition is a disability, not an inability.

UNDERSTANDING DYSLEXIA

Dyslexia is sometimes called a perceptual handicap. This designation is not precise because in dyslexia the organs, such as the eye and the ear, correctly perceive. It is the neurological impairment of the perception which causes the trouble. (Perception can be disturbed for many reasons which are not involved in dyslexia; emotional disturbance, deafness, blindness, mental retardation. These cases are not relevant to this discussion.)

Conceiving the process of learning through hierarchies of experience is helpful in understanding dyslexia. These hierarchies may be designated *sensation, perception, imagery, symbolization* and *conceptualization* (Johnson and Myklebust 1967). For example, any peripheral nervous system impairment in *auditory or visual sensation* can disturb the first stage of the learning process. At whatever point an integral requisite for learning is blocked, each step beyond this level is also blocked. The second process is *perception,* which is an awareness relative to ongoing sensations. Factors which interfere with perception can cause inadequate transducing of symbols from auditory to visual or from visual to auditory. The third process, *imagery,* is the cognitive functioning of auditory and visual stimuli; the dyslexic is deficient in this process of imagery because of faulty association of the visual and the auditory symbols. Fourth is *symbolization,* translating experience into words or other symbols, and vice versa; this process organizes past experiences into meaningful units and permits output of information from the language center of the brain. The dyslexic has a deficiency in symbolization due to inaccurate imagery. The fifth process is *conceptualization,* the ability to recognize relationships among experiences. A child learns the experience of a chair, then *his* chair. Then he abstracts or classifies into all chairs. Finally, he conceptualizes into furniture. Students with difficulty in conceptualization cannot generalize and have trouble, for example, with proverbs and metaphors. Any dysfunction in the brain which alters the learning process also interferes with conceptualization. Therefore, this also is an area of concern in dyslexia.

We have said that, if we understand how a child with perfectly formed muscles and bones cannot walk due to a neurological impairment, it should also be understandable that an individual can have difficulty in reading, spelling, writing, and speaking due to neurological impairment. To repeat our previous definition, dyslexia, and a variety of other currently used terms, refers to a learning disability which prevents a child from reading adequately although he is of average, or in many cases above average, intelligence and has adequate vision, hearing, emotional adjustment, and adequate motor integration. The word "reading" as used in this context refers to a cerebral process that includes both the cognitive and the affective aspects of communication as related to human development. For our purpose it is limited to the field of formal language as developed in the combination of the spoken and the written word.

THE ACQUISITION OF READING ABILITY

The beginning of normal word-meaning acquisition is by means of sound related to experience, and then sound and sight related to experience. The experience is related into sound and sight symbols—words spoken, heard, or written, which have meaning. Normally sound and sight symbols become integrated so that they are automatically conjoined as one. However, it is actually a two-track system. An otherwise normal and intelligent individual's ability to receive information, to establish relationships, and to express the resulting integration of information (to hear and speak, to comprehend, and to read and write) may be impaired if one or more of the connecting lines between sound and sight is lacking or faulty. When an individual cannot automatically effect this conjoining, the process of learning to read does not follow the usual pattern.

Children normally acquire a relatively large speaking vocabulary before learning to read. They express themselves orally with simple syntax. They understand much more complex syntax when it is spoken to them. At the level of beginning reading, the symbol system involves the form of the alphabetical letter associated with the sound it represents. In addition it involves much more complex integration processes of developing comprehension. The symbol system eventually evolves into logical thinking, conceptualization, and expression.

Learning to read, however, will be difficult if something obstructs the rapid establishment of an increasingly automatic and unconscious connection between sounds and their written symbols. In such cases, the mind seems to try to treat the printed page as totally divorced from aurally learned language. Reading and writing become inaccurate translation processes which are increasingly distasteful and seemingly useless, even to individuals with good intellectual capacity. Unable to profit normally in what is generally considered "academic learning" (particularly the current traditional school program), these individuals are led to consider themselves "dumb" and are often so considered by others. Educational practice today all too often equates reading facility with intellectual capacity. Not only is this a fundamental error, but in addition the concept works a double hardship on those truly intelligent individuals whose learning hierarchies are neurologically "different"—in other words, dyslexic.

A dyslexic may be denied, in varying degrees and combinations, the following abilities of the normal reader:

1. Ability to associate meaning with graphic symbols.
2. Ability to understand words in context and to select meaning that fits the context.
3. Ability to read in thought units.
4. Ability to understand language units of increasing size; the phrase, clause, sentence, paragraph, whole selection.
5. Ability to acquire word meanings.
6. Ability to select and understand main ideas.
7. Ability to follow directions.
8. Ability to draw inferences.
9. Ability to understand a writer's organization.
10. Ability to evaluate what is read, to recognize literary devices and identify tone, mood, and intent of writer.
11. Ability to apply ideas and to integrate them with past experience.

The foregoing limitations are mentioned here with immediate concern for their effects upon reading, used in its broadest sense as a human intellectual activity. However, extrapolating one's thinking about the possible effects of these handicaps into all areas of an individual's relationships with his environment inevitably brings the conclusion that these handicaps may also significantly affect many diverse, "normal" human capabilities—for example, directional and distance perception, physical dexterity, automobile operating judgment, social relations, value judgments, capacity for self-understanding and fulfillment. The belief that habilitation of dyslexics can significantly affect the most fundamental aspects of their lives inspires a unique dedication on the part of those individuals who have struggled in the face of many odds and much misunderstanding to develop effective diagnostic and corrective measures in this field.

EDUCATIONAL EVALUATION OF DYSLEXIA

It must be understood that it becomes necessary, in analyzing, diagnosing, and dealing with verbal learning disabilities, to take apart the various learning systems of an individual in order to understand all of the complex aspects of a disability in reading, a disability in spelling, a disability in writing, a disability in arithmetc. This is necessary in order to discover and label what needs to be treated. However, these systems then must be synthesized into the whole being, the individual child, with a thorough understanding of the bits and pieces of various systems which are out of order. Possibly, it is this approach which has lead to the belief that dyslexia or a verbal learning disability is an umbrella for many conditions.

Returning to the more specific consideration of dyslexia and reading, an illustrative example not infrequently experienced in diagnosis and therapy is the student who has an IQ of 120 or better, has adequate vision, hearing, motor coordination, and emotional adjustment, but who cannot read, cannot write even the sequential order of the letters of the alphabet, cannot sequence letters in a word for proper orthography. One important reason for this is faulty transducing, or lack of association between the auditory and the visual symbol. As mentioned previously, the normal development of the language continuum in the human proceeds from the experience, to the sound, to the sight.

For instance, a child of six months discovers a dog. He can watch it, stroke it, hear it bark. This is the experience. Someone labels the experience by saying /dog/. Later on when the child attends school the teacher writes "dog" on the blackboard. The child must connect what he sees on the board with what he has heard—/dog/—with the actual experience of the dog. Therefore, reading can be defined as a symbol system twice removed from reality: experience to sound to sight. This definition of reading is of paramount importance to the understanding of dyslexia.

The ability to sequence is as essential to reading as it is to reason and logic. Dyslexics may evidence sequencing difficulties by seeing *gril* for *girl*. Reversing may appear in spelling or syllabification—*conversation* for *conservation, reserve* for *reverse*.

Inversing is another manifestation—*u* for *n*, *b* for *p*, *d* for *g*. Spatial concepts of time, size, shape, distance and direction can be distorted in dyslexia—particularly auditory dyslexia.

TYPES OF DYSLEXIA

There are, incidentally, two general types of dyslexia—visual and auditory. Some children can copy perfectly but cannot read what they copy. There is no auditory association with what they see. Some can read but have no association with what they hear and therefore cannot take notes from a lecture. In these children the eye perceives correctly. Ophthalmologists state that it takes a 50% refractory error to interfere with reading as far as the organ of the eye is concerned (Cole and Walker, 1964). The ear perceives. A 35-decibel error in the organ of the ear usually is present before reading is disturbed as far as the organ of the ear is concerned. The perceptions are made but the information does not have a clear neurological pathway to the brain and is not properly integrated in the language area in the cortex of the brain. In habilitation for dyslexics, a connection or link must be created by drill and repeated association in order to lock in a pattern that will accomplish the necessary integration. Ideally, this involves a simultaneous, triangular synthesis of visual symbol, auditory symbol, and kinesthetic representation. A clear-cut, single pattern is seldom seen in dyslexia. There is usually multi-involvement. Disorders of auditory language, dysgraphia (inability to write or spell) and dyscalculia (inability to form numerical concepts) may all be involved in a dyslexic.

DIFFERENTIATION BETWEEN
AUDITORY AND VISUAL DYSLEXIA

Dyslexics with auditory disorders are much more difficult to habilitate than those with visual disorders. Audition is the primary channel for language acquisition and interpersonal communication. The disorientation of spatial concepts involved in auditory dyslexia is difficult to correct. Even teenagers with auditory dyslexia might fail to grasp the meaning of prepositions and adverbs like *under, on, around.* Told to "draw a line around" a word or a symbol printed on a page, a dyslexic might say "I can't because I can't get behind it." The concept of "around" becomes confused. It is a different concept in the "the bus travels around the city," and "a line around a word" on a printed page. The word *around* in "line around the word" has a vertical plane while the word *around* in "around the city" has a horizontal plane. The words *since, while, before, after,* cause trouble because the concept of relative time is involved. The normal reader acquires these concepts automatically. The function and meaning of adjectives is also difficult to grasp. The concept *characterized by* was very hard for a dyslexic student with an IQ of 140 to grasp. The concept must be approached by another route—*belonging to* or *pertaining to*. Homonyms, as well as words which perform two functions cause trouble; e.g., *cover* as a verb and *cover* as a noun. Here the process of symbolization in the development of learning is fragmentary or absent and requires careful and patient habilitation or construction by means of an understanding of grammar and the function of various parts of speech.

VISUAL DYSLEXIA

The visual dyslexic has other problems, particularly in spelling. Spelling requires the ability to reauditorize and revisualize letters or combinations of letters in sequence. The visual dyslexic frequently has topographical disorders and cannot read graphs, maps, globes, or floor plans. He cannot spatialize symbolically, which interferes with geography and mathematics. The visual dyslexic often has not learned whole words. He must be trained to recognize word parts and then to synthesize them into a whole. The auditory dyslexic can see whole words but has not yet learned to relate visual components of words to their auditory equivalent. He frequently cannot hear double consonant sounds and cannot discriminate among short vowels. A disturbance in auditory sequence sometimes results in disturbance in articulation such as *emeny* or *meny* for *enemy*. The visual dyslexic learns from the partial method, while the auditory dyslexic learns from the global or whole method.

Dyslexics sometimes have deviant motor patterns in varying degrees of severity. There is no gross motor involvement but there can be aberrant locomotor coordination, balance, and manual dexterity. They may find it difficult to manipulate small pieces. They may be awkward and perhaps subject to tripping and falling. They may possess an unusual degree of cerebral laterality distribution. However, these characteristics by themselves cannot be considered in any sense diagnostic.

ACADEMIC IMPLICATIONS OF VERBAL LEARNING DISABILITIES

In the context of current educational methodology, including teacher training both for general education and for the traditional discipline areas (English, Mathematics, Social Studies, Science, Foreign Language, etc.), it is not surprising that little is understood or done, except in specific corrective reading training, about the effects of a learning disability such as dyslexia upon a student's capacity to achieve in academic pursuits. Nonetheless, relating the symptoms and limiting characteristics of such a disability to the learning requirements of these discipline areas makes immediately obvious the frustrations these individuals experience. Inability to sequence, and to integrate auditory and visual symbols, as explained earlier, can be devastatingly disruptive in the presently normal method of learning either one's own or a foreign language.

Mathematics is a symbolic language dealing with magnitude, with relationships between figures and forms, and with relationships between quantities (both observed and logically projected), to arrive at conclusions or hypotheses. Inability to perceive accurately, to sequence, and to integrate, quite obviously may create insurmountable stumbling blocks in mathematics also. The learning process in the natural and social sciences and in the humanities involves the same hierarchies of learning described earlier and also infinite combinations of the verbal and mathematical language continuums. All are affected in varying degrees by verbal learning disabilities.

Habilitation of the language continuum for disabled verbal learners requires the concept of programming with reinforcement based on operant conditioning paradigms. The goal is accuracy in reading in its broadest sense leading to effective discrimination among concepts for reception, internalization, and expression. Whether the disabled individual has an IQ of 100 or of 140, with the proper help he can learn to function more nearly commensurate with his own inherent ability. Ideally, this could be accomplished most effectively by utilizing appropriate aspects of programing with reinforcement in all academic discipline areas. This approach was described at the October, 1969, Orton Society meeting by C. Wilson Anderson, Jr., Project Director, Language Disabilities Program, Robbindale Junior and Senior High School, Minneapolis, Minnesota. Specific Language Disability (SLD) classes in English and Mathematics are a regular part of the curriculum. They are structured with specific techniques for students diagnosed as SLD cases and established as a constructive alternative to the widespread practice of shunting such students into courses designed for low intelligence pupils. The good results to date have brought acceptance of the desirability of developing parallel SLD courses in social studies and science. So far as is known, similar multi-disciplinary approaches exist only in small tutorial private schools.

BASIC PHILOSOPHY FOR TEACHERS OF SPECIFIC LEARNING DISABILITIES

For any teacher who is working with children with learning disabilities, we repeat again that it is necessary to understand that the child's first experience with words is hearing them spoken orally. At this stage of development, concepts become associated with the spoken word, meanings become understood. Long before a child learns to read he understands a large number of spoken words, learns to imitate them and to use them with meaning. The child's understanding of the world around him is built on these words and on unspoken experience. The words come to have meaning in his experience through many channels, including the senses of sight, hearing, taste, smell and all the haptic experiences (touch, kinesthesia, proprioceptia). He learns what *hard* means through the tactile or kinesthetic experience of touch. In contrast, he also learns what *soft* means. These haptic experiences provide physical sensations which develop the emotions of pain and pleasure, fear and security, surprise, anger, grief, etc.

A toddler's world formerly consisted only of what he sensed in his own physically limited environment. Today, the extra dimension of the world of television is added to a child's environment. With this addition to his formerly more limited environment, he may build up an experience of situations far beyond what we have believed are natural limits of comprehension in terms of emotional maturity. The results of such early vicarious experience comprise an area in which a great deal of research must be accomplished. For example, we currently have no knowledge of the effect, good or ill, of television upon existent or potential learning disabilities.

As the child builds up a world of words through hearing, he articulates by imitation. Faulty imitation can exist at this stage, such as *psaghetti* for *spaghetti*. In most children these out-of-sequence sound symbols correct themselves and there develops a secure funneling of experience and information with no obstacle. In other children, persistence of out-of-sequence sound symbols may be indicative of difficulty in the language area. Pursuing the systems approach, the connection of sound to experience is the first system which a child uses. If there is actual difficulty, it often shows up next in the association of the sound symbols and the sight symbols. Many children understand sound symbols, words spoken to them, but are unable to make the connection between the sound and what visually represents these sounds. This connection between what is heard and what is seen is essential to the ability to read. We may define reading as the ability to connect a concept with its sound symbol and also with its sight or printed symbol in proper sequence. Many children make this transition very smoothly without any difficulty. Other children, equally as intelligent, are unable to do so, and may require special training in order to be able to make the necessary connection properly.

The fact that a child may have proceeded thus far without apparent difficulty, effectively relating experience to sound symbol to sight symbol, unfortunately does not preclude the possibility of a reading disability. Although this achievement should result in effective reading ability, it by no means is the end of the verbal process. It is further necessary to be able to speak and to write words meaningfully. In addition to intellectualizing concepts and their auditory and visual symbols, it is necessary to be able to reauditorize and to revisualize these symbols in order to reproduce them; that is, to hear a sound, to see the printed or visual counterpart, and to represent the result vocally or kinesthetically in writing. The latter involves visual motor coordination, the ability to see something on the printed page, to revisualize it, and to reproduce the same form in writing.

If a child cannot remember how to form a "t" in order to write the article "the," all of his energy is taken up trying to remember how to form the "t." He may well be able to recognize the "t" on the printed page. He can recognize "the" when he hears it and understand that it is an article, but he may not be able to get it down on paper. His entire concentration is consumed in trying to remember the feel of the letter. Needless to say, this often precludes having little energy left over to think about whatever it was that he wanted to put into a sentence.

To make a present-day analogy, using a systems approach and thinking of the brain as a computer, let us imagine that this computer receives a pattern of different signals fed into it automatically. After the signals have been integrated in the brain, the response emerges. If the input is faulty in any one of its signals the response is equally so. The so-called GIGO phrase, "garbage in, garbage out," is precisely what can happen with children who have reading disabilities. It is not the inability to think, but simply that the input from one or more systems is faulty. Therefore, the output can only reflect this fault. If the child *sees* "The girl came in the house," and yet *reads* "The gril was on the horse," it is not necessarily a sign of mental retardation but simply that the input was inaccurate. Therefore, so was the output. Such a child might not be able to internalize—to "read"—*sun* because it "looks" to him like *snu*. As previously explained, this is not an ophthalmologic problem. Children who twist symbols in a word are those whose visual organization is not secure. The integration of the sight signal (what is "seen," the alphabetic representation of words) and the sound signal (the word as used auditorially) is imperative. To correct this condition, this integration must be drilled by repetition until it becomes automatic.

PROBLEMS OF DISORDERS OF AUDITORY LANGUAGE

Another observed difficulty in sound symbol-sight symbol integration, which for obvious reasons appears intensifying today, is sound overload. This is a handicap that is still little understood. Many children who have learning disabilities are able to read accurately but are unable to screen out noises and sounds in the environment. This may produce either a constant or a periodic overload. An inability to discriminate among sounds in the environment, or to connect sounds with their appropriate meaning unless there is visual reinforcement, is present in varying degrees in disorders of auditory language.

For example, a child who functions effectively one day may not function effectively in the same activity on another day. The teacher cannot understand why Billy was able to take out his book and turn to the correct page one day whereas on the following day when she gave the same instructions he was unable to do so. The difference probably was that on the first day, when Billy was able to follow directions, the teacher pointed to the proper textbook and possibly wrote the page number on the blackboard. This was visual reinforcement and the child could understand. The next day the teacher may have done nothing but give the instructions orally and the student was unable to interpret the oral instructions without visual reinforcement. Once again, the auditory stimulus and the visual stimulus must become synthesized into one system in order for it to be effective.

Very little is really understood about children with auditory language disorders. These children may suffer under a variety of handicaps. Most of them have a certain degree of body disorientation in space, finding difficulty in establishing the exact location of their own body in reference to objects spatially represented in the environment around them. Concepts of relative locations may be difficult, particularly when it involves a change in frame of reference; for example, if A is west of B and north of C, what is the location of B relative to A and C? Concepts of shape, size, weight, height, distance, and direction may be distorted. In some cases, this can interfere with driving a car. These individuals need to have the environment verbalized for them. They need a great deal more explanation and definitive teaching than children who simply are unable to connect or integrate the visual form or symbol with the auditory symbol. Certain aspects of disorder of auditory language may exist in a dyslexic classified primarily as visually handicapped.

Hearing is the individual's primary distance scanning mechanism. The individual maintains constant contact with his environment through this channel. It is also a sense of social perception, so to speak. In cases of extreme disability, children may be classified as either deaf or mentally deficient. The actual case may be that the child hears, but because auditory perception in the central nervous system is blocked or distorted, he cannot properly interpret a spoken word or an environmental sound. For instance, a child may hear the sound of an airplane but not be able to associate it correctly with the visual object which is the airplane.

There are three types of disorders of auditory language: generalized auditory deficiency; disorder of receptive language; and disorder of expressive language (Johnson and Myklebust 1967). Generalized auditory disorder involves inconsistent response to sound. As described earlier, at times a student seemingly hears what the teacher says, while at other times he appears not to be listening and is reprimanded for lack of attention. It is not lack of attention, but a tuning out of the environment at some undetermined point at which he can no longer cope with the sounds. Because these children have considerable difficulty identifying and understanding what they hear they fatigue very easily. They will, therefore, seemingly withdraw from the situation.

REHABILITATIVE TEACHING TECHNIQUES

Students with a generalized auditory deficiency must be trained to identify, locate, discriminate, and memorize sound. They must be helped to isolate and identify both verbal sounds and nonverbal environmental sounds. Differentiation of sound is difficult for them. Traffic sounds, telephone, voices, airplanes, dogs barking, radios, newspapers crackling are all environmental sounds which have to be assigned a relationship within the environment as well as a meaning. In addition to being taught to isolate and identify sound, the student must be taught to comprehend sounds. He must learn which to ignore in order that he does not respond to extraneous and irrelevant noise. For instance, with sounds of traffic, telephone, voices, airplanes, dogs barking, radios, newspaper crackling in the environment, if the student is looking for father behind the crackling newspaper, this sound becomes the most important one and all the rest are extraneous. If the dog is lost, then a dog's barking becomes the most important environmental sound. The student's responses to sound become more suitable as he learns to associate sound with the experience to which it is related.

Following identification of the sound, the student may have difficulty locating it—for instance, ascertaining from what direction a car is approaching from the sound alone. Fine discrimination of sound may be difficult. To differentiate between a knock on the door and a ring of the telephone is not difficult, but to discriminate between the ringing of the telephone and that of the doorbell is much more difficult. Increasing the intensity of the sound is rarely beneficial for students with auditory disorders; it usually merely produces confusion. The primary problem is inability to associate sound with the proper unit of experience. Increase in volume of sound is no solution.

Auditory memory, a part of general auditory capability, is critical for language development. Retaining a sequence of sounds within words, and words in sentences, is essential for comprehension and for expressive use of words. Children with disorders of auditory language are apt to have memory problems. It is imperative that corrective measures include a great deal of structural repetition.

Unlike those individuals with generalized deficiencies, students with auditory disorder in receptive language may easily comprehend nonverbal social sounds but are unable to relate spoken words to the appropriate unit of experience. They are described variously as possessing receptive aphasia, sensory aphasia, auditory verbal agnosia, or word deafness. These children frequently suffer from agnomia: they are unable to name an object or situation even though they themselves comprehend the meaning and actually know what they are talking about. A primary characteristic of a receptive disability is difficulty in producing the correct spoken word.

Sometimes a student can respond to "point to the one we use to lock the door" but not to "point to the key." He has to be taught that objects and situations can be named as well as described. He must learn that adjectives represent qualities, not objects, or actions. In another context, he may confuse the meaning of the action of pointing with the instrument used in the action of pointing, such as the finger or a pencil. These students have great difficulty with parts of speech other than nouns, particularly with adjectives, adverbs, and prepositions. The symptoms are the same as those previously described for dyslexics.

A child with this type of disorder must learn what verbal symbol represents what experience. The meaning units in a flow of words must be differentiated. In older children, improperly differentiated words show up not in spoken form but in written form. They are apt to leave out medial syllables and endings—"intresin" for "interesting." These disorders affect reading, writing, and arithmetic as well as spoken language. The student usually cannot formulate good sentences spontaneously. In arithmetic, the student can calculate but is unable to do word problems or form abstract numerical concepts. He may be able to calculate adequately for the reason that number symbols are more stable than words. Their meaning does not vary to the same extent. In reconstructing receptive auditory disorders, auditory configurations must be drilled. *Sub, sat, sit* are difficult for auditory aphasics because they tend to be unable to distinguish the short vowel sounds. Sometimes the vowel is left out completely—*bnd* for *bend*. It is easier to distinguish between longer words in which fine discrimination is not necessary, such as *construct* and *believe*.

Those individuals must be taught parts of speech in a specific way. In teaching nouns, the primary purpose is to establish the principle of naming. Following this, it is necessary to teach concepts in addition to the labels. For instance, it is important to first teach the label, i.e.: *shoe,* then various kinds of shoes—tennis, baby, loafer, football. If there is a disturbance of body image, there can also be confusion as to the relationship of the shoe to the body. Teaching nouns is important because these students may not be able to name a *dentist* as such but understand that he is the one who fixes teeth. Students may have difficulty distinguishing between units and categories. Peas, carrots, beets are unitary labels; lamb, beef, pork are unitary labels. The categories are vegetables and meat respectively. Continuing larger units of experience must also be structured, such as the concept that the categories of meat and vegetables comprise food.

The basic goal is to teach an understanding that words represent not only names of objects but also actions. Inherent in this is the tense of the verb, which must be related to a time concept. The internalizing of yesterday, today, and tomorrow is necessary before the concept of verb tenses can be mastered. It may also be necessary to establish a distinction between agent and action. In showing a student various pictures of a cat walking, leaping, sitting, or sleeping, it can be difficult to get across the point that the cat is just the agent doing the action of walking, leaping, sitting, or sleeping.

The adjective is taught to show that words, in addition to names of objects, and actions, can represent qualities. *Beautiful* is not the name of an object. The sentence must name a beautiful something. In trying to get across this point, substitution is sometimes useful. The baby was in a buggy. The beautiful was in a buggy. The beautiful baby was in a buggy. The adjective also represents relative qualities of size, space, feelings which can only be meaningful in relation to other experiences. In order to understand *big*, you have to understand *little*. Where there is a deficit in visual spatial ability the student is unable to differentiate size and distance and cannot comprehend *long, short, wide,* or *narrow*.

Prepositions and adverbs are the most difficult for these students to understand. Children sometimes fail assignments not because they are unable to do the work but because they cannot follow directions when they include prepositions. Prepositions and adverbs denote the concept of location in relation to certain spatial and time organizations. *On, in, under, behind, before, after,* are all related to objects or circumstances which may be constantly changing.

In habilitating disorders of auditory language, it is necessary to isolate the deficits. The input should be evaluated before the output, the auditory before the visual, the concrete before the abstract. Each system should be habilitated by means of the process of association.

Students with disorders of auditory language have low auditory memory span. Auditory memory span is the amount of auditorially received information an individual can retain in proper sequence for the purpose of immediate action or recall (Johnson and Myklebust 1967). These students have difficulty in understanding a series of commands or in comprehending complex verbal instructions. A differentiation between a partially deaf child and a child with a limited auditory memory span should be made. The latter student is constantly being reprimanded in school for lack of attention. He can be a distracting influence in the classroom. He fails his assignments not because of an inability to do the work but because he cannot remember the sequence of instructions. For older students in this category to take class notes, much effort is required since they cannot both remember what they hear and write at the same time. This disability affects all areas of the life of the individual, not only the academic. Unless habilitative techniques are instigated, such an individual may be unable to take instructions from employers and may be thought inattentive and incompetent. Emphasis should be placed on meaningful associations, organization, and retention in a practical manner so that it is useful in everyday activities. Organizational skills for performing routine activities in studying or in working should be developed. Visual clues, making use of maps or diagrams, are helpful techniques for training, as is practice in building a meaningful series out of related units.

PROBLEMS OF EXPRESSIVE LANGUAGE

We have been considering receptive disorders of auditory language, and now turn to expressive disorders of auditory language. There are three broad groups of individuals with disorders of expressive auditory language (Johnson and Myklebust 1967). First are those with a deficit primarily in reauditorization and word selection. These children can understand words spoken to them. They are unable to use these same words to express this understanding. They often will do well in activities until a spoken reply is required. Second are those who have a deficit in auditory-motor integration and experience difficulty in saying words. They comprehend but cannot execute the necessary motor patterns for speaking. Third are those with defective syntax. These individuals are able to use single words or short phrases but cannot organize words into complete sentences. They omit words and use incorrect verb tenses long after these abilities should be acquired in the normal development of the language continuum.

For those children with a deficit in the ability to speak appropriate words, this ability can be developed. Once this is developed, the ability to recall words can be developed. Occasionally, inability to recall words occurs only in certain categories. Words of great import to the intended meaning are sometimes most difficult to express. Children experience tremendous frustration when they are unable to communicate. In trying to describe events or objects, they cannot remember how to say what they have in mind. This condition has a parallel in the inability of the child with dysgraphia (writing disturbance) to remember the feel of letters in order to write them on paper. As an example, a boy might have the electronic knowledge to construct a radio but be unable to explain how to do it for the reason that he cannot remember or name the articles used. Non-specific words such as, *you know, the stuff, the junk, the what chamacallit,* might be used to describe his activity. Inability to recall a sufficient number of specific words might lead to a simple response indicating that he couldn't explain it and a conclusion on the part of the listener that he was stupid.

Many children need the reinforcement of the actual object in order to recall the appropriate word. They might try to ask for milk but be unable to do so until a glass or bottle of milk was seen. This condition can be better understood by envisaging a monolingual English-speaking individual trying to communicate with a monolingual Spanish-speaking person. The English-speaking individual knows what he wants to communicate but does not know the corresponding Spanish words. As soon as the object is designated, communication is established. For these students who can name it if they see it, techniques of visualization are necessary to teach reauditorization. Sometimes children can give only functional definitions. As in the case of receptive agnomia described earlier, instead of *knife* and *fork,* a child might say, "It's what I eat with. One you cut with." When a child is unable to recall a word, he may substitute one from within the same general category or one similar in meaning (*cake* instead of *pie, dog* instead of *cat,*) in spite of the fact that the alternative selected is known to be incorrect. Some children can use writing as a means of recall, while some cannot evoke the auditory symbol even after writing it. Others can say the correct word if they see it, using the visual symbol as a cue to auditory recall. In teaching a person with reauditorization deficits, the major objective is training him to recall the proper word at the appropriate time.

The second category of expressive language deficits comprises those of auditory-motor integration (Johnson and Myklebust 1967). An individual limited in this area can understand what is said to him, can read visual symbols, can understand syntax, but cannot control the physical act of articulation. He has never acquired an accurate motor pattern for the spoken word; he has not learned adequately that he can produce a particular sound by placing his tongue and lips in a certain position. This child is unable to retain a motor pattern, so he distorts words by reversing sounds. In some cases, in addition to making the association between audition and articulation, it is helpful to have the child watch the speaker's lips. These students cannot just listen and do, but they can listen, look, and do. Others can only look and do because they cannot associate the visual-auditory patterns.

Individuals in the third group, those with defective syntax, understand what they hear and can use single words and phrases but cannot organize words according to correct language usage. They omit words, distort the order of words, use incorrect verb tenses. Ability to form sentences is a complex skill, involving comprehension, sequencing, memory, and connection of auditory and visual symbols. Johnson notes that while the normal child cannot remember every sentence he hears, he does retain certain structural patterns and relationships of words, and then generates sentences of his own (Johnson and Myklebust, 1967). Students with a deficiency in oral expressive language must be instructed in this development by using specific techniques. Many children can distinguish errors but cannot correct them. Children with syntactical disturbance are referred for language training at an older age than those with other language problems. Since most have acquired some vocabulary, parents and educators tend to take the position "He will outgrow it. Give him a few years." This is usually not the case. Habilitative techniques are necessary to correct these deficiencies.

HABILITATIVE TEACHING TECHNIQUES

Some children express concepts in telegraphic language: "boy go store." Omitting articles, prepositions, and connectives, the essentials only are retained. For children with this type of telegraphic symptom, a sense of syntax must be developed to help them learn the structure of language. Grasping the full structure of a concept is understanding it in a way that permits many other things to be related to it meaningfully. To learn structure, in short, is to learn how things are related. A grammatical organization into which the student can insert appropriate words is one habilitative technique. Pictures are often useful in developing concepts of syntax and sentence structure. It is possible to arrive at tenses of verbs in the following manner. Show the child a picture of a dog. While the picture is present ask the child "What do you see?" "I see a dog." Then remove the picture and ask "What did you see?" "I saw a dog." In this way a modification of the experience promotes modification of the language structure. It also gets at some sense of time relationship. Pictures can be selected for work with prepositional phrases: *Mother is walking — to the store — to the school.* Gradually more variables can be introduced so that the student can say and write, "The boy is riding to the park on his bicycle." Photographs can be selected and phrases provided to help the child understand that a descriptive word generally precedes the name of an object. For example, several pictures can be shown of things which are funny. The purpose is not to develop the concept of funny (although this can be used in nonverbal techniques) but to establish the position of an adjective in relation to a noun.

These and other methods will gradually fill the syntactical void characteristic of those with auditory language deficits. Sentence building is one of the most difficult skills to teach, yet it is imperative for academic success. Students with learning disabilities of auditory language form one of the most difficult groups to habilitate, yet it can be accomplished with patient use of the proper reconstructive language techniques.

NONVERBAL LEARNING DISABILITIES

"Comprehension" is an area of concern which classically has been considered as part of "reading ability," for obvious reasons. However, if we define reading as a symbol-system twice removed from reality, we do not include comprehension. For our purposes thus far, we have considered reading to be primarily the ability to articulate alphabetical symbols on a printed page in temporal sequence. I have found more and more cases of students who are able to read and write commensurate with grade level, in some cases far above grade level, but are not able to use the information which they read. The usual complaint on the part of the teacher is that the student is disorganized and cannot correlate what he reads, or in other words is "weak in comprehension." In many cases, I do not believe that this is the primary problem. It is my observation that some students do not have an understanding of what they read because they are unable to understand their social environment. In other words, they are unable to understand life as it goes on around them by observing situations and interpersonal relationships. This inability to understand the general social environment through observation is a disability which we will label *nonverbal*. This does not mean that the child cannot read more than adequately or cannot write more than adequately. It means that the knowledge gained from this reading and writing is not transferred to the child's environmental or social world for use in his personal life — the obvious goals of education.

REQUISITES FOR NONVERBAL LEARNING

Three talents are necessary for understanding the actual physical and sociological environment. The first talent is the ability to interpret body language, or the movements, expressions, actions, and various nonverbal characteristics of other people. An interpretation of body language, for example, requires an understanding of what a tapping foot might mean on the part of an individual who is waiting for an appointment. Expression by means of body actions can be very meaningful. The interpretation of these actions is a necessary medium of knowledge. The expression on a face, a gesture, the actual movement of an individual from one place to another, the manner in which he moves, may indicate a great deal about the individual.

The second talent necessary is the ability to interpret object language. A student should be able to read object language by understanding the meaning behind objects such as the American flag, the swastika, the Red Cross, smoke, fog. Meaning can be inferred from observing the physical relationships of one object to another.

The third talent is the ability to infer from situation language. Some students cannot interpret a situation from merely observing it. They cannot understand what component relationships within a situation mean unless they are verbalized. This inability contributes to lack of comprehension in academic subjects. It interferes with interpretation of literature as well as of life situations. If a student is unable to comprehend that a series of events or situations resulted in an effect, that an action specifically caused a reaction, unless these relationships are verbalized, the acquisition of knowledge in any academic subject is more difficult. If the student cannot understand why something happens as a result of a previous action, the study of history has little meaning. Experimental science and mathematics have similar characteristics. If a student cannot understand situation symbols in his own immediate environment, he cannot understand them when he reads about them. This type of deficit may be termed a *nonverbal learning disability*.

DESCRIPTION AND HISTORICAL BACKGROUND OF NONVERBAL LEARNING DISABILITIES

In order to educate the child of today effectively, academic or verbal learning must be synchronized with experience. Knowledge can be acquired by two separate systems of codifying information; *verbal* (the alphabet and the numerical system) and *nonverbal* (objects, body action, and situations which are symbolic of the thing, idea, or event for which they stand). Some children have learning problems primarily with verbal language and some have learning problems primarily with nonverbal language.

The possibility that a nonverbal learning disability existed came to my attention several years ago. Some cases referred for verbal evaluation because of an assumed reading disability were found to be proficient in verbal skills of reading, writing, and arithmetic. Upon further observation, these students seemed to be unable to acquire the overall understanding of their environment which would be presumed from their mastery of the traditional skills of reading, writing, and arithmetic, and their apparent inherent intelligence. From experience in handling cases of verbal learning disabilities, it seemed probable that a category of nonverbal disabilities (as unrecognized and as silent as the verbal disabilities have been in past years) does exist in sufficient degree to warrant further study and the development of appropriate techniques for habilitation. After discussing ideas for habilitating techniques for nonverbal learning disabilities with Dr. David Wechsler[1] in the summer of 1968, I embarked upon further research and practical experimentation. Reinforcement was discovered in the previous work of Johnson and Myklebust, whose findings are included in the following discussion. Continuing observation of diagnostic symptoms has served to strengthen the original hypothesis. Tentative habilitation techniques were developed and utilized in appropriate cases. Because the whole concept of nonverbal learning disabilities is so new, virtually unrecognized and unexplored in standard literature, the conclusions described in

---

1. Author of Wechsler Intelligence Score for Children and Wechsler Adult Intelligence Score.

the following paragraphs are otherwise undocumented and admittedly in need of further validation, experience, and standardization.

A child who has a nonverbal learning disability is one who does not have difficulty acquiring knowledge from reading, writing, or speech (the usually assigned cause for academic difficulties in an intellectually normal child) but who cannot understand the significance of a variety of nonverbal aspects within his own environment. He cannot anticipate situations. He cannot learn the implications of the actions of others from the usual means of gestures, facial expressions, nonverbal sounds, or body language. He may exhibit symptoms previously described as characterizing some dyslexics, in that he may not understand the concepts of time, size, direction, or space related to his own environment. He has difficulty in daily living even though his level of intelligence falls within or above the average. This deficiency in social perception is as crippling a disability as dyslexia or any of the related verbal learning disabilities.

RATIONALE FOR EXISTENCE OF
NONVERBAL LEARNING DISABILITIES

A case in point is that of a nine-year-old boy with a Wechsler IQ of 140 able to read and acquire information which is printed or spoken, able to comprehend the information within the level of his maturity and answer pertinent questions, yet whose mother is afraid to leave him alone in the house because of his lack of comprehension of the practical implications of his physical environment. She is equally afraid to have him cross a busy city street with all the concomitant hazards. This boy might read about these hazards, correctly answer relevant questions, but be unable to apply this knowledge to his own environment.

According to Johnson and Myklebust (1967) a disturbance of the brain processes can affect nonverbal as well as verbal behavior. One can be affected while the other remains basically intact. The supposition is that the brain categorizes experience on the basis of whether it is verbal or nonverbal. At this point, we are handicapped by general lack of knowledge of nonverbal learning, as well as of nonverbal learning disabilities.

Johnson analyzes the learning process in general by means of the previously described hierarchies of experience of sensation, perception, imagery, symbolization, conceptualization. Verbal learning disabilities occur at the level of symbolization and automatically affect the higher level of conceptualization. Nonverbal learning disabilities fall at the level of perception and imagery, and constitute a more fundamental distortion of the total experience. Most basic experiences are nonverbal. In a nonverbal learning disability the experience itself is distorted, not the ability to use language (spoken, written or read), which describes it. In normal learning every word assumes a referent, a unit of nonverbal experience which it symbolizes. In order to illustrate this point, Johnson likens the child with a nonverbal learning disability to the child who lacks color vision. He has no difficulty learning the word *red* but he cannot acquire the experience *red*. When he uses the word as required by daily activities, it connotes a vague impression with little relationship to the actual experience of red. The perception and the imagery are distorted.

Bruner (Haber 1968) in his study of the development of perceptual readiness in the human being states that perception is a decision process, and that this process involves the use of discriminatory cues. Proceeding from a cue to an inference of identity is the most primitive cognitive activity. The use of cues for the purpose of inferring categories depends upon the learning of environmental probabilities. Bruner gives four general types of mechanisms necessary for perception: one, grouping and integration; two, access ordering; three, match — mismatch signaling; and four, gating. Concerning integration there must be a record of the likely transitions and contingencies of the enviroment. If in nonverbal disabilities the experience of the environment is distorted (another way of saying that object language or situation language is not constant and therefore cannot be put into categories), then habilitation techniques should be structured so that some degree of environmental security is learned. In the realm of social perception, where the problem of incorporating knowledge and experience into categories is complex, the most bizarre effects of inappropriate category systems are found.

Bruner refers to accessibility as the ease or speed with which a given stimulus input is coded in terms of a given category under varying conditions of instruction, past learning, and motivation. He gives the example of perceiving a *B* or a *13* being dependent on anticipation of the category based on what has preceded the perception. If an individual with a nonverbal learning disability is incapable of anticipation or expectation perhaps habilitation techniques should be directed at this area.

Bruner further reasons that an important feature of learning involves perceptual readiness. He mentions that some people are characteristically tuned in for a narrow range of alternatives in the situation in which they find themselves. If the environment contains events and sequences which are anticipated, then the individual will do well and perceive without a closer examination. Students with a nonverbal learning disability have difficulty in this area of anticipation. Therefore, the ability to shift categories and judge accordingly is another ability which may require special learning techniques for children who have nonverbal disabilities.

Illustrative of this point is the case of a lady recuperating from a fractured hip. Her physician had instructed her not to walk or put any pressure on her leg. The frame dwelling in which she lived caught on fire during the middle of one night. A rescuer trying to aid her in escaping the second floor of the building requested that she try to walk down the stairs with his support. She refused to move since her instructions from her physician had been not to put weight on the fractured hip. In this case the individual was unable to shift categories from a matter of cure to a matter of actual survival.

Bruner proposes that failure to perceive is not a lack of perceiving but an interference with perceiving. Gibson (Haber 1968), also a student of the development of human perception, mentions that the ability of the child to select and abstract information from the world grows as he grows. Space is perceived and time is remembered; space concerns adjacent order and time concerns successive order. Conscious remembering may be an occasional and incidental symptom of learning in the same way that sensations may be occasional and incidental symptoms of perceiving. Recognition is *perceiving* or *identifying* and can exist without memory or recall. In a child with a nonverbal learning disability, if the perception of body language, object language, and situation language is deficient there may be little environmental learning from these visual languages.

VERBAL AND NONVERBAL LEARNING AS PARALLEL SYSTEMS

The rationale of the devised approach for habilitating nonverbal learning disabilities, subsequently described, stems from the fact that verbal and nonverbal learning seems to be based on different but parallel systems within the brain (Johnson and Myklebust 1967). Nonverbal learning develops before verbal learning and is more basic to the environment. A baby learns to cry, smile, suck, and clutch long before he learns the words which symbolize these actions. He expresses himself in nonverbal language by crying, smiling, and waving. Later in normal development the action codification is taken over by the verbal codification. By adolescence, the verbal means of communication predominates. Nonverbal learning, however, must still be an ongoing process if the continued acquisition and utilization of knowledge is to be properly effective. Nonverbal learning is "felt" to a greater degree than verbal learning since nonverbal impressions evoke a greater pressure for response than verbal impressions (Ruesch 1956). The perception of nonverbal language is immediate while the perception of words requires a longer time due to the volume required for explanatory purposes. The most important reason for the need to increase knowledge of nonverbal learning, as well as to increase the ability to enhance the process, is the fact that an individual's evaluation of social events and social environment is based largely on this type of learning. As population, technological and other modern pressures continue to multiply, this evaluative capability is assuming even more significant proportions for effective social and environmental adjustment on the part of maturing individuals. The growing recognition of "sensitivity training" is a comparable and related current development.

Verbal statements and visual statements can take parallel forms. Thinking by visualizing and revisualizing nonverbal language is as important a skill as thinking with words. In discussing verbal learning disabilities, the problem of revisualization was described as particularly important to both integrative and expressive functions. Verbal language is a code which substitutes words for things, with general agreement on percepts. The learning of the language code as a vocabulary is different from the child's learning to consolidate his knowledge by prediction. He gets information just by focusing, enhancing, detecting, and extracting it from nonverbal stimulation. Later, the extracting and consolidating go on together.

As nonverbal learning develops prior to verbal learning it is essential that once verbal learning is initiated the two types of learning proceed together, rather than separately. This integration, as well as the nonverbal learning process in general, will be adversely affected by the hitherto little-known disabilities with which we are here concerned. Students with nonverbal learning disabilities need to develop skills in sequencing (not alphabetic letters as in verbal learning disabilities) the relations of events and objects visually perceived. Neither verbal learning nor nonverbal learning alone is sufficient to produce optimum achievement in learning.

VISUAL LEARNING

Visual learning is the extraction of information by understanding visual language; the three areas of body language, object language, and situation language. It is necessary for nonverbal learning. Visual language can be an international language. Words by nature are symbolic or referential but the mother tongue must be understood in order for the communication of words to be understood. Visual language involves objects, symbols, situations, and actions that can be seen and experienced in a meaningful way. This includes communication from one human being to another both intentional and unintentional. In the natural development of visual literacy, the child acquires a visual vocabulary which is passive at first. He then learns to respond to this visual vocabulary in an active manner, integrating and giving meaning to observed changes. There is a difference in the meaning of the visual perception of a car parked at the curb, and of a car pulling away from the curb. It is the same car, but the process of the car has different implications. In order to understand nonverbal language this difference or change must be interpreted.

Before a child develops word concepts, he learns to respond to visual sequences. The sequence of father's driving into the yard and putting his car in the garage is followed customarily by dinner. This passively received visual information comprises a nonverbal vocabulary which becomes active with integration and is the means of nonverbal learning.

The child soon learns to communicate by using his own body and actions from an expressive point of view. In developing a visual language (nonverbal vocabulary), children select the actions of body language, objects, or situations in their environment which are the most important to them. Thereby they develop discrimination and judgement.

It has been pointed out that children from the inner-city distrust a verbal message. They have learned that the visual message is a more true and trustworthy form of communication. They have lived their lives until the age of school in a visual environment where the verbal "I like you" is not trusted unless it is accompanied by visual reinforcement. Children of all groups and categories are much more visually literate today than in the past. Inability to extract information from nonverbal language can be a greater handicap than a verbal disability.

EDUCATIONAL EVALUATION OF VISUAL LANGUAGE

Through the medium of television, children now passively receive sophisticated visual information almost from the time they are able to sit up. This impact has been deplored as being time-consuming and nonconstructive, if not destructive. Attempts to determine the true impact of TV on a child's development are in their infancy. Theories about mass media as expounded by Marshall McLuhan and others have called attention to this influence without arriving at determinative conclusions. Obviously, TV involves both verbal and visual language, but the nonverbal language is the predominating influence. Television and other nonverbal pressures pose a modern-day educational problem.

Historically, our schools have been, and to a large extent still are, oriented to verbal learning. It appears that within the academic framework an additional function of formal education should be the development of nonverbal learning skills. Teaching the recognition and inferences of body language, object language, and situation language may well be the responsibility of educational institutions. If a student is proficient in feeding back facts of mathematics, science, literature, and history, but has little understanding of his fellow man and is unable to learn by visual language, he may be described as having a *nonverbal learning disability*. If perception of nonverbal or visual language is not followed by the ability to make inferences, effective learning for the world of tomorrow cannot take place. The impact of mass media, the population explosion, and the increasing tempo of technological living may well change educational methodology to the degree that visual learning will be superimposed on verbal learning rather than verbal superimposed on visual. Nonverbal learning techniques should be utilized as a structured, goal-oriented educational medium rather than be left to chance and the vagaries of commercial television.

Lines, shapes, forms, color, and movement have a language of their own; reading it takes time. It is not enough to look. You must "see," and *see* means "read." Spoken and written language are not the only language media necessary to develop the capability of the individual to learn. Babies learn a visual vocabulary long before they can talk, just as they learn a spoken vocabulary long before they can read. Inattention to, or misreading of, cues is a common fault in our young society. Motion pictures, a symbol for reality, have been in some measure the means of counteracting the real impact of visual perception as a means of acquiring information. One cause is the required passive acceptance of the message of motion pictures and television serials.

When the child sees violence and gun battles on television, there is nothing he can do about it. Appropriately, in these circumstances, nothing should be done. This generation of children has grown up conditioned to passive acceptance of violence. The number of people influenced by this passive acceptance of violent visual messages may far outnumber the number in the past influenced by the adventures read in the classics. The enormous impact of the automatic reception of a visual message filed away without meaning is beyond measuring. The subject of nonverbal learning is all the more important because radio and television today bridge the spatial and temporal gap of contemporary living.

Picture language existed long before the symbol language of the phonetic alphabet. Through ideographs, people of different tongues were able to communicate when otherwise they would have difficulty. Pictorial representation is the exact reproduction of the object, action, or situation at the moment. In the natural development of a child, understanding the concrete object precedes understanding that a picture can represent the concrete object. Both of these steps precede the phonetic symbol system. Comic strips are another modern-day version of nonverbal or visual communication.

BODY LANGUAGE

Nonverbal language can be used for intentional as well as unintentional communication. An intentional message can be encoded in visual or nonverbal language just as it can be encoded in written or verbal language. As the child decodes speech before he can encode it, he develops the ability to decode body language before he can encode it. Body language can be a powerful instrument for learning. Movements can be read for information as a book can be read for information.

To be visually literate includes the ability to perceive, interpret, and make inferences from the three general categories previously mentioned. Body language is communicated by action language which involves appropriacy of movement, precision, accuracy, rhythm, speed, and rate of change of movement. For instance, the sound of a walk characterizes an angry man and sets the mood before the man is seen. The dance is a form of body language in which the human body itself is used for expression. The creator and the creation is one and the same. Gesture, physical expressions, pantomime are means of communicating. The action of walking, or taking off a coat, can communicate a message far better than the verbal description of these actions. An action can be learned by means of the traces left by an action. The world of detectives is proficient in the skill of learning from traces left by actions. Body actions can be a silent but powerful means of communicating with other persons.

Facial expressions, included under the category of body language, are an important means of conveying emotion. The observation of nonverbal messages of emotion can implement actions far more quickly than the description of emotion in words. Intensity and quality of emotion often have far more influence when perceived visually than when verbalized. Emotion can establish roles in interpersonal relationship, in group relationships, and in community relationships. The interpretation of emotion is an important skill and one a child with a nonverbal learning disability may not possess. Skills for recognizing changing roles and situations through nonverbal language may need to be specifically taught to such children.

OBJECT LANGUAGE

Object language is an important method by which anthropologists evaluate or "read" ancient civilizations. Art involves object language as well as situation language. It is a medium which codifies and interprets. This medium was used during the Middle Ages to teach religion to illiterates. Object language may or may not be symbolic or referential. It exerts an effect on the individual vastly different from spoken words perceived as sound signals, and from printed words perceived as sound and visual signals. It needs no commas, periods, or paragraphs. Objects occur and are arranged so that the eye perceives imaginary boundaries.

Lack of perception of constancy of shape sometimes occurs in nonverbal learning disabilities. This also can occur in many reading problems involving visual perception of the letter form. Object constancy is necessary for identification. Identification comes before ability to make inferences. The perceptual process seems to be disturbed in these disabilities. If a child cannot grasp object constancy it must be taught.

SITUATION LANGUAGE

To acquire meaningful information by perceiving and integrating cues or signals, including spatial and temporal, the perceiving of the cues cannot be separated from perceiving the situations in which they occur. When these two lack synchronization, there is then a concomitant problem in learning. This can be termed lack of social perception. Since a message can be codified in pictorial language as well as in the language of words, those individuals who lack social perception must be trained to perceive visually coded messages, to interpret them, and express them.

Bruner mentions economical perception as the ability to avoid distraction and to concentrate on one thing at a time within many environmental influences. To accomplish this perception, one must be quick and efficient rather than slow and contemplative. As a result, the information registered about objects and events becomes only what is needed, not all that could be obtained from the environment. This he refers to as the schematic tendency of perception. Unless the perception of the action, object, or situation is followed by focused integrative reasoning, it is not an effective means of learning. These skills may be trained by means of discriminating among relationships.

REHABILITATION TECHNIQUES FOR NONVERBAL LEARNING DISABILITIES

On the theory that visual literacy is based on the ability to elicit information and inferences from the three visual languages — body, object, and situation — the habilitation of students with nonverbal learning disabilities should begin by developing an awareness of objects visually represented in space for the purpose of sharpening awareness of the world they live in. The first step could be a demonstration that all form consists of lines and mass. This precedes attention to the mass, or what is inside (also helpful in drawing inferences). A brief illustration of the mechanical aspect of the human body is useful. There are certain definite connections of muscles and bones which limit the types of possible body movement. The plumbline of balance, the gravitational line, might also be demonstrated. The predictability and limitation of movement of the human body is in a large measure affected by these factors.

The second step could be a demonstration of perspective, without which objects in spatial organization cannot be understood. Selected photographs and drawings can be used as teaching aids. Space in pictures is purely an idea, and it is the idea of space which is essential to create in students. It seems reasonable that this may be accomplished by creating an understanding of the principles upon which space is visually perceived and represented two-dimensionally. The rules of diminution, foreshortening, convergency and other aspects of perspective are excellent tools for intellectualizing space and spatial relations.

Perhaps some of the confusion in children who lack understanding of spatial concepts comes from the fact that in the observation of perspectives, real seems make-believe and make-believe seems real. J. Kolbuszewski (*Journal of the Royal Society of Arts,* 1953) described 150 experiments, the conclusion of which was that the eye likes to see equal distances in perspective in a way different from that recorded by a camera or determined by rules of perspective. In this report, Kolbuszewski mentions that the wise circulation of good photographs for over a century has had its effects on the visual appreciation of educated people, particularly those of Europe and America, who are probably perspective-conscious as never before; and the implications are of interest. From the numbers of students who are not visually literate, this influence of photographs has not had the intended effect in some cases.

Lawrence of Arabia reportedly made portrait sketches of the Arab tribesmen during his leisure hours in his desert campaigns. He was a very capable artist, but his Arab soldiers had no tradition for visual representation. They did not even know how to hold a portrait drawing right side up. Therefore it may be that techniques for visual literacy must be taught to certain individuals. The motion picture camera, with its close-up, fade-out, zero-in mobility, could be responsible in part for fostering an insecure sense of spatial relationships in the children of today.

Understanding of the organization of a picture, if we are to teach visual literacy, is a paramount factor. Pictures are composed of shapes made by using line, tone, shading, and color. The organization of these shapes guides and directs the observer's eye, controls the speed of the eye movement, and serves to direct the eye to the intended climax. Learning to pick out basic geometric shapes within the organization of a picture is an important skill. Most objects viewed can be reduced to the fundamental shapes of circle, square, and triangle. This should be demonstrated so that the student is able to see it. To "see," to be visually literate, could be some combination of physiological and psychological factors plus experience and learning. Some of this should be the result of intensive training with the proper techniques.

The ability to anticipate from a situation might also be trained. Elementary techniques of balance and imbalance with basic forms of circles, squares, and triangles could be used. A sense of action about to happen could be trained using these same basic forms. By changing the shapes and directional thrusts, a sense of changing the anticipated outcome can be fostered. This is the first step in making inferences from situations. The second step is showing how different relationships of objects change the meaning of the objects. The third step might involve analyzing important values by eliminating extraneous detail. The fourth step might be the use of situation photographs for the purpose of sequencing events and projecting possible outcomes. The instrument for teaching all four steps is selected photographs.

In addition to the foregoing, training in the identity of facial expressions as indicative of emotion might also be accomplished by means of appropriate photographs. Actors use facial expressions to convey various emotions through muscle control of the face. For every expression, there appears to be a special movement of each separate feature: the eyebrows, the eyes, the nose, the mouth, the cheeks. Muscles control expressions by shrinking. This causes the skin to assume an expression. Study of facial expressions in actual photographs might be a means of teaching the student to interpret expressions. The inference of various emotions such as pleasure, scepticism, disgust, anger, fear, disdain, determination, love, mirth, and joy from facial expressions in photographs should lead to the ability to identify these same emotions in everyday situations.

A picture is a medium for almost instantaneous transmission of information. Books and music use words and sounds. Page must follow page in unfolding the slow reception of information and sound. Looking is not always seeing, but seeing can be trained. For most students, a casual glance can give enough information for everyday use. Other students with a nonverbal learning disability must be trained by the foregoing methods. Seeing is divided into practical, specialized, and reflective. Practical seeing is protective. Specialized seeing is that which is viewed by someone with highly technical skills which are related to the seeing. Reflective seeing is that which calls to mind related things from the past. The only type of seeing with which we are concerned in habilitative techniques is the practical seeing. We are, therefore, interested in historical pictures, descriptive information pictures, and situation pictures telling a story or depicting social situations.

SUMMARY

To summarize, in children who fall in the intellectually normal, or above-normal, range on the Wechsler Intelligence Score for Children, having no sensory, emotional, or gross-motor deficiencies, two broad categories of learning disabilities have been observed; verbal and nonverbal. *Verbal disabilities* include problems in reading, spelling, writing, and auditory language. Verbal disabilities can occur either at the level of recognition or at the level of recall. A child who fails to recognize words visually cannot read. A child who is able to recognize words but cannot revisualize them can read but cannot write. A child who cannot reauditorize cannot communicate or give any feedback of knowledge. These conditions can be habilitated by specific techniques in associating visual and auditory symbols, sequencing, training in visual-motor coordination, and building a sense of grammar and syntax. *Nonverbal disabilities* include problems in comprehension of environmental factors due to inability to gain information and make inferences from body language, object language, and situation language. This condition can be habilitated by specific techniques using analysis of forms, shapes and spatial relations, and selected photographs describing sequence of cause and effect in environmental situations.

REFERENCES

Allen, James E.: The right to read—target for the 70's. Paper presented to 1969 Annual Association of State Boards of Education, Los Angeles, Calif.

Ausubel, David P.: *The Psychology of Meaningful Verbal Learning.* New York, Grune and Stratton, 1963.

Buford, Thomas: *Toward a Philosophy of Education.* New York, Holt, Rinehart and Winston, Inc., 1969.

Bruner, Jerome: *Toward a Theory of Instruction.* Cambridge, Harvard University Press, 1967.

Childs, Sally: Sound reading. *New Frontiers in Reading.* 1960. Reprint, International Reading Association.

Clemmens, Raymond L.: Obscure causes of school failure—a pediatric viewpoint. Presented at the 42nd International Conference of the Council for Exceptional Children, April, 1964.

Cole, E. M.: Specific reading disability: a problem in integration and adaptation. *American Journal of Ophthalmology, 34*:226–232, 1951.

Cole, Edwin M.: The language clinic and the cortical function test laboratory. *Massachusetts General Hospital News,* Boston, October, 1961.

Cole, E. M. and Walker, Louise: Reading and speech problems as expressions of a specific language disability. Reprint from *Disorders of Communication,* Vol. XLII; Research Publications, Association for Research in Nervous and Mental Disease, 1964.

Cole, E. M.: Specific reading disability: a problem in integration and adaptation. *American Journal of Ophthalmology, 34,* February, 1951.

Cole, E. M. and Walker, Louise: Familial patterns of expression of specific language disability in a population sample. *Bulletin of the Orton Society, Inc., XV,* 1965.

Crowell, Thomas Lee, Jr.: *A Glossary of Phrases with Prepositions.* Englewood Cliffs, Prentice-Hall, 1957.

Cruikshank, William M., ed.: *A Teaching Method for Brain-Injured and Hyper-Active Children.* Syracuse, Syracuse University Press, 1961.

Cruikshank, William M., Ed.: *The Teacher of Brain-Injured Children.* Syracuse, Syracuse University Press, 1966.

DeHirsch, Katrina: Diagnosis of developmental language disorders. *Logos, 4*:5–9, 1961.

DeHirsch, Katrina: Concepts related to normal reading processes and their application to reading pathology. *J. Genet. Psychol., 102*: 277–297, 1963.

Della-Piana, Gabriel M.: *Reading Diagnosis and Prescription.* New York, Holt, Rinehart and Winston, 1968.

Fernald, G.: *Remedial Techniques in Basic School Subjects.* New York, McGraw-Hill, 1943.

Gallagher, J. Roswell: Specific language disability (dyslexia). Reprint from *Clinical Proceedings of the Children's Hospital, XVI*:1, Boston, January, 1960.

Gallagher, J. Roswell: Can't spell, can't read. Reprinted from *The Atlantic Monthly,* and from *Understanding Your Son's Adolescence,* New York, Little, Brown & Co.

Gillingham, Anna: Is a school with no reading problems possible? *The Independent School Bulletin,* January, 1963.

Gillingham, Anna: Pedagogical implications of specific language disability. Reprint from *The Independent School Bulletin,* January, 1952.

Goldstein, Kurt: *Language and Language Disturbances.* New York, Grune and Stratton, 1948.

Haber, Ralph, ed.: *Contemporary Thinking and Research in Visual Perception.* New York, Holt, Rinehart and Winston, 1968.

Hagin, Rosa A.: Some practical applications of diagnostic studies of children with specific reading disability. Presented at the 11th Annual Meeting of the Orton Society, Inc.; October, 1960.

Hermann, Knud.: *Reading Disability: A Medical Study of Word-blindness and Related Handicaps.* Springfield, Thomas, 1959.

Johnson, D., and Myklebust, H.: *Learning Disabilities: Educational Principles and Practices.* New York, Grune and Stratton, 1967.

Jung, John: *Verbal Learning.* New York, Holt, Rinehart and Winston, 1968.

Kephart, Newell: *The Slow Learner in the Classroom.* Columbus, Ohio, Charles E. Merrill, 1960.

Keyes, Kenneth: *How to Develop Thinking Ability.* New York, McGraw-Hill, 1950.

Lenneberg, E.: Implications of biological origin of language. Paper presented at The Twentieth Annual Meeting of the Orton Society, 1969.

Manis, Melvin: *Cognitive Processes*. Belmont, Wadsworth, 1966.

Money, John, ed.: *Reading Disability: Progress and Research Needs in Dyslexia*. Baltimore, The Johns Hopkins Press, 1962.

Money, John, ed.: *The Disabled Reader: Education of the Dyslexic Child*. Baltimore, The Johns Hopkins Press, 1966.

Myklebust, Helmer R.: *Development and Disorders of Written Language*. Vol. 1. New York, Grune and Stratton, 1965.

Myklebust, Helmer R., ed.: *Progress in Learning Disabilities*, Vol. 1. New York, Grune and Stratton, 1968.

Myklebust, Helmer R.: *Auditory Disorders in Children*. New York, Grune and Stratton, 1954.

Orton, S. T.: *Reading, Writing and Speech Problems in Children*. New York, Norton, 1937 (reprinted 1961).

Orton, J. L., ed.: Specific language disabilities. *Orton Society Bulletin No. 13*, June, 1963. (Reprints of papers by Orton, Dozier, Bender, DeHirsch, etc.)

Peter, Lawrence, Jr.: *Prescriptive Teaching*. New York, McGraw-Hill, 1965.

Rabinovitch, R. D., *et al.*: Research approach to reading retardation. *Ass. Res. Nerv. Ment. Dis. Proceedings: 34*:363–399, 1956.

Reger, Roger, Schroeder, W., and Uschold, K., ed.: *Special Education: Children with Learning Problems*. New York, Oxford University Press, 1968.

Ruesch, Jungen, and Kees, Weldon: *Nonverbal Communication. A Study of Visual Perception*. California, University of California Press, 1969.

Silver, Archie A.: Diagnostic considerations in children with reading disability. Presented at the 11th Annual Meeting of the Orton Society, Inc., October, 1960.

Slingerland, Beth: Meeting the needs of dyslexic children. *Academic Therapy Quarterly*, Vol. I, No. 2. Reprint No. 101, published by DeWitt Reading Clinic, San Rafael, California.

Stern, Catherine and Gould, Toni S.: *Children Discover Reading*. New York, Random House, 1963.

Subirama, A.: The relationship between handedness and language function. *Logos*, 4:67–85, 1961.

Talland, George A.: *Disorders of Memory and Learning*. England, Penguin Books Ltd., 1968.

Tansley and Gulliford: *The Education of the Slow-Learning Child.* London, Routledge & Kegan Paul, 1960.

Tarnpol, Lester, ed.: *Learning Disabilities.* Springfield, Charles C. Thomas, 1969.

Wapner, Seymour, and Werner, Heinz, ed.: *The Body Percept.* New York, Random House, 1965.

Weintraub, Daniel J., and Walker, Edward L.: *Perception.* Belmont, Wadsworth, 1966.

Weintraub, Daniel J.: The last skill acquired (interview in *New Yorker Magazine*). September 14, 1963.

Weintraub, Daniel J.: How to teach the hard-to-reach. Reprint from *Grade Teacher Magazine,* May-June, 1967.

Weintraub, Daniel J.: Northfield: Operation talent salvage. Greenfield (Mass.): *Recorder-Gazette,* August 19, 1964.

Weintraub, Daniel J.: A memorandum on certain reading and spelling difficulties for my academic colleagues, teachers, parents and anyone else. Reprinted from Vol. VII of the *Orton Society Bulletin.*

Wolfe, Clifton W.: An experimental investigation of specific language disability (dyslexia). *Bulletin of the Orton Society: XVI,* 1966.

Chapter V

IDENTIFYING THE
CLINICALLY RETARDED READER

PAMELA FERRARO

Much time and effort has been spent in the attempt to discover a poor-reader syndrome (cluster of symptoms) and ascribe an appropriate label; e.g., "dyslexia." Among the characteristics suggested are physiological and behavioral abnormalities such as defective auditory, visual, and motor skills, minimal brain damage or dysfunction, seizures, confused laterality, hyperactivity, distractibility, poor spatial orientation, dependency, aggression, withdrawal, etc. Intellectual capacities of the poor reader tend to follow the normal curve for the general population (Monroe, 1932; Witty and Kopel, 1939) with some subjects demonstrating varying patterns on certain subtests of the Wechsler Intelligence Scales. In addition, poor concept formation, inadequate body image, relative superiority in mathematics, poor speech, etc. have been offered as identifying characteristics. Overall reading performance generally falls 3 years below grade level for grades 4–12, or 6 mos. to 1 yr. for grades 1 through 3. However, such limits are varying and arbitrary. More specific skill deficits may occur in auditory and visual perception and discrimination, left-right directional orientation, word recognition, word meaning, oral fluency and comprehension, silent comprehension, listening comprehension, rate and flexibility, study skills, spelling, and writing. To a large extent, attempts at classification have remained unsuccessful since any one child may exhibit some behaviors and not others, the experts from various interested disciplines being unable to agree on which symptoms should receive priority and in what degree for identification purposes. Consequently, the only behavior shared by all children in question is a deficiency in reading skills inhibiting academic learning and/or personal and social adjustment. It is this deficiency, rather than possible etiology and identifying symptoms or application of labels, that becomes the chief and immediate concern of the reading clinician.

DIAGNOSTIC GOALS

Referral of a child with a recognized learning disorder to a reading clinic obviously implies that a reading difficulty indeed exists. Insufficient reading skill is likely to be part of almost any learning disorder since reading and writing activities comprise such a significant part of the modern learning process and its evaluation. The responsibilities and goals of the reading clinician are two-fold: 1) Confirmation and thorough identification of the nature of the difficulty is a most obvious task; 2) However, the ultimate goal of any diagnostic assessment must be treatment. Thus, the most significant responsibility of the clinician is to discover strengths as well as weaknesses in order to make a series of suitable *prescriptive* recommendations for instructional purposes. The next question is how the above goals may best be accomplished.

EXPECTATIONS AND INTERACTION

Inevitably, the child referred to any educationally-oriented clinic brings with him an extended and often complex network of individuals and groups concerned with his problems. At times, it appears that the various parties involved have become so obsessed with diagnosis, potential causes, and classification of disorder that they cease to regard the child as a human being in need of immediate assistance but merely view him as an interesting clinical specimen. It thus becomes imperative that the child, as an individual, remain the focus of attention and as such be included as a *full* participant throughout evaluation and instruction. To facilitate this involvement, those initiating referral (parents, school, other clinics) must prepare the child as fully as possible for the clinic visit. This includes explanation, in language the child can comprehend, of reason for referral, what may occur during the clinic visit, and what the child can hope to gain personally through full co-operation and participation. Upon arrival for the clinic visit, the clinician provides further preparation through discussion of the child's purpose for attending the clinic as he and others see it, what the assessment will include and why, and perhaps of utmost importance, assurance that once evaluation is completed, he will be included in a post-diagnostic "feedback" session. Such a policy may prove threatening for some parents, educators, or clinicians, but if the co-operation of the child in the learning process is desired, and indeed it is absolutely necessary for successful remediation, then strengths, weaknesses, and goals must be made clear to the child in terms he can understand: i.e., *he* has the problem and *he* must assume the responsibility for dealing with it effectively, the instructor and materials merely serving as vehicles for attaining mutually established goals. Needless to say, such information as specific IQ scores need not be stated, but a child does require some information as to the nature of his personal capabilities. Without knowledge and acceptance of such, he cannot possibly begin to establish realistic personal goals. In terms of actual reading skills, discussion of grade levels attained and desired may prove most satisfactory.

Obviously, parents must also be included in discussion of difficulties and instructional goals. Valuable information concerning the child's problems, as seen by the parents, can be gained from both application information and a pre-diagnostic question and answer session with the clinician. Direct observation by the parents *during* diagnosis, facilities permitting, is often useful for demonstrating exactly what the child can or cannot do under specific conditions. This offers a concrete basis for subsequent topics concerning the parental and familial role in remediation.

The third party most often and most necessarily concerned with diagnosis and treatment of the child with a learning disorder is the school. Since in most cases it is desirable for a significant share of the remediation to be given or supplemented within the school, it is essential that clinic and school personnel communicate freely. A clinician may wish to observe the child in question as he functions within the typical classroom setting prior to diagnosis. This provides an opportunity to make a realistic assessment of the remedial situation potentially available within the school and to discover the child's needs as seen by the teacher. It is then hoped that the classroom teacher and other school personnel likely to become involved in planning and executing the remedial program will be released from their school duties to observe *and* participate in the clinical evaluation and post-diagnostic conference. Such an exchange permits both clinic and school personnel to observe the child's behaviors under two very different sets of conditions. In some cases, wide discrepancies become immediately apparent. Sharing of common observations and understandings form a basis for the accurate, effective communication and mutual trust requisite to commitment from both school and clinic in terms of follow-up activities. Hence, the clinic may expect the full participation of the school as the party most likely to share in the implementation and/or supplementation of remedial procedures in exchange for detailed clinical information pertaining to the nature of the problem and most importantly, specific, realistic, prescriptive recommendations for instruction; i.e., what needs doing, at what level, how, and with what anticipated results. Of course, constant reassessment must be considered an integral part of maintaining an appropriate remedial program.

In the case of cross-referral from one clinic to another, a free exchange of pertinent diagnostic results and interview information is assumed. Total sharing not only facilitates accurate diagnosis, but potentially eliminates needless repetition. For example, should a psychologist have thoroughly evaluated a child's intellectual capabilities, there would be little value in repetition by the reading clinician. However, careful analysis by the reading clinician of verbal responses and other behaviors recorded by the psychologist may contribute toward an understanding of a child's approach to various tasks. Occasionally, the question arises as to how much or which "confidential" information should be circulated among clinical personnel. Certainly parental consent should be obtained, but it is felt that total exchange is generally advisable for two reasons. First, what might not be of major concern to one clinician in an inter-clinic case could be of significant use to another in understanding a child's difficulties and needs. Hence, withholding selected information may inhibit accurate diagnosis and selection of effective treatment strategies. Second, if the clinic personnel concerned with the welfare of the child wish to gain parental trust and confidence, they must certainly demonstrate the same behaviors among each other as professionals.

To summarize, the reading clinician needs the full co-operation of *all* parties concerned with a child's difficulties for accurate assessment of strengths and weaknesses and developing effective remedial strategies. In exchange, the clinician is responsible for rendering specific, viable instructional recommendations appropriate to the child's present level of functioning. Above all, personnel must focus attention on the child as an individual in need of assistance, but capable of assuming many responsibilities in the learning process. Who actually treats the child will depend on the severity of the difficulty, the facilities available, and specific nature of the problem.

AREAS AND STRATEGIES OF CLINICAL INVESTIGATION

How a clinician approaches a specific case is determined by several factors: knowledge of the child's difficulties as seen by the child himself and by others, his age, and the ultimate purpose of the evaluation. In addition to isolating and identifying specific areas in need of remediation the clinician must seek to discover under which conditions the child *can* learn, this being the first step toward looking at a child in a helpful way. The pre-investigative procedures would consist of collecting test and interview data previously supplied by the school, other clinics, etc., and eliciting further pertinent background information from the child, his parents, and the school in the application and/or interview situation. The diagnostic strategy itself would include both formal and informal tools of observation; i.e., standardized individual and group tests to determine the individual's present level of functioning relative to a specific norm population as well as less formal and more subjective observations such as response to frustration, praise, and various instructional approaches and materials which might later be included in remedial procedures.

Four basic areas might be identified for clinical investigation: 1) *mental potential,* 2) *physical performance,* 3) *attitudes and interests,* 4) *and reading skills.* Obviously, assessment of reading skills is the central concern, the other areas being included more

for screening purposes to confirm previous reports, eliminate possible sources of academic discomfort or disability, or serve as a
basis for further referral, rather than supply exhaustive diagnostic
information.

Mental Potential: Screening for mental capability might include
one of several short intelligence tests whose scores remain independent of reading skill or several, selected subtests of more
extensive intelligence scales. A low score or observation of response inconsistency may lead the clinician toward a more
thorough investigation of learning potential during diagnosis or
through subsequent referral. Objections are frequently raised when
standardized intelligence measures are used for minority-group
children. Certainly, many items could be termed "culturally
biased" and as such fail to discriminate on the basis of intellectual
capability alone. However, results do have value in that they may
be indicative of how well a child is prepared to cope with the
white, middle-class demands usually, if unjustly, imposed in the
schoolroom. And, as with any measuring instrument, *it is the
interpretation and application of information that is important,
rather than actual scores achieved.*

Physical Performance: Physiological assessment involves such
functions as visual and auditory acuity; i.e., how well can the child
see and hear? Telebinocular screening should reveal whether the
child has adequate vision for nearpoint activity during reading
and the degree to which the eyes operate together. Should difficulties be noted, referral to the appropriate visual specialist is in
order. An audiometric sweep test at 15dB for frequencies critical
to speech (500–4000 Hz) is generally sufficient to detect any gross
auditory inadequacies and provide a basis for threshhold testing
(depth testing at all frequencies) and/or further referral to a
hearing specialist. In addition to visual and auditory screening,
tests of various motor and perceptual-motor skills are usually included. It should be noted that how a child responds to directions
and performs specific tasks is often more important than what he
actually does. Thus, style of approach, observable responses to
frustration and failure, etc., must be accurately recorded for meaningful interpretation of actual scores derived.

Attitudes and Interests: Investigation of attitudes and interests is often useful in discovering how a child feels about himself and his difficulties. In many instances, a poor reader will have a poor academic self-concept and be anxious about his scholastic abilities. Under the circumstances, such feelings may well be appropriate to the reading situation and thus are not indicative of need for psychological attention. However, should such doubts and anxieties extend to all life situations, further evaluation may be advisable to discover whether anxieties stem from or appear to be independent of poor reading skills. If the former be the case, then it is likely that remediation will alleviate the problem. If numerous other factors are operating independently or in conjunction with retarded reading skills, then further referral for potential counseling concomitant with remediation may be the wisest choice. However, should counseling not be available, remedial personnel need not postpone instruction, for children (even those with rather severe emotional disturbances) can often *learn* to distinguish between safe and threatening instructional situations. In such cases, the tutor may be tempted to treat the emotional problems along with the skill deficits, but this is not advisable unless special training and experience have been received in the area of psychological counseling. Thus, teaching and learning remain the central concerns for both reading instructor and student.

A second function of attitude testing is to determine whether a child has made a realistic response to his reading difficulties. In many cases a child has genuinely failed to recognize, or refuses to acknowledge (to himself or others) that any problem exists. If, despite thorough explanation and personal involvement in the diagnostic assessment and follow-up conference, a child of eight years or more still cannot, or more significantly, will not adjust to the realities of the situation, he may not be ready for remedial instruction. Naturally, the door to assistance is not closed permanently, but temporary postponement of instruction until the child has been guided toward establishing his own purposes for remediation may be advisable. To begin prior to inner acceptance or acknowledgment of need may merely reinforce an already unsuccessful experience with reading.

Furthermore, use of interest inventories and direct discussion often provide the reading clinician with valuable insights concerning potential means of motivation in the learning process. The instructor can capitalize upon expressed interests in such self-motivating activities as experience charts, stories, etc.

Reading Skills: The major portion of any clinical assessment of a child referred to a reading clinic with a learning disorder will, as stated above, consist of an evaluation of reading skills. Again, specific tools chosen will be dependent upon the suspected nature of the difficulty, the child's age, and ultimate purpose of the diagnosis. The following is a discussion of skill areas which might be selected for investigation. Note that both formal (standardized) and informal means can be used for varying purposes.

WORD, RECOGNITION TESTING

Auditory Discrimination: Not to be confused with acuity, discrimination testing is designed to determine how well a child can hear significant phonemic differences; e.g., "man" vs. "men." Should difficulty with this skill (it *can* be trained) be noted, the child will be unable to establish the accurate letter-sound association requisite to initial reading success and competent spelling. Obviously, a phonics technique would be inappropriate as the central mode of instruction for this approach would emphasize a weakness rather than capitalize on strength.

Visual Discrimination: As with auditory discrimination, visual discrimination is concerned with the ability to visually distinguish significant differences in letters, words, phrases and sentences; e.g. (b,d) (p,q) (d,p) (was, saw). Again, the skill can be trained, the technique focusing on the principle that to learn what a "b" is, is to learn what it is not; i.e. "d." Thus, the two letters are taught together rather than in isolation. Alternatively, a matrix is provided as a point of reference; i.e., "b" vs. "d." Certainly, inadequate visual discrimination will result in lack of initial reading success, or at best, inaccurate word recognition and numerous substitutions if contextual skills prove strong. Discussion of visual discrimination leads to the controversy concerning the significance of reading and writing reversal errors noted in children with reading disorders. For further information see Delacato (1963), Robbins (1966), Hildreth (1934), Hillerich (1964), Smith (1950). My experience indicates that reversal or more complex orientation difficulties can be treated very successfully when viewed as a mechanical problem responsive to left-right directional training.

Sight Vocabulary: A child's sight vocabulary consists of those words mastered to the extent of instant recognition. Smooth, reasonably speedy reading depends heavily upon the number of words immediately available to the reader, particularly those not amenable to other types of analysis; e.g.; phonetically irregular basic sight words.

Context Clues: If a reader cannot readily identify by sight a word appearing in sentence or paragraph reading, he may succeed by using the contextual clues available from the meaning or structure of the sentence. This technique is a function of overall comprehension skill as well as intelligence and experience. Under varying circumstances, use of context can be viewed as a strength or weakness. A child with serious word recognition problems in isolation may demonstrate true strength in use of contextual clues for word identification and comprehension. On the other hand, a child with an extensive sight vocabulary and adequate comprehension may be overly dependent on context for word recognition, resulting in what may be meaningful but frequent substitution errors, with few skills at his command for expanding reading vocabulary as the difficulty of the reading task increases.

Phonetic and Structural Analysis, Syllabication: Each of these skills serves as an additional tool for identifying those words not present in the reader's sight vocabulary or available to him through contextual clues. Each strategy consists of dividing the unknown word into smaller, recognizable parts. Phonetic analysis relies on accurate grapheme-phoneme association while structural analysis develops from the individual's knowledge of roots and affixes. Accurate syllabication is dependent on an awareness of vowel sound significance in word structure and vowel-consonant letter patterns and accent characteristic of a particular language. It should be noted that these techniques are usually of little value to word or passage comprehension unless the word in question is already part of the reader's listening or speaking vocabulary. Accuracy of response can, of course, be confirmed by reference to a dictionary.

Spelling: At times, it is difficult to determine the basis for classification of spelling skills in the reading program. Obviously it is a *tool* of written expression but it can easily be taught in conjunction with word recognition skills as the need arises. A formal or informal test of competency can provide valuable information concerning a child's left-right, letter-sound association and syllabication skills. Note that errors bearing no recognizable relation to the word in question may be interpreted and treated quite differently from "word salad" errors in which all or most of the correct graphemes are present but not in proper phoneme-grapheme sequence. Again, it is the interpretation of error type that is important rather than actual score achieved.

Comprehension During Oral-Reading: Obviously, fluency in oral reading reflects word identification skills, knowledge and awareness of sentence structure, and at least minimal comprehension. However, an important task distinction must be made between oral fluency and oral comprehension. Failure to demonstrate adequate comprehension following oral reading does not *necessarily* indicate an inability to understand what one has read. At one time, the chief task of the reader may be to relay a message, the listener assuming responsibility for comprehension. At another, the reader's task may include both fluency and comprehension, especially for diagnostic purposes. In either case, the task must be stated clearly to the reader prior to performance if results are to be considered valid for the task. Further, it is significant to note that young and/or inexperienced readers may rely heavily on oral reinforcement for meaning; i.e. vocalization is necessary to maintain attention and/or they have not made the transition characteristic of the more mature reader from listening orally to "listening" silently. Thus, oral reading passages contribute primarily to the identification of word recognition and fluency strengths or weaknesses. Comprehension questions following oral performance may serve as a screening device for more intensive investigation of comprehension skills especially when viewed relative to silent and listening comprehension. Final interpretation of oral reading results will depend upon the age and experience of the reader, the specific nature of the task, and factors included in the test instrument itself.

Silent Comprehension: The purpose of formal or informal silent reading passages is to observe how well a reader can function independently without oral reinforcement. Questions may vary from simple recall to interpretation and application. However, once the application level is reached it must be kept in mind that intelligence and experience may heavily influence performance.

Listening Comprehension: For many very poor readers, listening comprehension becomes a true asset and hence a most important mode for the learning of classroom content during the clinical treatment period. Spache (1963) suggests that the average child can listen approximately two grade levels above his expected age-grade placement, listening comprehension scores correlating approximately .80 with intelligence. However, *poor* listening comprehension may be a function of attending behaviors or other factors rather than intelligence. Thus, tests of listening comprehension may be used very cautiously as a rough indicator of mental capacity in terms of verbal comprehension (when other data are lacking), and as a measure of how much a child might be able to learn from class lecture and discussion, taped lessons etc. This is particularly true when results are in a positive direction from measured oral and silent reading skills.

Study Skills: For the older reader with severe reading difficulties, a study skills assessment is often included in the diagnosis. Can the subject direct and adjust his own reading according to purpose, knowledge of passage structure, utilization of heavy type and end-of-chapter questions; to "survey, question, read, recite, and review?" Can he recognize significant thought relationships signaled by key words; e.g. cause-effect cued by such indicators as "because," "therefore," etc.? Does he have an efficient system of note-taking permitting sufficient summarization and self-testing procedures?

Criteria Teaching: Determining exactly what a child can learn, and under which conditions, is the most important function of any diagnosis in that it points to the appropriate treatment: mere statement of strengths and weaknesses is insufficient. One example of criteria teaching might consist of exposing a student to nine new words, three each through the sight, phonics (analytic or synthetic) and tracing methods. Response to, and success with each strategy should be recorded during and immediately following presentation and after a longer period of intermittent activity (1–24 hours). Results may indicate equal success or difficulty with all three or suggest superiority with one or two approaches. Continued evaluation during treatment should confirm or negate the original findings.

Reporting Results: The primary and ultimate purpose of a diagnostic report is communication of information leading to the successful *treatment* of reading difficulties. Topics included should consist of 1) background information pertinent to interpretation of the subject's difficulties, 2) actual tests used and specific scores received, 3) objective interpretation of data collected, noting patterns which suggest appropriate level for initiation of instruction, as well as 4) subjective impressions supported by actual behaviors observed. 5) Finally, the repor*t must* supply a series of specific, prescriptive recommendations (what to do, why, how, at what level, and with what expected results) based on strengths and weaknesses evident during diagnosis. A final word must be included indicating the need for continual reassessment of skills and goals during the actual treatment in order to preclude a static and hence useless learning experience. Certainly, specific prescriptions for remediation with appropriate follow-up are far more valuable than mere confirmation of previously identified difficulties or ascription of frequently ambiguous and sometimes damaging labels.

The following case study should clarify some of the procedures discussed above and demonstrate the relationship between test interpretation and instructional planning.

Name: Paul C.
Age: 8 years, 4 months
Grade: 3

Referral: Paul was referred to the reading clinic by his parents as "possibly dyslexic" at the suggestion of the school. Concern was expressed for "Paul's apparent inability to progress in reading despite mental capacity and one year of remedial reading instruction."

Medical History: Paul's appearance is one of a rather normal but somewhat anxious eight-year-old boy. Coordination appears slightly, but not seriously, retarded for his age level. No serious illnesses have been reported by the family or the school, but Mrs. C. has stated that a foot cast was necessary at age 3–6 months to correct a muscular deformity. General development appears to have occurred within the normal range.

Family History: Paul is the oldest of five adopted children. Mrs. C. reports that Paul is aware of these circumstances and takes great pride in the fact that he is adopted. Both parents report excellent health although Mr. C. is a somewhat older parent than normal for a child of eight. Paul's parents express great interest in all their children and the environment is felt to be both secure and stimulating.

Educational History: Paul has progressed through school at the normal rate despite an obvious reading disability. According to the school, Paul is well adjusted and learns exceptionally well orally. Consequently, retention did not seem advisable and is not in question at the present time. However, the school has recently noted that Paul has resorted to thumbsucking in school, a habit frequently practiced at home according to Mrs. C. In addition, Paul appears to be rather restless unless he is able to physically participate in an activity and consequently is very distractable during school-oriented tasks. The school psychologist reports that reading skills in grade two were "almost non-existent" and Paul may be "dyslexic, although bright, well-adjusted generally, a leader, and well motivated." Poorly developed perceptual-motor skills were felt to be factors inhibiting successful reading and writing.

Relevant Test Results:

Intelligence Testing:

Peabody Picture Vocabulary Test, A	Mental age—10 months
	Percentile—96th
WISC (as reported by school)	Intelligence Quotient—126
Verbal = 125	
Performance = 99	
Full Scale = 114	

Detroit Tests of Learning Aptitude	(Used to determine relative strength and weaknesses, not as a measure of general mental age.)

		Mental Age
#9.	Visual Attention span for Objects	11-9 (simple)
		12-3 (weighted
#13.	Auditory Attention Span for Related Syllables	10-6
#16.	Visual Attention Span for Letters	9-9
#18.	Oral Directions	9-9
#6.	Auditory Attention Span for Unrelated Words	8-0 (simple)
		8-9 (weighted)
#7.	Oral Commissions	8-3 (highest possible)
#5.	Motor Speed	7-0

Wechsler Intelligence Scale for Children	
Block Design only	Standard Score 10

Emotional Testing:

Bender-Gestalt	No evidence of inappropriate emotionality present.
Incomplete Sentence Blank, Child Form	No evidence of inappropriate emotionality present.

Physical Testing:

Keystone Visual Survey	Left-eye suppression evident at near point. Acuity at near point is questionable, and directionality appears confused; left, right and top, bottom consistently reversed.
Bender-Gestalt	Error Score—5
	Age Norm—2.5
	Perceptual Motor Age—7.0–7.5

Informal Tests of Motor Skills

Task	Performance
1. Cutting line made by magic marker containing sine curves.	Successful, but not smooth.
2. Walking forward on line.	Successfully completed.
3. Walking backward on line.	Done with difficulty.
4. Running maze.	1st trial 65″ (unsuccessful) 2nd trial 35″ (successful) 3rd trial 25″ (successful)
5. Running upstairs.	Completed successfully.
6. Running downstairs.	Done with some difficulty.
7. Touching nose with alternate index fingers with eyes closed.	Right hand—normal. Left hand—contact at second knuckle.
8. Hopping on right foot Hopping on left foot	Completed successfully. Done with difficulty.
9. Skipping	Completed successfully.
10. Jumping jack	Subject grasped task, but has difficulty coordinating hands and feet.

Skills Testing:

Informal Test of Alphabet, Written

Cursive—7 min. plus.
Manuscript—3 min.

Visual Discrimination Testing

14/15 word discrimination.
12/12 consonant blends.
26/26 alphabet—upper and lower case.

Wepman Test of Auditory Discrimination

X score = 5
Y score = 1
Age norm = 3 or less

Visual Tracking (Discrimination)

1st trial 4min. 10sec.
2nd trial 2min. 39sec.
3rd trial 2min. 14sec.

Informal Test of Learning Rate for Five New Words (Fernald tracing technique)

100% recall following one hour of intermittent activity.
100% recall after 4 days of intermittent activity.

Spache Diagnostic Reading Scales

Grade Score
Oral Reading Based on Errors—2.0
Oral Reading Based on Comprehension—2.5
Silent Reading Comprehension—1.9
Listening Comprehension—High 4th—Low 5th

Durrell Analysis of Reading Difficulty

Grade Score
Visual memory   1.5
Phonic Spelling   Below 4.0
Spelling   Below 2.0

Botel Phonics Survey A

Word Recognition

Independent level—none
Instructional level—pre-primer—primer
Frustrational level—1
Consonant sounds—95%
Consonant blends—100%
Consonant Digraphs—83%
Rhyming knowledge—100%
Vowel sounds—30%
Double vowels and R control—22%
Knowledge of syllables (auditory)—30%

Test Interpretations: Intelligence testing during diagnosis confirms previous reports that Paul's verbal ability falls within the bright-normal range and informal testing indicates that learning rate is high. Consequently, poor ability and inadequate rate of learning must be eliminated as factors inhibiting successful reading. Retention of meaningful wholes rather than isolated parts (see *Detroit* test #13 versus #6) may indicate a preference for an analytic learning style; i.e. working from the whole to part.

At present, Paul is experiencing perceptual-motor difficulties, the *Bender-Gestalt* suggesting a one year retardation in this area. This lag was further confirmed by a test of motor speed (see *Detroit* test #5). Informal observations of gross and fine motor activities indicate more "clumsiness" than expected for a boy of this age. In addition to perceptual-motor retardation, Paul appears to suppress his left eye, especially during near point activity. Acuity at this distance is also questionable. It was noted that on tests 4½, 5, and 6 of the *Keystone Visual Survey,* Paul consistently reversed left with right and top with bottom. This behavior may either confirm evidence of perceptual difficulties, or suggest a need to apply appropriate conceptual labels to that which he successfully discriminates. Visual memory is an area of general strength, but attention span for letters and words is relatively weak (see *Detroit* tests #9 and 16 and *Durrell* test of visual memory). This discrepancy may reflect Paul's lack of experience with letters through reading since he has demonstrated adequate discrimination skills (see *Betts* tests of visual discrimination).

Auditory discrimination skills appear poor for his age but may reflect a temporary ear infection present during testing, lack of training, or a maturational lag. "F," "v," and "th" were particularly difficult for Paul (see *Wepman* test of auditory discrimination).

Writing skills are inadequately developed for Paul at this time. It was observed that during cursive writing tasks he became so involved with the circular and connecting motions that he was unable to perceive when the individual letter had been completed and shift to the next. Again this is likely a reflection of immature fine motor skills.

Reading skills tests indicate that Paul is potentially capable of reading at or above grade level as evidenced by the scores involving listening comprehension and strong use of context for meaning (*Spache Diagnostic Reading Scales*). Certainly he appears most able to learn content presented orally and participate fully in intelligent discussion.

Oral reading comprehension is an area of strength, reflecting intelligence and experience. This is most likely due to Paul's excellent use of context and the fact that oral reading forces him to attend to the task. Strong auditory stimulation is, of course, absent during silent reading, and may account for numerous signs of distractability observed during independent silent reading. (Compare *Spache Diagnostic Reading Scales* oral comprehension score with oral error score, and oral comprehension with silent comprehension.)

Sight vocabulary is poorly developed with no independent level observed. Instructional level is pre-primer to primer with frustration at 1–1 (see *Botel Reading Survey:* word recognition and testing, and compare with oral reading comprehension demonstrated on the *Spache*). It may prove difficult for Paul to focus on this weakness at first due to the exceptional context skills demonstrated in passage reading tasks. Phonics of any kind are extremely weak beyond the use of consonants, consonant blends and rhyming words. Much work will be needed in this area.

To summarize, Paul's strengths include intelligence, recall of meaningful wholes, visual discrimination, knowledge of consonants and consonant blends, use of context for meaning, listening comprehension and learning rate. Weaknesses include slight perceptual-motor retardation reflected in directional inconsistencies and poor writing skills, poor visual memory for letters and words, vowel sounds, dependence on oral reinforcement for meaning and possibly auditory discrimination.

Recommendations: Based on the test interpretation and observations stated above, the following instructional recommendations are made.

1. It is recommended that Paul receive intensive remedial training in a clinical situation in an attempt to develop basic reading skills in as short a period as possible. At this time, prognosis appears excellent in light of Paul's desire to succeed and strong mental capacity. The remedial program should include intensive instruction in basic sight vocabulary, followed by development of phonics skills once sufficient letter-sound association has been established. Specific phonics instruction should emphasize vowels, vowel combinations, and use of syllables. Special attention should be given to the development of left-right directional consistency. Commercially printed materials designed to enforce these 1st and 2nd grade word identification skills would serve as suitable supplements to meaningful reading passages.

2. A tracing technique, utilizing visual, auditory, kinesthetic and tactile sensory modes is suggested for the building of a meaningful sight vocabulary, establishing directional consistency and letter-sound association. Words may be printed with a waxy china marker on paper placed over a piece of common window screen or sandpaper. This should provide a clear model with raised letters. Such a technique proved extremely successful during the diagnosis for development of sight vocabulary and spelling. It should be continued until no longer efficient.

3. Because of the poor fine motor skills evident at this time, it is suggested that Paul not engage in cursive writing activities. Further development of manuscript should ease the task of written expression as well as contributing to greater legibility. Typing would also contribute to a similar end-product as well as provide motivation.

4. Further evaluation during the tutoring period is suggested to

determine the advisability of referral to an ophthamologist for questionable acuity at nearpoint and possible left eye suppression. Evaluation of perceptual-motor skills by the pediatric clinic at the medical center appears warranted.

5. Exercises in spatial orientation and visual and auditory discrimination are recommended in order to establish directional consistency. These should provide a sound basis for future phonics instruction at the first and second grade levels. Materials and techniques for this purpose might include commercially published programs to develop perceptual skills directly related to reading or any teacher-made materials to introduce Paul to relevant shapes.

6. Because of Paul's present disenchantment with reading and school-related activities, it is suggested that emphasis be placed upon the development of a sight vocabulary which is important to him personally. A thoroughly analytic approach from whole story, to sentence, to phrase, to word, to word-part should capitalize on Paul's ability to attend to and recall meaningful wholes and minimize poor recall of the isolated fragments employed in a phonics technique. An experience story approach would be useful for this purpose and Paul appeared quite enthusiastic at the prospect of writing his own material. Vocabulary words should be placed on cards for future reference; Paul should be encouraged to make his own word models to be added to a personal word file.

7. The school may complement the more intensive clinical program by providing supplementary phonics materials to develope knowledge and application of individual vowel sounds, combinations, and common syllables found in comercially published materials designed for this specific purpose. Instruction should begin at the high first grade level and continue until mastery is achieved. It may also be helpful for Paul to build a file of personally selected words demonstrating the use of the sounds cited above. A tracing technique as previously described can be encouraged for building a school-oriented sight vocabulary and mastering spelling assignments. Paul is now capable of demonstrating this technique for his teachers and may be responsible for selecting words for study. Evidence indicating

a maturational lag in the development of fine motor skills requisite to successful cursive writing suggests that Paul be allowed to complete assignments with manuscript. A typewriter might also be used. Once manuscript appears well-developed, cursive may be introduced in small stages using extremely simple letter forms. Because of Paul's intelligence and well-developed listening skills, he should be encouraged to participate fully in all class discussions, particularly those relating to content. Further acquisition of content may be facilitated by employing a class partner to read material above low second grade level until Paul has achieved the skills necessary for independent work. Oral examinations are also advisable to provide a valid indication of content mastery until reading and writing skills are adequately developed.

Follow-up: Paul visited the medical center for further perceptual-motor skill evaluation. He was diagnosed as slightly immature in development of these skills with somewhat poor co-ordination and slight suggestion of hyperkinesis. He was thus placed on medication to determine whether improvement might be observed but there was no noticeable change in behavior and medication was discontinued. Re-examination one year later indicated no further need for involvement of medical personnel. Tutoring over the next 18 months resulted in rapid growth in all skill areas with all recommendations apparently appropriate for Paul's specific difficulties. In June of the 4th grade, Paul's word recognition and comprehension skills were at the 5th grade level, while listening comprehension measured above the 7th grade level. At this time, no further remedial help was deemed necessary. At the end of 5th grade, Paul was experiencing no difficulty with academic subjects.

Hopefully, presentation of this case study has demonstrated sufficiently that diagnosis implies far more than mere accumulation of descriptive data. From the diagnosis must come an appropriate remedial program which is continually re-evaluated and altered to suit the changing needs of the child.

Summary: The preceding chapter has attempted to define the role and strategy of the reading clinician in the evaluation of a child referred for a learning disorder. The goals consist of accurate diagnosis and realistic, prescriptive recommendations for treatment. In addition to these responsibilities, the reading clinician must be concerned not only with the application of his diagnostic tools to the skill problems involved, but with his relationship both to the child as an individual capable of assuming responsibility for learning and to the parents, school, and professional collegues sharing in the concerns of evaluation and remediation. It is the combination of accurate diagnosis, appropriate, realistic recommendations, and effective participation and communication among all concerned that contribute to a successful remedial program.

REFERENCES

Bender, Lauretta: Bender Gestalt Test. American Orthopsychiatric Association, Inc., 1946.

Birch, H. G., and Belmont, L.: Auditory-visual integration, intelligence, and reading ability in school children. *Perceptual Motor Skills Journal, 20*:295-305, 1965.

Bond, G., and Tinker, M.: *Reading Difficulties: Their Diagnosis and Correction.* New York, Appleton-Century-Crofts, 1967.

Botel, M.: *Botel Reading Inventory, Word Recognition and Phonics Survey.* Chicago, Follet Publishing Co., 1961.

Critchley, M.: *Developmental Dyslexia.* Springfield, Thomas, 1964.

Dechant, E. V.: *Improving the Teaching of Reading.* Englewood Cliffs, New Jersey, Prentice Hall, 1964.

Delacato, C. N.: *The Diagnosis and Treatment of Speech and Reading Problems.* Springfield, Thomas, 1963.

Detroit Tests of Learning Aptitude. Indianapolis, Bobbs-Merrill, 1959, revised.

Durrell, D.: *Durrell Analysis of Reading Difficulty.* New York, Harcourt, Brace and World, Inc., 1955.

Fernald, G.: *Remedial Techniques in Basic School Subjects.* New York, McGraw-Hill, 1943.

Ferraro, P.: An interdisciplinary approach to learning disabilities. In Greene, F. (ed.): *Reading: Reasons and Readiness.* Syracuse, Syracuse University Press, 71–81, 1970.

Harris, G. J.: Lateral dominance, directional confusion, and reading disability. *Journal of Psychology, 44*:283–294, 1967.

Helmuth, J. (ed.): *Learning Disorders,* Volumes I, II, and III. Seattle, Special Child Publishers, 1965.

Hildreth, G.: Reversals in reading and writing. *Journal of Educational Psychology, 25*:1–20, January, 1934.

Hillerich, R. L.: A study of the relationship between eye-hand dominance and the reading achievement of selected primary pupils. *American Educational Research Journal,* pp. 121–26, March, 1964.

Johnson, D., and Myklebust, H.: *Learning Disabilities: Educational Principles and Practices.* New York, Grune and Stratton, 1967.

Keystone Visual Survey Tests, Keystone Viewing Company, Meadville, Pennsylvania, 1961.

Koppitz, E. M.: *Bender-Gestalt Test for Young Children.* New York, Grune and Stratton, 1964.

Money, J.: *The Disabled Reader.* Baltimore, John Hopkins Press, 1966.

Money, J. (ed.): *Reading Disability: Progress and Research Needs in Dyslexia.* Baltimore, John Hopkins Press, 1962.

Monroe, H.: *Children Who Cannot Read.* Chicago, University of Chicago Press, 1932.

Myklebust, H. (ed.): *Progress in Learning Disabilities,* Vol. I. New York, Grune and Stratton, 1968.

Orton, S. T.: *Reading, Writing, and Speech Problems in Children.* New York, W. W. Norton Company, 1937.

O'Sullivan, M. A., and Pryles, C.: Reading disabilities in children. *Pediatrics, 60*:369–375, 1962.

Peabody Picture Vocabulary Test. Circle Pines, Minnesota, American Guidance Service, 1959.

Pope, L.: *Guidelines to Teaching Remedial Reading to the Disadvantaged.* New York, Faculty Press, Inc., revised 1970.

Rabinovitch, R.: Reading and learning disabilities. In, Arieti, S. (ed.), *American Handbook of Psychiatry.* New York, Basic Books, 1959.

Robbins, M. P.: The Delacato interpretation of neurological organization. *Reading Research Quarterly, 1*:57–79, 1966.

Smith, C. B., Carter, B., and Dapper, G.: *Teaching Reading Difficulties: The Role of the Principal, Teacher, Specialist and Administrator.* Washington, U. S. Government Printing Office, 1970.

Smith, H. P., and Dechant, E. V.: *Psychology in Teaching Reading.* Englewood Cliffs, New Jersey, Prentice-Hall, 1961.

Smith, L. C.: A study of laterality characteristics of retarded readers and reading achievers. *Journal of Experimental Education, 18*:321–329, June, 1950.

Spache, G.: *Diagnostic Reading Scales, Examiners Manual.* Del Monte Research Park, California Test Bureau of McGraw-Hill, 1963.

Wechsler Intelligence Scale for Children. New York, The Psychological Corporation, 1949.

Wepman, J. M.: *Auditory Discrimination Test,* Chicago, 1958.

Wilson, R. M.: *Diagnostic and Remedial Reading for Classroom and Clinic.* Columbus, Ohio, Charles Merrill, 1967.

Witty, P., and Kopel, D.: *Reading and the Educative Process.* Boston, Ginn and Company, 1939.

Chapter VI

SEVERE MULTI-SENSORY DISORDERS AND LEARNING DISABILITIES

W. SCOTT CURTIS and EDWARD T. DONLON

Are there issues in the field of learning disorders which might be developed more fully if studied from the viewpoint of clinicians and researchers interested in other populations? This is the general question we approach in the presentation of some findings on children with severe multi-sensory (deaf-blind) problems. Our first reaction to this opportunity was that there is basically an antagonistic relationship between these populations — being at opposite extremes of the disability continuum. Probably for those readers of the old school, that feeling will be shared. The "new wave" of special educator, who apparently wants to take on responsibility for large numbers of children in school, may not share our attitude. We hope that all our readers will separate the objective methodology of the Behavioral Observation Protocol and the subjective attitudes of the authors as they read.

In general, our research problem has been to seek ways to unravel the semantic web which encumbers psychoeducational testing and reporting procedures. These semantic problems affect not only the research but also teacher training programs generated by our profession. In short, we must look at words to see children. And we must look at children to see issues, if the cycle of observation is to be pragmatically perpetuating.

For example, the child with learning disabilities has been with us under several pseudonyms, going back beyond the neuraphrenic described by Edgar Doll in the 1940's. Such characteristics as perseveration, hyperirritability, hyperkinetic behavior, distractibility, and other well-known descriptions have been listed for him as well as for the aphasic child, the aphasoid child, the neurologically-impaired child, the brain-injured child, the interjacent

124

child, the emotionally disturbed child, and most recently . . . the child with learning disabilities (or disorders). It may be that in severe extremes children identified in the above administrative groups differ, but it is also true that these parameters are used throughout the entire range of behavior and across all groups.

That is to say, it is very likely that a child fitting any one of the above administrative or diagnostic groups would probably have a familiar list of descriptive adjectives applied to him at some point in his records and files. It may be that the terms would only be used to indicate that he is normal in those categories, but more than likely some limitations of performance in an area would be described in a pattern not too different regardless of the labels of the major diagnosis.

It is quite possible to use those same descriptions in identifying the characteristics of the multi-handicapped child. We do not, however, do it within the frame of reference described by Curtis and Donlon and particularly as elaborated in our 1969 Descriptive Adjective Report. We have found through unfortunate experiences with the severely multi-handicapped child that to say a child is distractible or hyperactive etc., tells very little about him. It is certainly not wrong to use these words to help clarify a general behavioral pattern or overall tone of the child if the terms add meaningfully to the descriptive process. However, it is wrong to ignore their limits. Many teachers may feel that indicating the extent to which a given child is the victim of each of these traits gives a clear picture of the child's performance. This is hardly true. Unfortunately, case records do not indicate that all teachers are aware of the meaninglessness of some of our jargon.

In light of the above it may seem inappropriate to present one more *schema* for the description of children or the inspection of their behavior and it is probably true that in time this examination terminology may prove equally unsatisfactory. However, the terminological matrix which we consider when examining a multi-handicapped child while rating him through a video-tape protocol technique forces the examiner to systematically inspect and rate nine important components of the child's behavior patterns.

The matrix identified in Figure II is an outgrowth of the model developed in Figure I which is a result of preliminary research conducted through support of the Office of Social and Rehabilitation Services Administration in 1967 and 1968. This research was one of the few attempts, to our knowledge, to apply the deductive rather than inductive method to model development. That is, instead of beginning with what ought to be said about children when looking at children and then examining children we reversed the process and catalogued those things which had been said about children in reports by a variety of professional people. Based on these descriptive terms a model was developed which would include a concept and verbal constructs used to describe the children. This approach may be absurd in that it implies that what has been said about children is what ought to be said about them. One could argue that this is not the case, and worse, that errors which have been made before would then be compounded into a model for a future proliferation of errors. Such *could* be the case.

However, we presume that when more than 20 examiners from 10 professional backgrounds tested 100 children — each examiner using the terminology and the tests and observational methods of his profession and his own personal distinctive background and training within the course of this most interpersonal interaction— there would be a reasonable display of terminology which might be sufficient to describe most children in that population. Based on this assumption, a collection of such terminology was divided according to the model described by Donlon (1969) for severely multi-sensorily handicapped children.

The purpose of the ensuing presentation is to familiarize the reader with some aspects of the video-tape protocol for the examination of severely multi-sensory handicapped children (1971) which may be of value when applied to the problems of children with learning disorders. The following report will present:

1. A description of the terminological matrix for behavioral observation.
2. A discussion of the differences between the learning-disordered and severely multi-handicapped populations which must be considered if the model is to be generalized.
3. Some direct testing and observation suggestions based on

experience with the technique which seem general enough to apply to learning-disordered as well as to multi-sensorily handicapped children.

4. Some theoretical issues.

THE TERMINOLOGICAL MATRIX

The nature of the examination procedure which we have developed for the inspection of severely multi-handicapped children may be applicable to those children with learning disabilities in the sense that both populations do not readily demonstrate their incapacity on traditional and standardized tests. This is perhaps the most important reason for using some of the principles from the field of multiple disability as an approach to examination and treatment in the apparently unrelated field of learning disabilities even though the two populations are remarkably different in their overall ability to sustain themselves in society.

The observational technique which we have employed is derived from a three-by-three design with (1) *communication,* (2) *adjustment,* and (3) *learning* displayed on one axis; and (1) *people,* (2) *situations,* and (3) *tasks* displayed on the other axis.

This display presents the examiner with a total of nine cells in which he *must* make observations and record a point of view concerning the child, based on test data, historic information, the behavior which he sees, and his understanding of the nature of the problem.

Consequently, the examination of communication calls for an inspection of the ability to communicate with (1) various people in (2) varied situations while (3) engaged in a variety of life tasks. The observation of adjustment calls for a reaction to the individual's ability to adjust to (1) a variety of people in (2) various situations and (3) to the tasks that confront him in real life as well as the testing situation. And finally, the appraisal of the child's learning ability is seen as it occurs in relation to (1) various people, and his ability to learn in (2) varied situations and (3) a variety of tasks.

This all seems too elementary. However, it is the failure to carefully inspect the child throughout these categories that has led to some of the important and critical problems in education for the handicapped and perhaps for the normal child as well.

The model in Figure I shows the original construct upon which the research and terminology for describing severely multi-sensorily handicapped children was based. This model was developed on the basis of information mentioned earlier in this report and reported more fully by the authors (Curtis and Donlon, 1969). Basically the model is concerned with three topics. First the types or categories of behavior to be observed; second, types or categories of situation or condition in which the observation will take place, and third, the terminology which will be used in reporting the observations.

The behavior to be observed in handicapped clients will probably vary with the objectives of the professional responsible for the observation and the type and severity of problem the client manifests. In observing the behavior of the severely multi-sensorily handicapped child, our purpose was to force the examiners to be cognizant of the major problems of the populations and to lead them away from the more traditional psycho-educational procedure of examining for detail at the expense of information about gross pathological behavior patterns. In brief, although it is delightful to have a detailed catalogue of the child's idiosyncracies, it is imperative that we have clear-cut statements as to his effectiveness *now* and his *potential for growth* in certain broad critical behavioral categories. One presumes that the teacher or the therapist or the parents will quickly observe the overt and superficial behavior patterns of the child and that these need not be reported except as examples nor dwelt on by experienced professional examiners. The job of the competent professional in psycho-educational management is to make broader and more operational statements about the child's behavior, its meaning and its implications, than to merely catalogue that which is visible to the layman or inexperienced professional. As the model indicates, the members of our team believe that *communication, adjustment* and *learning* are the major fundamental categories which must be dealt with by the examiner for this population of multi-sensorily handicapped. There are other obvious important areas of behavior such as *mobility, health care, family life,* etc. which could well be important observational categories for other populations. It is our hope that the information presented in this report will allow those involved with children having learning disorders to consider the behavioral categories which are appropriate for observation of that population.

Figure 1
A MODEL INDICATING THE PARAMETERS OF THE BEHAVIORAL
OBSERVATION USED IN CLINICAL
EXAMINATION

Terminology Available
For Reporting Observation

BEHAVIOR OBSERVATION
1. Communication
2. Adjustment
3. Learning

VARIATION OF PERSONNEL	VARIATION OF THE PHYSICAL SETTING	VARIATION OF TASKS AND STIMULI
1. Number	1. Room size	1. Table tasks
2. Relationship	2. Background structure	2. Motor skills
3. Etc.	3. Figure objects	3. Problem solving
	4. Etc.	4. Ect.

The second question indicated by our model for observation asked the question, "How shall we vary the observational settings and what shall we vary within these settings to give a brief, but true exposure of the child's behavior in each of the above-mentioned observational categories?" Ideally, one would do as Ann Sullivan did with Helen Keller—one would move into the child's home and become a part of his real environment. In most situations, even in the relatively small population of deaf-blind children this is unreasonable in today's world. For that reason, a simulated observational experience or a very structured and brief observation within real-life situations must be conducted. We determined for the purposes of our population that there were three major characteristics which could be varied in the clinical observation situation. First, we believe we could vary the number and type of people introduced into the observational situation. To enhance our observation, we see the child alone, we see him with parents, we see him with his peers, we see him with unfamiliar normal children, we see him with a teacher, we see him with a demanding person, or a sympathetic person, etc. Specifically, we hope to introduce into the observational situation as many types of people and stimulate as many interpersonal relations as can be interjected in the allowed time period.

Secondly, we attempt to vary the physical setting in which the observation is conducted. Under some conditions the greatest amount of variability which can be set is simply room size, which is one important part of the child's momentary attitude. Other aspects of the physical setting which we may vary are room, lighting, the amount and types of furniture, objects in the room, functions of the room, familiarity or unfamiliarity of the room to the child, reverberancy or sound absorption, and the child could be outside or in a space or area such as a hallway not usually called an observation room. Briefly, then, we have observed that not only does the child's behavior vary with the people around him but also in relation to where he is.

Our final variation in the observational situation is based on the belief that the third factor which influences behavior is the task or stimuli presented (or in a sense, those which are being inflicted on the child) by the examiner as part of the testing situation or as part of a series of natural events which the observer can record. For our research population we believe it is important to attempt to show the child engaged at table tasks which are a part of the usual psycho-educational examination such as block sorting, figure matching, block stacking, form board work, and other close eye-hand tasks. We also attempt to show the child engaged in the tasks of daily living such as dressing himself, bathing, brushing his teeth, toileting, and organized play. As a major part of the task orientation within our observation schema we presented a host of isolated stimuli to the various sensory avenues of the child. Some examiners with particular background in sensory measurement might be inclined to think that the observation of a child's reaction to discrete stimuli such as light and pure tones ought to be distinguished in a fourth category from both tasks which are described as table tasks, and those which are life activity tasks. It is our belief that this kind of separation for our population is inappropriate (but it may well be considered an appropriate separation for other populations). Indeed it would certainly be an appropriate distinction to be made for the normal child.

Having determined to make observations of communication, adjustment, and learning as we see that the child moves through a succession of interactions with a variety of abstract and concrete tasks, we are left with the final problem for which this research was primarily developed. That is the problem of breaking down the semantic inaccuracy which is a large part of the confusion seen in clinical reporting about children. Thus, although we found as many as 8,000 terms have been used in the description of the severely multi-handicapped children, we found that this kind of battery of descriptions was probably unreasonable and unrealistic in view of the fact that some 70 children examined and reported on by this verbal array had such markedly disordered natures that little behavior was in fact, evidenced, and that that behavior was highly similar within the population. In other words, if 8,000 words are required to describe a small, relatively non-behaving and somewhat homogeneous population, how many descriptions would be required to describe the broad range of behaviors observed up through minor disorders and into the normal populations. The number of adjectives and adverbs would certainly be astronomical. And of course, as the number of such descriptive words increases, so does the problem of semantic error.

In addition to the problems of observational organization and altered semantic patterns, an important part of the research which subtends our current report is the application of video-tape recording to permit storage of behavior samples for concrete referents to the terminology used. Thus, issues which arise can be re-evaluated and studied over time for clarification. Through the video-taping process we have, in effect, developed a behavioral dictionary which can be seen by anyone interested in what we or our research judges believe to be a type and/or level of behavior. By reference to the written summaries of judges' reactions in the research reports, the probability of agreement between judges as to the type and severity of behavior can also be considered.

Consequently, our purpose was to narrow down the observational report into a brief series of ratings so that rather limited definitions could be developed for each of the terms rated and a simple numerical category could be developed for the whole concept of severity. The rating forms developed on this basis for the analysis of communication, adjustment and learning have been reported and are available to professional workers (Donlon and Curtis, 1972).The specific rating forms which have been developed are probably only models with respect to a learning-disordered population and undoubtedly reflect limitations because of their design for multi-sensorily handicapped children which would make them inapplicable to some other less severely handicapped groups.

Figure II shows the general terminological matrix which should be applied to the examination of a handicapped population if the preliminary success of our initial research effort is transferrable to a learning disordered population. Until such time as those workers in the field of learning disorders identify behavioral skills to be rated in planned environments, then probably the matrix suggested in Figure II will be helpful. At least it may prevent the proliferation of a semantic jungle through which examiners and teachers may never reach each other in their efforts to communicate about children.

The following suggestions of differences between children with multiple disorders and children with learning disorders may be of help in developing an expanded terminological matrix for the learning disordered population.

A TERMINOLOGICAL MATRIX ILLUSTRATING CELLS
FOR BEHAVIORAL OBSERVATION OF
SEVERELY MULTI-SENSORILY HANDICAPPED CHILDREN

Behavioral Environment

Behavioral Skills	People	Situations	Task	Composite
Communication				
Adjustment				
Learning				
Composite				

Figure 2

POPULATION CHARACTERISTICS

If these observational principles and techniques are to be applied to the learning disordered population, it is very likely that the details of the observational environment will have to be altered and that the categories of *Child Behavior* observed will be expanded.

As we consider the characteristics of a terminological matrix for classifying the observation of children with Learning Disorders, it will be important for the reader to review some differences between the severely multi-sensory handicapped and the learning-disordered populations.

1. *Institutionalization.* The severely multi-handicapped group will probably be institutionalized during some period of their life. Children with learning disabilities will almost never face institutional treatment. When we make observations about the adjustment of the two groups of children in an abstract frame of reference we must bear in mind that adjustment to the relatively structured living conditions of an institution as opposed to the random and unstructured daily life experiences of the child living outside an institution are quite different. If adjustment is defined as the ability to perform comfortably and productively at one's own educational expectancy level, in his own real life situation, then probably the multiply-handicapped child is better adjusted than the child with learning disabilities.

2. *Test Discrimination.* Children with learning disabilities fail tests because the tests are not discriminating enough whereas children with multiple disabilities fail tests because the tests are too discriminating.

3. *Daily Living Skills.* Activities of daily living are almost always a problem of extreme concern in educational planning for the multiply-handicapped group. Children with learning disabilities (other than the effect of general constitutional clumsiness) will not face this problem.

4. *Placement Goals.* The placement goals for children in learning disabilities programs primarily relate to a return to the normal classroom. The placement goal for children being

treated for multiple disabilities is movement into a classroom for children with a severe unitary disability.

5. *Parental Concern.* Parental concerns for the two groups differ sharply. Parents of the multi-sensory handicapped are concerned with such things as whether or not the child is retarded, whether or not he will need medical care and whether or not he will require institutionalization, whereas parents of learning disabled children are perplexed by the inability of their normal-appearing child to "please the teacher" and the extent to which the child will cause family embarrassment by failure to achieve while appearing normal.

6. *Appearance.* Cosmetically, children with learning disabilities tend to appear normal while children with multiple disabilities carry physical characteristics which mark them as atypical.

7. *Sensory Acuity.* Children with learning disabilities traditionally pass tests of sensory acuity. Children with multiple disabilities traditionally fail tests of sensory acuity but, both show disturbances of performance in receptive modalities.

8. *Reward—Punishment.* Another problem in dealing with the multi-handicapped child, distinct from that of the child with learning disabilities, is that the teacher is unable to use superficial types or rewards which are often applied in the classroom situation. That is, the multi-handicapped child is not stimulated by a star on his work board nor is he stimulated by a smile from the teacher or an extended recess period. He is not usually able to associate these "rewards," if he perceives them at all, with some changes in his own behavior. Children with learning disabilities, however, can respond to a very carefully graded "reward per behavior change" program.

9. *Quality of Behavior.* One of the problems of the multi-disabilitied group is that if the teacher plans to use the traditional reward and punishment approach in dealing with the behavior which the child exhibits, a surprising difficulty will be encountered when it is discovered that the child has not produced much behavior at all. In the absence of behavior the application of punishment and reward is a difficult process. When the behavior that does occur is largely that which one would wish to extinguish, the preponderance of punishment

to reward becomes so great that the child learns to expect only this, which of course, to an extent defeats the reward-punishment option.

That is, the child does not produce enough rewardable behavior on his own part, within the framework we now use to view behavior of children, to allow the use of contrived rewards. To this extent it would seem that other methods need to be used for producing behavioral change.

10. *Stimulus Selectivity*. One of the distinctions to be made between the multi-sensory handicapped and the learning-disabled child is that the sensory mechanism, and to some extent the response mechanism, of the multi-handicapped reacts on an all-or-nothing basis in contrast to a child with learning disabilities who is able to produce some control over the degree of response he will make to stimulation. In fact, it appears that stimulation of any sensory modality of the multi-handicapped child will produce what might be called an undifferentiated response, in the sense that the response can occur regardless of the modality through which stimulation occurred. That is, stimulus and response are not as systematically related as they are in the more nearly normal child with learning disabilities. One is tempted to think of the learning disabled child as exhibiting characteristics similar to those described above, but he reacts inappropriately to selected stimuli (perhaps certain school tasks) whereas the multi-sensory handicapped child reacts across senses and grossly to nearly all stimuli.

11. *Pedagogical Approach*. When the child with multiple disabilities approaches a very simple learning task and achieves anything at all he is rewarded profusely. When the child with learning disabilities approaches a learning task and fails anything at all he is often punished profusely. There is a striking difference in pedagogical approach to the two children which undoubtedly reflects in their adjustment to learning situations, schools, teachers and themselves. It is interesting, however, that when the child with multiple disabilities is contrasted with the child having learning disabilities he will in daily social life seem considerably more maladjusted. One

might say then that resolving the dilemma of managing success and failure as seen in the irrational extremes of the educational management of these two populations is not critical to life adjustment outside the educational setting of either of these groups of children.

12. *Stress.* Children with multiple disabilities live and perform in a relatively stress-free environment. The goals set for them are minimal and realistic, or if anything, unrealistically low. Consequently adjustment problems arising from inadequacies in confronting the learning situation (reinforced through negative social feedback) are not great for the multi-handicapped child. On the contrary, children with learning disabilities seem to show excessive maladjustment to minimal learning difficulties. Perhaps this is the result of the difference in an unrealistic expectation for this child to perform normally at a time in his life when he cannot. Both groups probably have inner stresses that we do not understand.

13. *Testing Procedures.* Whereas deafness or blindness *alone* may be characterized by stating the degree of disability in decibels and/or diopeters, multi-sensory disabilities cannot. They must be reported in terms of the number and types of discrete handicaps and in terms of degree of functional disturbance rather than degree of loss. In both instances, etiology may be appended to the descriptive label. Deafness or blindness as a unitary problem is not usually defined behaviorally in terms of learning, adjustment, communication or any other life process, but rather in terms of formalized test procedures done in an abstract or highly objective test situation; and producing quantitative indices of sensory loss, e.g., decibels and diopeters.

On the other hand when multi-sensory disabilities exist, these tests are not available or applicable or useable, and in most instances the definition of multi-sensory disability or diagnosis of multi-sensory disability is made on the basis of the traditional acuity tests in each of the two prime sensory avenues. However, the most useful definition for educational purposes should be based on a behavioral evaluation in the areas of learning, adjustment, and communication.

14. *Developmental Delay*. A general pattern of developmental delay in more than one behavioral category is characteristic of the multi-sensory handicapped. These categories roughly consist of the activities of daily living, formal learning abilities, and informal social, or recreational competencies. These functional delays will generally be below the level expected of a normal child by the third or fourth year of life. The learning disordered appear less problematical at this age. Later in life the children often appear to improve in the development of muscular and motor coordination and in gustatory/olfactory sense function to the point that such are not contributory to the larger deficiency.

15. *Health*. Early in life multi-handicapped children are frequently smaller and generally in poorer health than their peers.

TESTING SUGGESTIONS

When we face a problem which is so very severe that a child may be relegated to institutional life if the early years of observation, testing, evaluation, diagnosis, family guidance, medical treatment, etc., are not well done, we become enraged at and discouraged by some of the off-handedness which is tolerated in the educational examination of the not-so-handicapped.

The following list of suggestions was prepared for use by those testing the severely multi-handicapped. They are presented here as ideas that may affect the way one would work with less severely handicapped children. These ideas are not necessarily new but are still so often ignored that they deserve re-thinking. The reader should remember the population they were developed for, and apply the principle — when it fits — to other, more normal children.

There are undoubtedly some principles of child advocacy hidden within these suggestions. The reader may find subtle hints that the authors are concerned about the superficiality of many techniques applied by educational examiners. It is true that a great deal of concern for poor quality testing and planning is reasonable. Unfortunately, the severely multi-handicapped child frequently gets a better deal than most essentially normal children in ordinary classrooms.

1. Deal with children as if they can see and hear. It takes some time to overcome an initial sensitivity in asking blind children to look and see and asking deaf children to listen and speak. On occasion you might be embarrassed by unknowing examiners who will imply that you are unsophisticated in doing these things. Do it anyway! There's no one more foolish than someone who claims to be testing the hearing of a child while treating him as if he were deaf.

2. Remember that one of the aspects of traditional psychological testing often forgotten by the psychologist today in the routine working situation is that tests are supposed to provide maximum opportunity to achieve. If you do not begin your testing in such a fashion and if you do not structure the test situation so that the child can perform the tasks from which he will be judged, then you have done a poor job.

3. Remember that any single test situation you put a child through will have different implications to other people. For example: If you ask a child to stack blocks and he doesn't do it effectively, it may mean that he did not hear you, that he did not see the blocks, that his intelligence was unable to comprehend the task, that his language level was too low to translate the commands, that he was behaving negatively emotionally and rejecting your commands although he knew and understood what you said, or that some degree of neurological injury precluded his proper understanding and performance of the task. Consequently, although it might seem scientific and very objective to report only what was asked of the child and what he accomplished, it would at the same time allow for a great deal of possible misinterpretation of what actually took place.

4. If you are not used to testing multi-handicapped children look over your traditional or frequently used test material and then determine whether or not a sufficiently intriguing variety of materials is present. In the event of blindness, for example: blindfold yourself and manipulate your various

test objects to see if they are exciting, stimulating, or sufficiently different to be motivational and interesting to a child. Or for a very revealing experience, ask someone to test you as you would usually test others on a variety of skills, while you are both functioning in the presence of a loud radio you can put within a foot or two of your ear. This will give you some idea of the confusion of a child who is trying to follow partially audible instructions while additionally confused by distracting stimulation. In other words, try to get the best possible picture of your test materials—as they would appear to the child you are testing.

5. Consider the problem of sensory areas that you do not usually think of when testing children: olfactory, gustatory, tactile and temperature sensitivities. Think about your usual test procedures in terms of these things: Is the child's response to you related to a strong after-shave lotion, perfume, bad breath, the heat of cigarette smoke that you are blowing past him, a medicinal smell that he associates with a medical experience, an uncomfortable texture of your clothing that is irritating to him?

6. As the child appears lower and lower in competence, try to test from a point of view of what the child can *do* rather than what he *cannot* do.

7. Ask yourself why you are testing the child in general and specifically. You should test differently for the purpose of recommending what the mother might do next week with the child in order to improve his upright posture as opposed to whether or not you are going to make recommendations conconcerning institutionalization. It may be surprising, but we suggest that you must test much more critically and more specifically in order to make recommendations for the next week than for a life-time placement.

8. You should by all means play clinical hunches. Feel free to do anything or nothing with a client if necessary to discover his true competence, potential and abilities. Do not allow yourself the luxury of giving a test no matter how highly respected if, in your best opinion, knowing the result of that test will give you no information of value in dealing with the

child. It is better to spend your time creatively devising tasks that may in the end tell you something about a child than to use a test which has status but will not answer meaningful questions about the child. One of the most difficult tasks that we face in training students to deal with severely multi-handicapped is to get them to stop doing something to the child and instead to listen and observe.

9. Do your testing without much information on the child. It is important to know if there is any reason medically, or emotionally or otherwise why you should not do certain tasks which may present a danger to his physical or emotional well-being. We would not want a child to be over-extended physically by testing. We would not want a child to be triggered into a cataclysmic or rage response so that he becomes intractible. Other than these precautions, you should keep in mind that the child is at the widest extreme of the population and that the testing must employ the full capacity of your testing ability.

10. Rather than trying to imply learning ability in any given area of behavior from tests, isolate some status-quo behavior samples and modify them in several behavior areas. For example, find some visual behavior and try to change it; find some auditory behavior and try to change it; find some signs of adjustment techniques and try to modify them.

11. When the child is in the room or within sensory contact with you and you are interviewing his parents, teacher or others, assume that he understands everything that is going on and behave accordingly.

12. Be somewhat ritualistic in your behavior with the child. That is, do similar things in similar ways. When you talk, use gestures and signs at the level of your mouth. Use the same words, acts, gestures, and signs for the same activities repeatedly given. Do the same kind of testing in the same kind of place week after week. Shift physical environment for the various kinds of testing so that the child knows that he is coming to a demarcation point. Don't presume that he differentiates between tasks as you do.

13. Be cautious about token rewards. There is absolutely no rea-

son to use candy, ice cream, or any other kind of similar rewards to deal with any child at any level. "M & M's" are not panaceas.

15. When talking with parents, try to encourage them to accept the idea that you will work with the child's best skills without trying to label him or set a lifetime goal.

16. Insist that as part of the examination the parents stay with the child to observe him. It is also valuable for you to ask them to show off some of the things the child can do best.

17. When the child is low in general performance level and potential, it is important that you spend considerable time with him before making any statements about him at all or even dealing with him in a more formal testing procedure. You ought to plan just to "stand around" while the child goes through his day with other people and observe his behavior in his real world.

18. Find some device for working around the obstacle problems of referral. Do not refer to just any other person, teacher, psychologist, etc. Refer to the best person you know, *and for specific reasons*.

19. Don't suggest, recommend or sentence a child to any agency, institution, or person with which you have not spent time and with whose program you are not personally familiar in some detail.

20. Don't ever presume that someone else will coordinate the details of the child's total treatment. Search until you find that someone is doing it and until you are satisfied that his case will be professionally managed over a long period of time. If *such* a person is not available, you are obligated to remain responsible for the child's long-term placement regardless of your professional background. In line with that, it is important that you familiarize yourself with the variety of services available in this field.

21. As part of your testing procedure you must determine in early preschool clients how effectively they are going to be able to function with the parents in the home situation. You will probably be making recommendations for the parent to work with the child on certain selective "contracts" and to re-

appear for further examination at some later date. It is extremely desirable to use a contract plan with parents to give you some information on the areas wherein the child can learn and to tell you how effective the parents may be as teachers.

22. Most of the children don't do anything! Cause them to do something! Socially, academically, and communicatively.

23. If people don't follow your advice, stop seeing them.

24. Work as a team, and review the child with others in order to know the implications of problems you are not expert in.

25. Insist on the luxury of control of professional jealousy. Avoid paper and pencil experts. Don't be scared off by "the establishment."

26. Don't fear going out of business by requesting some conditions prior to seeing a child. Such things as anecdotal records kept by both staff and parents are important data. Adherence to a data collection routine is also important even though some might think the tasks are of minor importance.

27. Be aware of the "good boy" syndrome. Don't lavish praise unwarrantedly.

28. Remember that space, which is handled unconsciously by normal children, is a problem dimension to the sensorily handicapped.

29. Assume that the child is responding reasonably to his perceived environment and remember that what is your most unconscious or abstract perception of your life environment may be the multisensory disordered child's most conscious or concrete world.

30. Begin at infancy, but deal with problems of the child's life, not anticipated academic hurdles.

THEORETICAL CONSIDERATIONS

To this point, we have emphasized that children called "multiply-handicapped" are different from those with learning disorders. But, we have tried to suggest that some of the findings from both clinical and research experiences with the one population may be applicable to the other—perhaps to many populations within the handicapped domain. Most of the commentary to this point has been relatively empirical to the extent that it is highly behavioral rather than theoretical and that it is documented to a large degree on video-tapes (Curtis and Donlon, 1970) which were prepared as part of the research upon which this statement is based.

We would like to be subjective and offer some of the more fluid ideas that have developed during the conferences and observations which were a part of the experimental study and the clinical process. These ideas are not systematically related. They do not form a model. They are simply a set of discrete considerations discussed, puzzled over and remembered here.

Iatrogenesis. To what degree and in what ways are children's problems (or lives) made worse by education (or the specific educational procedures for a given population)? The concept of iatrogenesis has to do with the development of problems which arise as a result of treatment for other problems. Most educators who have been involved with children and young adults undergoing various kinds of psycho-therapeutic treatment are aware of some examples of this problem. We have seen the individual who has progressed through psycho-analysis only to show an undesirable flattened affect. We have seen the stutterer whose personality becomes hyperaggressive as his fluency increases. We have seen the victim of nondirective counseling who is now unable to make a decision or deal directively with simple life problems, and we have seen many examples of the results of physiological treatment which was necessary to sustain life, such as an amputation or enucleation, which have resulted in new emotional problems arising out of the treatment.

But these are iatrogenic ramifications of psychological and medical treatment. How does education hurt a child? We believe that if it were not for the educational establishment, there would be no learning disorders, and that if children with severe multi-sensory disabilities have "learning disorders" they are nothing more than what they are for any child—the result of being taught either the wrong thing or at the wrong time or by the wrong technique.

Some specific problems arise in this consideration; viz,

1. Should school start for a child on the basis of chronological age?

2. Why should children be weighed and measured physically but not psychoeducationally before placement in school?

3. Why should children be handed over to a single teacher for a whole year—a very critical year—without the parent interviewing the teacher or learning about her credentials in some way?

4. Why do we allow teachers and schools to grade children when it is the teacher and school who should be graded by the parents to see whether or not they (the system) are succeeding at the goals of education?

5. What happened to the idea that academic education is a privilege for some, but a necessity for many?

6. Why can't educators tell us what children ought to be able to do—so that children who do it can be free of school?

7. Why is it so difficult to accept the idea that children could do other things besides go to school?

8. Aren't two or three hours a day for six months per year about enough school to do the classical jobs of educators?

9. When are we going to start using an outpatient educational system consisting of telephones, television, broadcasting, programmed learning, parents, libraries, etc.?

Physiological Recruitment. Are our models of the sensory systems adequate? In the field of Audiology the concept of *auditory recruitment* has been used to describe hypersensitivity to minimal changes in stimulation. In the case of the multi-sensory handicapped child the unique problem of confusion or interchangeability of sensory avenues seems to exist and to be complicated by a phenomenon similar to the recruitment process in audition. That is, a stimulus of almost any type will seem to affect the entire organism provided it is over threshold, and a change in stimulus once over threshold is markedly incrementally perceptable for such a child in contrast to a normal sensing individual.

Another phenomenon associated with recruitment is that there is relatively short distance from the awareness of a stimulus to the point of discomfort or pain for that stimulus. This seems to be similarly true with sensory perception in all avenues for the multi-sensory handicapped. This may in some ways be similar to what happens to children in the learning disabilities group who respond in unusually strong and distorted patterns to a stimulus once it is focused into their sensorium through educational techniques. The problem of self-control or externally applied control becomes important when stimulus is placed within this narrow range from awareness to pain threshold in the "recruiter" type of sensory processes. It is important to remember that for multi-sensory handicapped children the perceptible stimulus alone may be a pleasurable sensation.

Double Reversed Teacher Training. Can the teacher fully exploit compensatory sensory learning avenues? One of the ramifications of the iatrogenic concept is the idea of the double reversed teacher training process which in reality amplifies a diagnosed problem of the child. Calhoon (1971) has prepared a fuller statement of the concept and some suggested alternatives. The concept of the double negative teaching approach which results from our teacher training program is as follows. If we wish to train a teacher to work with the deaf under our current procedures we teach them all about the nature of hearing, but the children that the teacher of hearing handicapped works with have no hearing to deal with to any great degree. The greater the hearing problem either in quantitative or qualitative measures, the less effective is the training of the teacher of the hearing handicapped to deal with that problem. By the same token, when training teachers to deal with the visually handicapped, we provide them with great information about the functioning of the eye, the anatomy of the eye, the nature of vision, the process of vision, visual learning, etc. However, as the degree of the quantitative or qualitative visual problem increases, the information which the teacher has to use in working with the child becomes increasingly useless. It is the kind of idea that one might have expected Lewis Carroll to point out in *Alice in Wonderland*.

We do not intend to suggest that teachers of the blind take one course in audiology or that teachers of the deaf take one course in anatomy of the eye. It is not a matter of a few simple courses traded between departments in existing university programs. It is a matter of separating our thinking from the medical model when we get down to teacher training. It is quite proper for a physician to study all of the features and characteristics of the organs and the functions of the organs which break down or fail. His job is to repair them, remove them, heal them, replace, etc. This is not, however, true for the teacher, and we believe we have in the past drawn some of our special education teacher training concepts from a medical model (this is certainly true in the field of Speech Pathology and Audiology). We need to establish in our minds the notion of the teacher as one who is trained to deal with competencies rather than one trained to be knowledgeable about deficits.

Sensory Interaction. What's wrong with simultaneous sensory stimulation? Word descriptions of responses to sensory stimulation are generally based and dependent upon terms relating to the sensory mechanism such as *visual* and *auditory acuity.* Terms relative to the stimulator such as *photo-* and *audio-* allow for a more accurate description of the behavioral responses. Thus, a phobic response to a sound or to a light source is more appropriately described as a *photophobic response* rather than a *visual phobic.* It also seems important to include a neutral or static descriptive variable since it is frequently noted that the children under observation have no specific response either toward or away from the stimulator. It is suggested that such terminology will help alleviate some of the problems which have heretofore been dependent upon a physiological rather than the behavioral orientation in describing such behavior.

The reason for discussing the concept of static behavior is that we are unable currently to distinguish between a diminished sensitivity toward a stimulus and a diminished responsiveness for behavior based on sensory stimulation through a given avenue. Consequently, it is important for us to have a term such as *audiostatic* which allows us to differentiate between the child who is essentially normal and responds to sound and that child who is afraid of sound (the *audiophobic* child). Similarly, we must distinguish between the child who is drawn to sound, the *audiotropic* child, and the child who does not fear or seek sound or does not definitely show an inability to respond to sound, but merely is non-reactive in the presence of sound. This child is the audiostatic child.

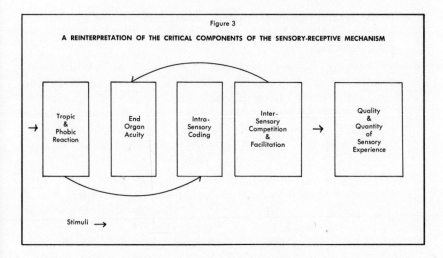

Figure 3. A REINTERPRETATION OF THE CRITICAL COMPONENTS OF
THE SENSORY-RECEPTIVE MECHANISM.

Figure III suggests the role of these general stages in the sensory process and how they reflect on each other. The figure suggests that a pre-sensory reaction to a stimulus may work to alter the effectiveness of a given sense organ, while the competition between sense organs may alter end-organ acuity. Either or both interference patterns may cause a misanalysis of the behavioral inadequacy of the sensorium.

In summary, there are several areas of mutual interest to students of both learning disorders and the severely multi-sensorily handicapped: a mutual interest in the study of sensory behavior; a common need for increasing the range of psycho-educational test sensitivity; a need for both professional groups to expand and drastically modify the tenets of the general educational establishment; and a common problem in the management of semantic errors which alter our ability to talk about children, their problems and their treatment.

BIBLIOGRAPHY

Calhoon, James R.: Learning Pathways, *International Journal For Education of the Visually Handicapped,* March 1971 (106–108).

Curtis, W. Scott: The evaluation of verbal performance in multiply-handicapped blind children. *Exceptional Children,* February, 1966 (364–367).

Curtis, W. Scott: Research problems in evaluation of deaf-blind children. *Conference Proceedings,* American Association of Instructors of the Visually Handicapped.

Curtis, W. Scott, and Donlon, Edward T.: *An Analysis of Evaluation Procedures, Disability Types and Recommended Treatments for 100 Deaf-Blind Children.* Multiple Disability Project, Syracuse University, Syracuse, New York, 1969.

Donlon, Edward T., and Curtis, W. Scott: *The Development and Evaluation of a Video-Tape Protocol for the Examination of Multihandicapped Deaf-Blind Children.* Multiple Disability Project, Syracuse University, Syracuse, New York, 1972.

Donlon, Edward T., Curtis, W. Scott, and Wagner, Elizabeth: *Deaf-Blind Children: Evaluating Their Multiple Handicaps.* American Foundation for the Blind, New York, New York, 1970.

Robbins, Nan: *Speech Beginnings for the Deaf-Blind Child,* Watertown, Massachusetts: Perkins School for the Blind, 1963.

Chapter VII

THE APPLICATION OF REINFORCEMENT PRINCIPLES IN THE CLASSROOM

SANDRA SMITH

WHAT IS BEHAVIOR MODIFICATION?

The notion of rewarding children for good academic and social behavior in the classroom is certainly not a new one. When this writer was attending elementary school, colored stars were very much in vogue. One year good behavior responses were kept at an optimum on the promise that the very best students would be rewarded at the end of the school year by a weekend outing chaperoned by the teacher. However, the application of rewards and also punishments in a *systematic* manner in order to shape and otherwise maintain certain behaviors while eliminating others is indeed a relatively new innovation, especially in the classroom setting.

By systematic application of reinforcement, is meant that the reinforcement, be it verbal praise or a piece of candy, is dispensed consciously after every occurrence of the desired behavior or in accordance with a predetermined schedule. Thus the reinforcement is said to be given contingent upon the desired behavior. Teachers have traditionally given praise, many have even given it abundantly, and they do not view behavior modification as anything new. What teachers often fail to understand is that typical classroom reinforcement is seldom given *contingently* and *consistently*.

The basic principle of behavior modification involves this systematic use of consequences to strengthen and weaken behaviors under specified environmental conditions. Very simply, behaviors which are positively reinforced or rewarded are more likely to increase in frequency. Behaviors which are negatively reinforced

149

or punished are less likely to occur subsequently. The withdrawal of rewards also results in a decreased probability that a behavior will occur again. This procedure is known as *extinction*. These principles which comprise the basis of behavior modification are drawn from a body of experimental literature dealing with the relationship between changes in environmental conditions and consequent changes in behavior.

To give an example, suppose a teacher complains to the school psychologist that a particular child is "hyperactive." The school psychologist may determine through classroom observation and discussions with the teacher that one of the behaviors exhibited by the child that is causing his teacher to describe him as hyperactive is frequent out-of-seat behavior. Thus the behavior the teacher wishes to increase in frequency is "staying-in-seat." The teacher might then be instructed to praise the child after *every* 10 minute interval in which the child does not leave his seat for other than a legitimate reason and to ignore out-of-seat behavior. The teacher would further be instructed to gradually praise the child on a more and more intermittent basis until the child's new behavior becomes self-sustaining.

WHY USE BEHAVIOR MODIFICATION?

Why all the recent enthusiasm about behavior modification, especially with respect to its application within the classroom? After all, the behaviorist approach was introduced by John Watson as far back as 1913. The answer to this question is rather complex, but one of the chief reasons is that psychologists have been faced with growing evidence in recent years that traditional interview therapies have limited efficacy (Bandura, 1969). They are applicable to only a small range of behavioral deviations, excluding from treatment such individuals as anti-social personalities, persons exhibiting gross behavioral dysfunctions, alcoholics and cases with neurological involvement. Of the restricted sample of persons for whom traditional psychotherapy is applicable, between 30 to 60 percent, as reported in Bandura, terminate treatment against the advice of their therapists. Approximately two-thirds of those who continue therapy are rated as exhibiting some degree of improvement but these ratings are usually based on subjective therapist accounts or questionable projective tests and question-naires. Although these statistics are based on studies with adults, the picture is not very different for children (Levitt, 1963). Fur-ther, traditional therapies are based upon the medical model which assumes that observable behavioral deviance is only sympto-matic of underlying psychic pathology. The behavior modifier argues on the contrary, that the behavior is the problem, that all behaviors including maladaptive behaviors are learned and thus can be unlearned (Wolpe and Lazarus, 1966). There is conse-quently no need to search for any hypothetical underlying pathol-ogy. Those who practice behavior modification in the school situation argue, moreover, that the constructs underlying tradi-tional psychotherapies have little relevance to what goes on in a classroom.

All the various traditional approaches boil down to one basic procedure. According to Bandura, they all involve a social rela-tionship (between patient and therapist) and place heavy empha-sis on the verbal interpretive method for inducing change in social behavior, except in cases with young children where play therapy may be used. Even if this general technique were effective, and there is little reason to suspect that it has been with children (Levitt, 1963), the typical situation of one school psychologist having a caseload responsibility of several thousand youngsters makes it inefficient at the very least. Thus psychologists working within the educational setting and elsewhere have been searching for a more efficient and effective method of dealing with problem children, and behavior modification has been found to hold prom-ise in this regard.

Clarizio and Yelon (1967) deal with the question of why teach-ers, specifically, should focus on the behavior of their students as opposed to its cause. The conclusion they reach is that the teacher usually has no other choice. She is not trained to probe into the causes of behavior and, there is little she could do to alter the cause in most situations even if it were known, e.g., brain lesions, a poor parent-child relationship. Still, the behavior must be dealt with in the classroom. Even in cases where the causes can be manipulated, the maladaptive behavior may still persist. In addition, symptoms are themselves incapacitating and as Clarizio and Yelon point out, may be producing emotional disturbance above and beyond the core disturbance.

Another reason to focus on behavior in the classroom, not mentioned by Clarizio and Yelon, is the extensive amount of objective evidence available in the last decade of the remarkable success many investigators have had in modifying a variety of behaviors in many types of settings and with many different types of children. No traditional therapeutic approach or other remedial program used in the educational setting has provided this amount of objective evidence in terms of scores of carefully controlled investigations. The evidence to be provided later in this chapter will necessarily be a test of such a statement.

A final reason to concentrate upon behavior through the systematic application of reinforcement principles is presented by Becker, Thomas and Carnine (1969). These investigators point out that "the teacher does not have a choice in the question of whether or not her children will be influenced by reinforcing and punishing events." That is, such events are always operative in the classroom, although not always in a recognized or systematic manner. Becker *et al.* feel that "the only choices the teacher has are 1) to use reinforcement principles systematically to optimally help her children develop, 2) to blindly and haphazardly approach the training of her children, and 3) to leave the training to less competent sources of reinforcement and punishment, such as other children" (p. 4).

SCOPE OF THE CHAPTER

This chapter is designed to serve as a basic introduction to the multitude of factors involved in the application of reinforcement principles in the classroom. Because of the individual nature of behavior modification programs, no easy formula for the implementation of such a program can be offered. No *one* reference can be recommended to those interested in setting up a particular type of program. Instead, this chapter is intended to serve as a reference source for those who are interested in implementing a behavior modification program and thus a large number of examples of

different types of programs are described. It is not expected that
the average teacher or psychologist without training in behavior
modification will, upon reading this chapter, be able to design
and carry out an extensive program with no difficulty at all. Until
the techniques involved in the utilization of reinforcement principles become more widely disseminated at every level of the educational hierarchy, the designing of most programs will require
the use of trained personnel, at least on a consultant basis. However, it is hoped that any reader will, upon reading this chapter,
be able to begin immediately to apply some of the principles discussed in this chapter, if only on a limited basis. Thus the aim
throughout this chapter is to make the reader aware of the issues
and practical problems involved in the design and administration
of any program.

Toward this end, the present chapter will deal almost exclu-
sively with recent applications of reinforcement principles in
terms of behavior modification programs in the classroom. The
programs will be broken down into predominant technique employed where one basic technique was emphasized. However, seldom is a program limited to one reinforcement technique in
isolation and thus the classification of programs will necessarily be
somewhat arbitrary in certain cases. It will be seen also that some
programs within a section may deal with modifying the behavior
of a single child or small group of children. Others will be
broader in scope, attempting to modify the behavior of an entire
class. As long as the basic reinforcement technique underlying the
programs is the same and as long as the issues involved do not
differ, no distinction between these types of programs will be
made. A section dealing with studies which have applied combinations of techniques will be presented as well as recent applications of behavior modification techniques in the teaching of
subject matter such as reading.

Issues involved in the individual studies and overall in terms
of methodology, teacher training and aspects of the various ethical
issues will be discussed. The chapter will be concluded with a
discussion of possible future directions in the application of behavior modification in the classroom as well as suggestions for
further research.

BEHAVIOR MODIFICATION PROGRAMS—
WHAT IS ENTAILED?

There are at any one time as many different behavior modification programs in existence as there are ingenious and imaginative psychologists and other school personnel to create them. The individualized nature of the behavior modifier's work is perhaps its key feature. Every program is designed specifically to meet the needs of the individual child or classroom with a number of other parameters taken into consideration, such as the setting, availability of ancillary personnel and monetary resources, to name a few.

There are several factors, however, which all behavior modification programs have in common (Lovitt, 1970). The first is the concern with reliable measurement and the discovery of events that alter behavior. Three principles are involved here: direct observation, continuous measurement and systematic manipulation. Before any manipulations take place, the persons designing the program or their assistants observe in the classroom for anywhere from days to months. This is done so that the behavior to be modified can be pinpointed and concretely defined, to obtain the baseline or typical level of inappropriate behavior before intervention and so that the observer can obtain some notion as to what behaviors of the teacher or perhaps peers are sustaining the behavior. If possible, the reliability of observations should be established by checking the agreement among several observers. Continuous measurements from the first day of observation until the last day of the program are also necessary in order to determine whether the experimental procedures were successful. Continuous measurement provides a quantitative record of how successful the procedures were and when during intervention the effects were observable. The observers will usually express their observations in terms of such measurements as rate per unit of time or in percentages. During the stage of systematic manipulation, one variable is altered in order to evaluate the effects of that variable alone. Usually this takes the form of altering in some manner the reinforcing consequences of the behavior. If the manipulation has resulted in a change in the target behavior, usually the design of experimental investigations of behavior modification call for a return to baseline procedures (this is seldom carried out for other than experimental purposes), that is, the conditions which existed before the experimental manipulation. This is done in order to demonstrate that it was indeed the particular variable manipulated which caused the change in behavior and not just coincidence. After a time, the experimental procedures are again instituted. More will be said about this general design, which is referred to as the ABAB design, in a later section on methodology.

The situation is comparable in the case of teaching an academic skill, as opposed to modifying an inappropriate behavior. The teacher must specify precisely what she wants the child to learn. The behavior must then be broken down into small steps to insure a maximum of success. An effective reinforcer is then identified and applied contingently. Objective measurement determines whether the skill was indeed learned.

A question often posed by teachers is, for what types of children is behavior modification inappropriate? The answer is that theoretically, as long as the specific behaviors to be modified can be defined and objectively measured and as long as some notion of what specific events are maintaining the deviant behavior can be identified, there is no type of child for whom behavior modification is inappropriate. However, the older a child becomes, the more complicated his reinforcement history becomes. The particular event maintaining maladaptive behavior may be occurring so infrequently that it is very difficult to identify. Also, general complaints such as depression or anxiety must be pinned down to specific behaviors in order to design a program to deal with them. There are children for whom it is difficult to establish what the most potent reinforcers are and also who the most potent reinforcing agent is. Conceivably, there will be times when the would-be behavior modifier will be stumped. However, the development of behavior modification techniques is still in its infancy. With increased knowledge, it is hoped will come increased practical applicability.

Thus behavior modification programs are carried out with a similar scientific approach and rigorous use of measurement and controls, as was the case with the laboratory research from which they are descended. Further, all programs eventually should be evaluated in terms of persistence of effects over time and across situations. If generalization across situations does not occur, however, the program should not be considered a failure unless specific attempts are made by the program designers to insure such generalization. If the aim of the program is the modification of the child's classroom behavior, and this is indeed achieved, this is all one can realistically expect from such efforts. The reader should bear this comment in mind in evaluating future programs.

POSITIVE REINFORCEMENT

Token Systems

Token systems all involve the presentation of secondary reinforcers such as poker chips or check marks contingent on behavior, which have gained reinforcement value through previous pairings with primary reinforcers such as candy, trinkets, privileges or toys, called *back-up reinforcers*. Tokens are accumulated for various periods of time and then cashed in for something the child wants or can "afford."

Token systems present a number of advantages over tangible or social reinforcement. The basic advantage is that tokens do away with individual differences in preference for different types of reinforcement. If the back-up reinforcements are varied enough, and are reevaluated and changed frequently, they should always contain something valuable for each child. Tokens are practical in that they do not have to interfere with ongoing activities in the classroom. The teacher or aide can unobtrusively give check marks or deposit poker chips near the child. They are economical as the schedule of reinforcement can be gradually decreased so that the child can be cashing in his tokens as little as once a week for a toy or trinket of less than 50 cents value. If a valuable tangible reinforcement had to be administered on a frequent schedule, the cost could quickly become prohibitive.

The disadvantage implied by any token system is that they all involve some delay of gratification. That is, the child must wait anywhere from minutes or days to weeks before his tokens may be cashed in for back-up reinforcers. For some children, e.g. severely retarded or autistic, almost any delay may be too long for them to form the association between the token and back-up reinforcer, thus making a preparation period of immediate pairings of token with primary reinforcer necessary. There is also the potential problem of the children becoming dependent upon the tokens; however, the studies reviewed do not present this as a disadvantage as this problem has been successfully dealt with.

As will be seen from the investigations reviewed, a successful program rarely provides tokens and back-up reinforcers in isolation. Since token systems are often implemented because a group of children have been found unresponsive to social reinforcement, a goal of token programs should be to transfer control of responding eventually from the token to other conditioned reinforcers such as teacher praise and grades. Thus the token is frequently paired with social reinforcement from the teacher and other adults in the classroom in successful programs. Also, other principles of reinforcement such as *ignoring* or *time-out* (removing the child from a positively reinforcing situation) are frequently applied simultaneously with a token system. Kuypers, Becker and O'Leary (1968) feel that all principles of reinforcement are needed simultaneously to make a token system work.

A number of ingenious and successful token systems have been devised. Teachers often complain of the amount of time needed to carry out a token system. One of the aspects of such a program which is time-consuming is the exchange of tokens for back-up reinforcers. This problem was eliminated in one program devised by McKenzie, Clark, Wolf, Kothera and Benson (1968) who involved the parents of the children they studied by having them dispense their child's allowance on the basis of his weekly grade report. These investigators attempted to modify the academic behaviors of ten students in a learning disorders class. The children were rewarded with teacher praise, attention, extra recess and weekly grade reports contingent upon a certain amount of academic progress. The authors reported that the program was not totally successful until the child's parents agreed to have their children earn their allowances on the basis of their child's weekly grades. This procedure resulted in a significant increase in academic behaviors. This type of token system has much to recommend it. For one thing, the involvement of parents in the program opens up lines of communication between the parent and child and between the parent and teacher. It also increases the probabilities of generalization of the new behaviors to the home. The main advantage, however, is that it saves teacher time as she no longer has to spend time overseeing the exchange of tokens for back-up reinforcers. This investigation is an example of how ingenuity can be very rewarding in terms of meeting the needs of both teachers and students in a successful token program.

Since token systems are rarely administered in isolation, it is important to establish that for any given program, it is indeed the tokens and not the other aspects of the program which are responsible for any behavior change. A study which addresses itself to this problem is reported by Birnbauer, Wolf, Kidder and Tague (1965) who initiated a token program to modify the classroom behavior of mildly and moderately retarded students in an experimental programmed instruction classroom. Correct responses were reinforced with knowledge of results, verbal approval and check marks which were exchanged for back-up reinforcers at the end of each class. These authors withdrew the tokens for a period of 21 days to determine if the token reinforcement was an essential aspect of the program. They found that 10 out of the 15 children were adversely affected in terms of percentage of errors and decline in amount of studying. The tokens were then reintroduced and the performance of the students returned to its pre-reversal level, thus establishing the essential nature of the tokens in the overall program. Another token system used to modify the instruction-following behavior of retarded students is reported by Zimmerman, Zimmerman and Russell (1969).

The problem of insuring generalization of new behaviors from an after-school token program to the child's regular classroom is dealt with by Wolf, Giles and Hall (1968). These investigators attempted a token reinforcement program in an after-school remedial education program with 15 low achieving fifth and sixth grade urban poor children. They used standard instructional materials, mastery of which was supported by a token system resembling a trading stamp plan. The children were given books containing pages of different colors in which the teacher marked points. The students were reinforced for work completed or corrected in their regular school classes and for their grades in school. This aspect of the program was essential in terms of insuring generalization to the regular classroom. They also received points for work completed in the remedial classroom and weekly report card grades. The investigators reported that the effects of the program in terms of report card grades was significant as compared to the gains of a control group which received no remedial program. In fact the experimental students gained a full year on the average in their achievement level. This program is also noteworthy in that the investigators provided reinforcement contingencies for the instructors, who received money when their students improved. The students also were reinforced for such accomplishments as attendance and good behavior. The student's regular classroom teachers were further involved in the program by giving them the right to give points or take away a child's right to the "store." In addition, the members of the student's family were involved as the student could buy presents for his family from the store. Since these were poor children, pressure from siblings was possibly a contributory factor although the authors do not specifically state this. It would be interesting as well as informative for a future study to systematically evaluate the effectiveness of involving the student's other "environments."

Teachers often comment on the fact that most token programs are carried out in a small class of rarely more than 10 or 12 students and with at least one aide present. Since this situation does not exist in most schools except for possibly in special classes, the teacher feels overwhelmed by the prospect of carrying out a token program with a regular sized class and when no ancillary personnel are available. With this criticism in mind, O'Leary and Becker (1967) designed a token program which could be readily carried out by one teacher in an average-sized classroom. The target classroom used in their investigation was a third grade class of 17 emotionally disturbed children. While the program focused on the behavior of the eight most disruptive children, the token system was in effect for the entire class. The children received teacher ratings of their behavior exchangeable for candy and trinkets. The children were also given group points based on total class behavior. O'Leary and Becker claim that their program can be used by one teacher in an average classroom on the basis of the fact that the teacher reported that with practice it took a maximum of three minutes to rate all the children, certainly a reasonable expenditure of time for any classroom. An abrupt and significant reduction in disruptive behavior for all the children was observed. The authors also provide anecdotal evidence that the children's appropriate behavior generalized to other school situations. In addition, the observers spent three weeks in the classroom before they began to make ratings in order to allow the children to get their "show-off" behavior out of their systems. This is an important methodological point in that baseline recordings can easily be inflated if this initial reaction to the presence of observers is not taken into account.

Token systems have been successfully carried out at the pre-school level. An example of the application of a token system to a preschool class is provided by Bushell and Wrobel (1968). These children were given plastic washers contingent on a variety of study behaviors. The tokens were exchangeable for special events such as a short movie, trip to the park and story time. After an acceptable level of study behavior was established, the special events were provided noncontingently for seven days. Study behavior declined as a result. The original contingencies were then reestablished and the initial level of study behavior returned within one day. Another example of the use of a token system with preschool children is provided by Homme, De Baca and DeVine (1963).

The failure of children to attend adequately in the classroom is one of the most common complaints a school psychologist receives. Often, the child's failure to attend is interpreted as an inability to attend and is explained in terms of labels like "minimal brain dysfunction" or "hyperkinetic syndrome." Sometimes attempts are made to control the distracting elements in a classroom by, for example, changing a child's seat to the front of the room. The difficulty of controlling the stimuli in the classroom which maintain this failure to attend by inadvertently reinforcing it has proved a considerable obstacle. Walker and Buckley (1968) attempted to deal with this problem in a situation where the initial reinforcement control over attending behavior was established in an individual conditioning program outside the classroom and then brought into the regular classroom. The subject of their study was a nine-year-old boy for whom an individual conditioning program was carried out for 40 minutes five days a week outside the classroom. The boy was reinforced with points which could be traded in for a model contingent upon attending behavior. The length of attending behavior required for a point was gradually doubled. Eventually, the subject was attending for 93% of the sessions. The boy was then placed on a reinforcement schedule in his regular classroom. He was rewarded with one point for each 30 minute block of attending behavior. This procedure was successful and is recommended by the authors to acquire initial control over behaviors which are difficult to modify in regular classroom settings where the maintaining stimuli operate in an uncontrolled fashion.

Sixteen low achieving urban elementary school children were the subjects of a study by Wolf, Hanley, King, Lachowicz and Giles (1970). The investigators used a "timer-game" in their token reinforcement program designed to reinforce behavior incompatible with high frequency out-of-seat behavior. Every 20 minutes a timer rang and every student in his seat earned five points. Out-of-seat behavior was reduced from 17 intervals containing out-of-seat behavior per child per session to two intervals per child. This study inadvertently serves to illustrate an important point. A timer game can be a very useful technique in the classroom but if the interval is kept constant as was done in this study by Wolf *et al.,* there is the potential danger that the children will simply learn to judge a 20 minute interval, for example, and will abandon their non-reinforced behavior just before the timer rings. However, if the timer is made to ring on a variable interval schedule, this possibility is eliminated.

The last study to be presented in this section is the evaluation of the Santa Monica Project provided by Hewitt, Taylor and Artuso (1969) which utilized an engineered classroom designed for emotionally disturbed children. These investigators defined their goals for the children in the engineered classroom in terms of a hierarchy of educational tasks: paying attention, making a response, ordering behavior (following directions and developing order in attending and responding), accurately and thoroughly engaging in multi-sensory exploratory behavior, gaining social approval, requiring self-care and cognitive skills and functioning on a self-motivated basis with achievement in learning providing its own reward.

The engineered classroom is divided into sections of activity and there are nine students, a teacher and an aide in each room. Each child carried around a work record with him all day and earned a maximum of 10 checkmarks every 15 minutes. In the phase of the study reported, the checkmarks were exchangeable for tangible rewards. The subjects were 54 children with learning and behavior problems. The first semester of the program three classes were engineered and three control classes were not. During the second semester, two control classes switched to engineered, two experimental classes switched to control, one experimental class continued as engineered and one control class continued as a control class. The dependent variables were student task attention and academic functioning level in reading and arithmetic. The authors report that task attention of students significantly improved in the experimental condition when that condition followed placement in a regular or control class. Task attention was facilitated by removal of the experimental condition from classes which had become accustomed to it over a semester. This result was explained by the authors as illustrative of the fact that the experimental classes which became control classes did not become totally dependent on the tangible reinforcers. They hypothesize that the teacher's social reinforcement became more effective after having been associated with the tangible reinforcers. Also these classes had acquired skills in attending during the experimental program which allowed them to continue to improve during the control period.

Hewitt *et al.* (1969) further report that reading achievement was not significantly improved by either the experimental or control condition but gains in arithmetic were associated with the experimental condition. The authors feel that the most important aspect of the engineered classroom is the emphasis on attention, response and order behavior. This study is presented here in detail not because it was a particularly successful study but because it

is one of the few studies which defines objectively, in educationally relevant terms, what the goals of education should be. As
these authors eloquently point out, behavior modification answers
the question of how to get there but it doesn't address itself to the
problem of where to go with the child. It is a methodology, not a
philosophy of education, and it is encouraging that some behavior
modifiers are also addressing themselves to the educational issues
involved.

To sum up the evidence concerning the use of token reinforcement systems, it appears that token systems can be successfully used
with a wide variety of children, among them children with learning disorders, mildly and moderately retarded, low achieving
urban poor, emotionally disturbed, preschool aged, as well as with
children in a regular classroom. In addition, token systems have
successfully modified a variety of behaviors, such as out-of-seat
behavior, attending behavior, instruction-following, academic behaviors such as arithmetic and study behaviors. The fact that children can be easily weaned from tokens is illustrated by the Hewitt
et al. (1969) study. That token systems can be administered with
relative ease in a regular sized classroom by a single teacher is
also a basis for optimism concerning their wide applicability. A
number of cautions concerning the proper administration of token
programs have been discussed, among them the need for frequent
reevaluation of back-up reinforcers, the need to build in generalization to other environments and the need to allow a warm-up
period before observers begin recording.

Tangible Reinforcer Programs

Very few studies could be found in which a tangible reinforcer
was presented directly to the child instead of indirectly through
tokens. This is probably because the advantages of giving tokens
have been widely recognized. Behavior modifiers are becoming
aware of the fact that M & M candies do not serve as positive reinforcement for every child and even if they are initially reinforcing,
children quickly become satiated on them. Also, there is simply
not enough experimental evidence that addresses itself to the problem of what tangible reinforcers are optimally reinforcing for
different types of children. The only alternative then, is to ask the

child what he likes. Another problem with tangible reinforcers is that you can't give one child candy or money in front of an entire class of children who are not being similarly rewarded. One solution to this problem often used by investigators is to explain to the class why the child is being rewarded and thereby hope to enlist their support. Perhaps a better solution is to have the child share his earnings with his classmates. This solution has merit because of the peer influence often brought to bear on the child. This method was implemented in a study by Patterson (1965) in his attempt to modify the hyperactive behavior of a nine-year-old child. A small box with a flashlight and electric counter was placed on the child's desk and operated by the experimenter who sat across the room. During each 10-second interval that the subject attended to his book, the light flashed on, the counter clicked and the experimenter deposited one M & M candy or a penny on his desk. At the end of the day the boy was to share his candy and pennies with his classmates. Consequently, the class served to socially reinforce the boy by such behaviors as applauding him when his performance earnings were announced. A significant decrease in the subject's hyperactive behaviors was reported. It is unfortunate that one cannot conclude that the tangible reinforcers were responsible for the boy's change in behavior as this study confounded the candy and pennies with the social reinforcement provided by the peer group.

A second study by Patterson, Jones, Whittier and Wright (1965) did not dispense the tangible reinforcers immediately but instead used an auditory signal which was previously paired with the candy and pennies to modify the hyperactive behavior of two children. However, at the end of each conditioning trial the children were given their rewards. Consequently, the auditory signal served a similar function as the light and counter in the previous study. The investigators reported a significant increase in attending behavior which was maintained over a four-week extinction period.

The conclusion to be drawn from this brief presentation of the use of tangible reinforcers in the classroom is that because of the difficulties in administering tangible reinforcers and because the most potent tangible reinforcer for every child is still to be determined, wherever possible token programs should be substituted for classroom use.

Positive Social Reinforcement

Positive social reinforcers involve the use of social stimuli such as physical nearness, contact, verbal behavior (such as praise) and physical appearance (smiles, nods) to strengthen the behaviors which they follow. These stimuli events which are a natural part of the teacher's behavior have been found to be quite influential in modifying the behavior of children.

In an excellent review of the experimental literature concerning social reinforcement of children's behavior, Stevenson (1965) discusses a multitude of variables which determine how effective social reinforcement is for a particular child. Some of the variables he discusses are the sex of the child, characteristics of the adult who is doing the reinforcing, the age of the child, the difficulty of the task the child is being reinforced for, the social class of the child and a host of antecedent variables such as history of social reinforcement from parents, deprivation of social reinforcement, and personality characteristics of the child. Stevenson presents a number of hypotheses arrived at by various investigators concerning the operation of many of these variables but it is obvious that we are still a long way from understanding the operation of all the variables which account for the differential effectiveness of social reinforcement.

Perhaps this lack of understanding of the variables influencing the effectiveness of social reinforcers is one of the reasons that Anderson, as recently as 1967 in the *Annual Review of Psychology,* concluded that the use of social reinforcers to modify behavior has "had very little impact in education" (p. 146). In the few years since Anderson's statement it is felt that the impact of investigations concerning the manipulation of social reinforcers to modify deviant behavior and to increase the learning output of children in the classroom is beginning to be felt and a store of knowledge in this area is starting to accrue.

There have been a number of creative ways in which primarily positive social reinforcement has been used advantageously in the classroom. Martin and Powers (1967) provide a discussion of common misconceptions held by many educators about a child's "attention span" in which they complain of the tendency to refer to a short attention span as though it were an absolute unchanging characteristic of mental retardation. They suggest instead that attention is task-specific and that a long attention span can be built into a child's repertoire of behaviors by presenting reinforcement contingent upon attending behavior and allowing incompatible behavior to go unreinforced. These investigators feel that teachers inadvertently reinforce behaviors incompatible with a long attention span by, for example, attending to a child's out-of-seat behavior.

A study by Allen, Henke, Harris, Baer and Reynolds (1967) provides an application of the suggestions of Martin and Powers (1967) concerning the need to build in attending responses with the appropriate reinforcement. These authors modified the hyperactive behavior of a four-year-old boy by having the child's teachers provide immediate attention and approval to the boy when he remained with a single activity for one continuous minute. The teachers withheld their attention for all other behavior. Within seven days the number of times the subject changed activities decreased substantially. Reversal to baseline conditions reinstated the hyperactive behavior. Allen *et al.* (1967) feel that there is now strong support for the notion that attending behavior is teachable, that it can be shaped and maintained by teachers. They noted that the boy's mother reported that he was also settling down at home.

When instructed to provide attention and praise systematically to correct the deviant behaviors of a few specific children in a classroom, teachers often question the effect this will have on the other pupils in the class who are not being similarly praised. Ward and Baker (1968) attempted to answer this question as well as the question of whether improved classroom behavior would generalize to other non-related behaviors and thus cause a child's overall functioning to improve. Ward and Baker attempted to reduce the disruptive classroom behavior of four first grade black children from an urban public school, through the systematic use of attention and praise. Twelve students were assigned to one of three groups; the experimental group selected from three classrooms, a control group consisting of children matched for sex to the experimental group and taken from the same three classrooms, and a second control group selected at random from another classroom to provide a baseline for test-retest changes. All subjects were given a battery of psychological tests including four subtests of the WISC, the Draw-a-Person and a projective questionnaire. In the experimental group teachers were instructed to give attention and praise for task-relevant productive behavior and to ignore deviant behavior. While there were no significant changes in behavior for the same class controls, the behavior of the experimental subjects improved significantly. Thus no evidence was presented for adverse effects on children in the class who are not the subjects of behavior modification contingencies. Also, no generalized improvement was obtained in psychological test functioning for the experimental subjects. Considering the fact that a more appropriate measure of improvement in overall functioning would have been amount of work completed in the classroom, the present results are not surprising. The psychological tests used to determine generalization, such as a test of general intelligence (WISC), seem too remote from disruptive classroom behavior to expect an appreciable amount of generalization and there are a number of other factors involved in their performance.

The question of whether abundant social reinforcement or contingent social reinforcement is responsible for the changes in the cooperative play behavior of a preschool child is the subject of a study by Hart, Reynolds, Baer, Brawley and Harris (1968). During the baseline period intermittent attention was provided the child with no contingency. The next phase increased the teacher's noncontingent social reinforcement. The third phase decreased the amount of social reinforcement and gave it only contingent upon cooperative play. In the fourth phase the teacher returned to increased noncontingent reinforcement. The last phase signified a return to decreased contingent reinforcement. These authors report that cooperative play was significantly higher under the contingent reinforcement phases. Thus this investigation provides evidence that the effective use of social reinforcement is dependent on its being contingent rather than abundant.

Sometimes the use of praise will inadvertently serve to discourage the very behavior one is wishing to increase in frequency. This point is brought home in a study by Allen, Hart, Buell, Harris and Wolf (1964) who report the use of positive social reinforcement to eliminate a nursery school child's isolate behavior. Attention from adults was given to the child only when she interacted or approximated interaction with other children. This procedure, however, was found to draw the girl away from other children as she would begin to leave the group in order to seek increased attention from the reinforcing adult. Thus the procedure was modified so that attention was directed to the child as a participant of the ongoing group play rather than individually. If the girl began to leave the group, the teacher busied herself with another child or equipment. As the subject began to interact with children more and more, adult reinforcement was made more intermittent. This procedure greatly increased this child's cooperative play with other children.

The use of positive social reinforcement has been found to produce behavior changes in brain-injured children. Hall and Broden (1967) point out that if one were to ascribe to the medical model, the failure of brain-injured children to engage in such behaviors as manipulative play, climbing or social play would likely be explained as a function of the brain injury and no attempt would be made to alter them. The behavior modifier most likely would not accept such an explanation. Hall and Broden successfully increased these behaviors in three brain-injured children by having adults provide attention and approval for these behaviors.

Other behaviors which have been successfully dealt with through the use of positive social reinforcement are the use of outdoor play equipment in a preschool child with motor and social deficits (Buell, Stoddard, Harris, and Baer, 1968) and the regressed crawling of a nursery school child (Harris, Johnston, Kelley and Wolf, 1964), to name but a few.

It should be noted that all of the studies reviewed utilizing positive social reinforcement as the basic technique used very young children. This is probably not mere coincidence. Teacher praise appears to be very effective with young children but for older children with behavior and academic problems teachers often become associated with negative experiences such as failure. Consequently, teachers of children who have experienced such failure in school are likely to be less potent as social reinforcing agents. In fact teachers are often "tuned-out" completely. For these types of older children, token programs or such reinforcers as privileges usually need to be invoked.

The Use of the Premack Principle

The Premack Principle states: "if behavior B is of higher probability than behavior A, then behavior A can be made more probable by making behavior B contingent upon it. In other words a preferred behavior can be used to serve as the reward for engaging in a certain amount of a less preferred behavior" (Homme *et al.*, 1963, p. 544). Three examples of the use of the Premack Principle will be presented, although many more examples are available as of late. It is felt that the use of such rewards as time for special projects or extra recess will be used even more frequently in the future, because they provide an alternative for teachers who criticize the use of token and tangible rewards on the basis that they are "foreign" to the educational environment. They are also easy to arrange, can be very potent if used properly and can be valuable to the child's education.

A study which investigated providing privileges (preferred activities) for the entire class on the basis of an individual's behavior was carried out by Barrish, Saunders and Wolf (1969). These authors modified the out-of-seat and talking behaviors of a fourth grade class by dividing the class into two teams "to play a game." Each out-of-seat and talking response by a child resulted in a mark which meant a possible loss of privileges by all members of the team. The privileges used as rewards were extra recess, being the first to line up for lunch, time for special projects, stars and name tags. If neither team got more than five marks, both teams could win, and this was almost always the case.

Schmidt and Ulrich (1969) demonstrated how teachers can program their classes from the very start so that maladaptive behavior is minimized by strengthening desirable behaviors (in this case a quiet classroom) compatible with educational goals. Thus behavior modification is being recommended by these investigators as a preventive approach. Schmidt and Ulrich used two minutes additional gym time and two minute breaks as the rewards for 10 minutes of quiet behavior as monitored on a decibel meter with 29 fourth grade students. Transgressions of the sound limit produced a delay of reinforcement as the timer was reset for the full 10 minute interval.

Another example of the use of the Premack Principle is presented by Homme (1966). This investigator attempted to teach literacy to 26 school dropouts or potential dropouts. A procedure was evolved from this attempt which is called "Contingency Contracting" by Homme. Each day when the students arrived, they found an individually designed Contingency Contract awaiting them which they had to commit themselves to. This contract specified a series of pairs of behaviors, each pair consisting of an amount of lower probability behavior (related to the literacy instruction) and a set time for higher probability (reinforcing) behavior. The students also progressed each day from their lowest probability behavior to their highest, getting their least liked behaviors over with early in the day. High probability behaviors used as reinforcers were, among others, a coffee break and discussion of what was read. Homme reports great success in motivating these students to work and attend classes regularly. The gain made in reading was disappointing, however, and this was due, according to Homme, to the lack of control exercised over the quality of the lower probability behaviors. This is being remedied in future work by including small tests (Progress Checks) routinely as a part of the lower probability behaviors. The Contingency Contracting technique appears to be a very promising one in terms of the use of naturally occurring reinforcers to motivate even the most unsuccessful students.

AVERSIVE CONTROL

Extinction

The procedure of *extinction* consists of merely withholding positive reinforcement. Under repeated nonreinforcement, the behavior decreases in frequency and eventually disappears. Only one study could be found in which extinction was the primary technique, making no provisions for reinforcing incompatible behavior or anything of the like. There are a number of reasons for this procedure being infrequently used in the classroom. In the first place, extinction in the classroom usually means failing to provide attention for deviant behavior. Although theoretically, behavior which is not reinforced will eventually cease, this procedure can take quite a long time, too long for a teacher to simply ignore a deviant behavior such as shrieking or running in the classroom. Also, as the behavior is reduced through non-reward, alternative responses will emerge. Thus, a child could substitute an equally unacceptable behavior, in the teacher's view, for the one extinguished. The behaviors which the child will substitute, according to Bandura (1969), will depend upon the options the individual has learned in the past will secure reinforcement. Thus reliance on extinction alone does not guarantee that a desired response will appear when the original behavior has extinguished.

Another difficulty with the procedure of extinction is that although the teacher may be conscientiously ignoring a child's deviant behaviors, the child's classmates may be providing the attention needed to maintain it. A final problem with the use of extinction alone is that when reinforcement such as attention is withdrawn, the child is likely to exhibit a temporary intensification of the deviant behavior in an effort to secure the teacher's attention. This should not be misinterpreted as a failure of the procedure; however, the behavior may reach intolerable levels by classroom standards even if only for a brief time. This can also cause the behavior to become contagious if the child's classmates see that no consequences are forthcoming.

The only example of the use of extinction alone will be presented because it illustrates an important point. Hart, Allen, Buell, Harris and Wolf (1964) modified the operant crying of two preschool boys by having their teachers give them no attention for crying unless they were hurt or expressing an appropriate response to mild distress. Within a week, the authors report the operant crying had practically disappeared in each case. Reversal of procedures reinstated the operant crying. The lesson to be learned in this instance, especially for teachers of young children, is that the attention they give a child for crying may act as the reinforcer for the very behavior they are trying to eliminate. The first day of school for a young child is often a frightening experience and several children cry, but if the crying persists beyond the first day or two, the teacher should take stock of the possible rewards for this behavior operating in the classroom.

In view of the disadvantages discussed in the use of extinction alone, it is recommended that extinction be combined with other procedures in the classroom, particularly positive reinforcement of incompatible response tendencies.

Reprimands or Negative Social Reinforcement

Madsen, Becker, Thomas, Koser and Plager (1968) state that "classroom control depends on teachers being aware of how their specific behaviors affect students in the classroom." They illustrate this statement effectively with an investigation analyzing the reinforcing function of "sit-down" commands, an often heard statement in the classroom. These investigators made baseline ratings of out-of-seat behavior and also recorded the number of sit-down commands and the number of times the teacher praised a child for sitting. In the second phase, the teacher was asked to triple her number of sit-down commands. They then went back to baseline frequency and then back to the high frequency of sit-down commands. In the last phase the teachers were asked to praise sitting and working behavior. As expected, teacher sit-down commands were found to increase out-of-seat behavior while praise resulted in a decline in out-of-seat behavior.

The effects of loud and soft reprimands on the behavior of 10 disruptive students in five classes is reported by O'Leary, Kaufman, Kass and Drabman (1970). During the baseline period, the frequency of disruptive behaviors and teacher reprimands was assessed. Almost all reprimands were loud. The teachers were asked to use soft reprimands, in the next phase, which would be audible only to the individual child in order to eliminate the reinforcing effects of being singled out before the child's peers. This manipulation resulted in a decline in disruptive behaviors in seven out of nine of the children. Soft reprimands increased the disruptive behavior in two children. This was explained as possibly due to the fact that teachers had to go near the child to deliver a soft reprimand and this proximity may have been rewarding for these two children. Thus, as these studies illustrate, teachers must be aware of the effects of their specific behaviors, because often the behaviors which they feel are punishing, as loud reprimands, may be accomplishing the opposite of what is intended, that is, they may be reinforcing and thus maintaining the inappropriate behavior.

Time-Out

Another technique used as a punisher is time-out from positive reinforcement. Time-out differs from extinction in that the child is removed from the source of reinforcement instead of the reinforcement being withdrawn from the child, as in extinction. If a class is being provided with positive reinforcement for certain behaviors, especially with tangible reinforcers or tokens, removal from the classroom would prevent the child from obtaining these rewards and would thus constitute a punishment. This technique has not been widely used, probably because of the fear that sanctioned escape from the classroom may be more rewarding to some children than staying in the classroom earning tokens. In fact it might come to be sought for its escape value. Teachers have traditionally used such so-called punishments as placing the child in the hall or sending the child to the principal's office. What they have typically found is that the same child is out in the hall or in the principal's office day after day. In this situation leaving the classroom had become positively reinforcing and thus was not operating as a punisher at all.

Nolen, Kunzelmann and Haring (1967) have employed the time-out procedure, adding the cautionary note that this procedure will only be effective as long as the classroom continues to provide the child with positive reinforcement. Zielberger, Sampen and Sloane (1968) trained a mother to use the "time-out" procedure to control her son's aggressive behavior at home. The child was simply removed to a bedroom devoid of toys or other diversions. This procedure may be a more suitable one for use at home where "escape" is not such an attractive alternative.

Punishment

Punishment, or the presentation of unpleasant stimuli immediately following an act in order to reduce the probability of the occurrence of that act, has not been recommended for use very frequently by behavior modifiers. There are a number of reasons for this, a thorough discussion of which appears in Clarizio and Yelon (1967). In the first place, the research evidence generally indicates that punishment does not eliminate a response, it merely suppresses it. It is likely to occur again, at a later time, when surveillance is not as keen. Also, punishment tells the child what not to do, but it does not indicate what behaviors are appropriate. Further, aggressive behaviors on the teacher's part provide an undesirable model for her pupils, the implicit message being, this is the way to deal with your anger. The emotional side effects of punishment, such as fear, anxiety, withdrawal and lowered self-esteem are maladaptive behaviors. Punishment is also a source of frustration to the child which may in itself cause the child to act aggressively. Lastly, the child's peers may identify with the aggressive teacher and imitate the punishment at a later time.

However, there are situations according to Mayer, Sulzer and Cody (1968) in which punishment can be used effectively. On the plus side, punishment immediately stops the behavior and reduces the likelihood of future occurrence for some time. It is informative to the student in that it teaches him what he has done wrong. The punishment also informs the child's classmates as to the negative consequences of misbehavior. If punishment is to be used, there are a number of aspects concerning its proper administration which should be kept in mind. Punishment is more effective when escape is impossible, when it is applied immediately and consistently after every occurrence of the misbehavior, when it is used sparingly (children learn to tune-out) and when introduced at full intensity. In order to be fair, however, teachers must provide clear guidelines as to what is acceptable behavior in the classroom and what behavior is not acceptable. The moral of the story, according to Mayer *et al.* (1968), is that it is very difficult for the teacher to apply the above principles correctly in the classroom. According to these investigators punishment is a good method to use if there is danger to the child or others. Generally speaking, whether to use punishment depends on the "seriousness of the misbehavior, the frequency of occurrence, time factors [can punishment be delivered immediately?], the public nature of the act [will it quickly become contagious?], control of the consequences, patience, ethics, and practicality" (p. 327).

No study could be found, other than those discussed above, which used punishment as the primary behavior modification technique in the classroom.

COMBINATIONS OF TECHNIQUES

Many behavior modification programs have successfully utilized combinations of reinforcement techniques. In some instances this is done because a particular combination has been found to be effective in dealing with a given behavior. In other situations, the purpose of using a combination of techniques, applied successfully, is to determine the technique or techniques which are optimally effective for modifying a particular behavior. Examples of each of these types of studies will be provided.

A study which combined the use of rules, educational structure, praise of appropriate behavior and ignoring disruptive behavior in a second grade class is reported by O'Leary, Becker, Evans and Sandargas (1969). Each of these techniques was applied successively to disruptive behavior such as aggression, noise, turning around, and motor behaviors, but none of these alone consistently reduced disruptive behavior. The combination of all of these techniques was almost totally successful in eliminating the disruptive behavior of one child. At this point a token reinforcement program with back-up reinforcers was introduced in the afternoons. This program succeeded in reducing the frequency of disruptive behavior in five of the six remaining children. Attendance and academic achievement were also improved during the token program, but no generalization of the appropriate behavior from the afternoon to the morning was indicated. O'Leary *et al.* explain that this lack of generalization is probably due to the fact that the teacher did not reinforce appropriate behavior in the morning and in addition, her standards of appropriate behavior tended to differ from morning to afternoon.

Another study which combined the use of approval and disapproval and an individual remedial tutoring program in reading in which tokens and back-up reinforcers were dispensed is reported by Thomas, Neilsen, Kuypers and Becker (1968). The aim of the program was to improve the reading as well as the classroom behavior of a six-year-old black boy. The remedial tutoring program followed the procedures of Staats and Butterfield (1965) and was started with pre-primers to provide a high probability of obtaining correct responses to reinforce. Social reinforcement was paired with the earning of points. Thomas *et al.* report that this combination of techniques was successful in improving the child's reading and decreasing his disruptive behavior in the classroom. The authors report that his general attitude toward school was also improved.

Two studies have investigated the combined effect of explicit rules, praise of appropriate behavior and ignoring undesirable behaviors. Becker, Madsen, Arnold and Thomas (1967) reported the first investigation in which the teachers were given specific instructions in how to use the above techniques with particular children. These authors report that explicitly stating the rules alone did not improve the target behaviors. Ignoring deviant behavior actually increased it. The critical combination appeared to be the ignoring of deviant behavior and simultaneous reinforcing of incompatible appropriate behavior.

Further evidence that the combination of ignoring deviant behavior while simultaneously reinforcing incompatible appropriate behavior is particularly effective is provided by Madsen, Becker and Thomas (1968). These authors systematically varied rules, ignoring inappropriate behavior and approval of appropriate behavior. The subjects were three children in two classrooms. After baseline recordings were made, the rules, ignoring and approval conditions were introduced one at a time. In one class a reversal of conditions was carried out. This study was an improvement over the 1967 study in that the components of the program were introduced one at a time, a reversal of conditions was made, and extensive recordings of teacher behavior were made. These investigators found, similarly to the 1967 study, that rules alone exerted little effect on classroom behavior and that the combination of ignoring inappropriate behavior and showing approval of appropriate behavior was very effective in achieving better classroom behavior. These authors feel, in addition, that the approval of appropriate behaviors is probably the key component in effective classroom management.

Two studies provide illustrations of the combination of approval and disapproval techniques. Thomas, Becker and Armstrong (1968) systematically varied the teacher's approving (praise, smiles, contacts) and disapproving (verbal reprimands, physical restraint) behaviors with 28 well-behaving elementary school children in order to determine the effects of each. The authors report that approving teacher responses served as positive reinforcement in maintaining appropriate classroom behaviors while disapproving responses resulted in increases in gross-motor and noise-making behaviors. Thus these authors demonstrate that approving appropriate behavior alone is a more effective discipline strategy than is disapproving unacceptable behavior used alone. McAllister, Stachowiak, Baer and Conderman (1969) report the successful use of the combination of disapproval of talking and turning around behavior in a high school English class and praise for appropriate, incompatible behaviors. This study focused on modifying target behaviors for the class as a whole without specific regard to the individual students involved.

The combination of positive social reinforcement (praise and attention) for appropriate behavior and ignoring of inappropriate behavior is a commonly used and generally successful technique. Hall, Lund and Jackson (1968) successfully modified non-study behaviors in first and third grade classes by having the teachers ignore non-study behaviors and attend to study behaviors. Zimmerman and Zimmerman (1962) report the successful use of this technique with an 11-year-old disturbed boy who required a good deal of attention for oral spelling. The teacher was instructed to send the boy to the board and to attend to the boy only after he had spelled the word correctly. Finally, Brown and Elliot (1965) modified the aggressive behavior of a nursery school class by ignoring aggressive acts and attending to cooperative ones.

The above presented methods of combining techniques to suit the needs of an individual classroom are just a few of the ones which are theoretically possible. Additional techniques, again, will depend on the individual behavior to be modified, the particular consequences which are reinforcing it and the creativity of the program designer.

MODELING

It is now widely recognized that modeling or imitation is an extremely potent and efficient technique for producing new responses in an individual's repertoire and also strengthening a variety of behaviors in children and adults. It is unfortunate however, as Sherman and Baer (1969) point out, that imitation procedures have not been extensively used to modify behavioral deficits. In addition, the role of imitation in modifying behavior in the classroom has remained largely unexplored.

Some evidence that imitation of teachers does indeed take place in the classroom is presented by Yando and Kagan (1968). These authors investigated the effect of a teacher's tempo on the children in her classroom. Tempo is operationally defined by Yando and Kagan as the score on a matching-to-sample task in which the subject must select the design among several which is identical to a standard. One hundred sixty first grade boys and girls were randomly selected from the classrooms of 10 impulsive and 10 reflective female teachers. The children were tested for the tendency to be reflective or impulsive in the fall and spring of the school year and their change scores were related to the tempo of their teacher. The authors report that the children taught by experienced reflective teachers displayed a greater increase in response time over the course of the year than the other children. The effect was more marked for boys than for girls. These authors suggest the role of modeling to explain their results but they also point out that the reflective teachers may have issued more frequent social reinforcement for inhibition and delay than the impulsive teachers.

An illustration of how modeling may be used to modify deviant classroom behavior is presented by O'Connor (1969). This investigator tested the efficacy of symbolic modeling as a treatment to enhance social behavior in preschool isolates. Six experimental subjects were shown a film depicting increasingly more active social interactions between children with positive consequences resulting in each scene. A narrative soundtrack emphasized the appropriate social behavior of the models. Seven control subjects viewed cartoon figures in a film which contained no social interaction. The experimental subjects increased their level of social interaction to that of their non-isolate classmates while the control subjects did not change their withdrawal behavior. O'Connor suggests that the use of "carefully designed therapeutic films" may be particularly helpful in modifying the behavior of the extreme isolate who performs so few approximations to appropriate social behavior that it is difficult to reinforce and thus shape appropriate behavior. The children in this study viewed the films individually; however, for the sake of efficiency, there is probably no reason why pupils in the future cannot view the films in groups. Also the post-test occurred immediately after seeing the film. Studies of this nature need to include long-term follow-ups to assure the durability of behavior change.

That children in the classroom identify with peer models is a fact often observed by teachers but little has been done to isolate and study this phenomenon directly in the classroom setting. Walters and Parke (1964), in a suggestive study, illustrate how important the consequences of a model's deviation are on the imitation of peers. These authors assigned 84 boys to one of four experimental groups: film model rewarded for deviation, film model punished for deviation, no consequence to film model for deviation and no film. The children who viewed the child model being rewarded or receiving no consequence for deviation tended to deviate in the same manner as the peer model during their own play sessions. The children who viewed the model being punished or saw no film deviated little from previous play patterns. This investigation demonstrates a phenomenon which probably occurs naturally to a great extent in the classroom and thus would be an efficient variable to manipulate in an attempt to modify behavior. For example, a child could view a peer (in person or on film) being reinforced for behavior incompatible with his own deviant behavior. The peer would simultaneously be providing a model for more appropriate behavior.

We must also begin to study with increased vigor the role of imitation in learning school-related tasks. Rosenblith (1959) reported that having a model demonstrate the Porteus maze task was more effective than merely giving the children additional trials. The sex of the model was a significant variable in this study, suggesting that future investigators take sex into account in the analysis of their data.

Bricker and Bricker (1970) have stated that "imitation is probably the easiest means for building language production responses into the repertoire of children with severe language handicaps" (p. 101). Baer, Peterson and Sherman (1967) reported their attempt to utilize imitation to establish an initial verbal repertoire in two severely retarded subjects. Each subject was taught a series of responses identical to responses demonstrated by an experimenter who served as model. Each response identical to the behavior of the model was reinforced with food. The authors reported the initial use of intensive shaping to establish imitative responses in the subjects. As the subjects began acquiring varied responses, the probability of imitating was greatly increased. The reinforcement schedule was gradually decreased and the imitative behaviors were maintained at high strength. The potency of this procedure especially provides grounds for optimism in view of the fact that these subjects were without spontaneous imitative behavior of any kind at the beginning of this investigation. The Baer et al. (1967) study illustrates well the basic role of modeling in behavior modification, that is, increasing the initial probabilities that a response will occur. Whether an appropriate response increases in frequency depends on whether it is reinforced, directly or vicariously, but the fact remains that the response must occur before it can be reinforced at all.

There is a real need to understand the variables involved in the natural imitation of peer models and teachers which occurs in the classroom setting, so that we can begin to use this very potent technique advantageously in the service of modifying the inappropriate behaviors of students. Toward this end, research in the applied setting is essential. It is urged that all those who would embark upon this study read the excellent review of research on imitating behavior provided by Flanders (1968).

REINFORCEMENT TECHNIQUES IN TEACHING READING

A number of attempts to apply reinforcement principles in the teaching of reading appear in the literature. A few of these studies will serve to illustrate the way in which reinforcement techniques can be used in the teaching of subject matter in general.

The effectiveness of social reinforcers versus tangible and token reinforcers in the teaching of reading to pre-school children is the subject of a study by Staats, Staats, Schutz and Wolf (1962). These investigators designed a textual program which builds up reading responses from words to paragraphs and then to short stories in four-year-old children. For three of the four-year-olds studied, only social reinforcers were given for correct responses. After the subjects requested discontinuance of the activity tangible and token reinforcers were provided. For the other three children, tangible reinforcers were given, then withdrawn and finally reinstated. The unit of response was the number of new texts acquired as a result of each of the 45 minute experimental sessions. The investigators concluded on the basis of their data that the acquisition of texts occurred more quickly and was maintained in good strength when the tangible reinforcers were given.

In a similar study using four-year-old children and the same textual build-up technique, Staats, Finley, Minke and Wolf (1964) investigated different schedules of reinforcement. They found that the multiple schedules which involve intermittent reinforcement generally produced higher rates of acquisition for a smaller expenditure of reinforcers than did continuous reinforcement schedules.

The application of reinforcement principles to teach reading to a 14-year-old culturally deprived juvenile delinquent is reported by Staats and Butterfield (1965). The program was specifically designed so that it would not require the skills of a professional reading remediation teacher. In fact, the program was carried out by the boy's probation officer. The program consisted of 40 hours of training over a four and a half month period with the Science Research Associates materials and a token system of reinforcement. The authors report that the boy learned and retained 430 new words, his reading grade level increased to the 4.3 grade level and he passed all his courses in school for the first time. This study serves to illustrate that even the most difficult cases in which children have suffered through years of repeated failure can be taught to read when the proper rewards are offered.

Whitlock and Bushell (1967) compared the reinforcement value of a counter alone which registered the number of correct responses with a subsequent presentation of the counter and back-up reinforcers in teaching reading to a six-year-old slow reader. The investigators report that although the counter was initially reinforcing for reading behavior, the original response rate proved to be not recoverable after a six-session extinction period. With subject-selected back-up reinforcers the reading rate before and after extinction was high and the total amount of responding was considerably greater than the amount of reading obtained with the counter alone as reinforcer.

A dissertation study by Hammer (1969) investigated the relative effectiveness of tangible and social reinforcers during individualized instruction of beginning reading to 14 culturally deprived black children. The children were divided into three groups, one group receiving candy as a reinforcer, one group receiving social reinforcement (that's good, fine) and a customary instruction group which received no deliberate reinforcement for each correct response. Each treatment group was also divided into high and low ability groups. The Scott Foresman basal readers were used as well as supplemental materials designed by the investigator. Hammer found that more correct responses are made by children of both high and low ability when tangible reinforcements are dispensed than under social reinforcement or the customary group instruction.

Thus we may conclude that there is considerable evidence that in teaching reading to young children, juvenile delinquents, culturally deprived and retarded readers, tangible or token reinforcers as opposed to social reinforcement or progress feedback alone seem to result in optimal performance. There is also some evidence to suggest that the inherent problem of the child which is causing the failure to read is not a crucial element to be considered in the remediation of the reading problem. Instead, the key factor may simply be a matter of finding the optimal reinforcement for learning for the particular child.

It is regrettable that many of the studies in this area are of the individual or small group case history variety, e.g., (Staats and Butterfield, 1965; Whitlock & Bushell, 1967). These studies do not use appropriate control groups to enable the investigator to conclude that it was indeed the reinforcers which are responsible for the reading gain and not just the attention and special materials provided. All studies in this area should include control groups which receive the attention and special materials without the reinforcement, such as in the Hammer (1969) study, so that definitive statements about the effectiveness of the reinforcers in producing reading gains may be made.

REINFORCING AGENTS OTHER THAN THE TEACHER

Peers

Teachers often provide anecdotal evidence concerning the operation of peer reinforcement in the classroom and how it can operate to thwart their efforts to control the inappropriate behavior of certain children. Often it is the class clown who is the target of reprimands and the teacher realistically recognizes that little will be accomplished in changing his behavior so long as his friends find him amusing and laugh and cheer at his antics. For some children, and this is unfortunately often the case with the class clown, this type of peer reinforcement is the most potent there is.

An illustration of how the failure to control peer reinforcement can thwart experimental attempts at behavior modification is provided by Egeland (1970). This investigator attempted to teach reading to culturally deprived children using tangible and later token and back-up reinforcers. He used two second and two third grade groups of boys as subjects. He found that the treatment was more effective for the second grade than for the third grade boys. Egeland explained his results in terms of the relative effectiveness of the reinforcers used in the experiment and that provided by peer group recognition. Anecdotal evidence provided by the teachers indicated that for the third grade boys, peer group recognition was simply more valuable than the back-up reinforcers provided for learning. Consequently, their attitudes and motivation toward learning did not change. For the second graders the back-up reinforcers appeared to be quite valuable and these students' attitudes toward learning are reported to have changed drastically during the year.

Thus, the operation of peer reinforcement is a phenomenon which occurs in the classroom to thwart a teacher's efforts at control and experimental efforts at behavior modification. It is time that we learn not only to control peer reinforcement when we are not interested in studying it, but also to learn how to use it in our attempts to modify behavior. As indicated by Patterson *et al.* (1969), "little attention has been given as yet to the training of peer groups for aid in behavior modification of classmates" (p. 293).

One possible way that the teacher could handle undesirable peer influences is by making the peers her collaborators. She can enlist their cooperation by providing group rewards contingent on the improvement in the target child's behavior. Once she has enlisted their cooperation, she can instruct them on precisely how they should behave toward the particular child, as Patterson (1969) suggests. Some evidence that peer group influence can be manipulated in this fashion is provided by Wahler (1967). This is the only study which could be found that set out to systematically manipulate peer group attention and observe the consequences on the social behavior of individual children. The subjects were five preschool children and their peers. These authors used an intra-subject replication design and demonstrated in a free field setting that peer social attention acted as positive reinforcement for four out of the five subjects to control their social behavior. The experimenters simply asked the peers to ignore certain behaviors of a child and give attention for other behaviors. They were then instructed to return to their original behavior. Wahler further noted that these preschool children apparently had little trouble following his directions. As Wahler suggests, "the child who presents behavior problems in the classroom might be more effectively treated by procedures which allow control of peer social attention contingencies as well as those of adults" (p. 293).

The utilization of group consequences for an individual's behavior is another way in which peer influence has been studied.

Based on the assumptions that most grade school children will approve of behavior which leads to such reinforcements as story periods or early dismissal from class and that peer approval has reinforcing properties for the underachieving child, Evans and Oswalt (1968) made early dismissal or story reading for the entire class contingent upon the performance of a few underachieving fourth and sixth grade children. This study is significant in that it is one of the few attempts to manipulate academic achievement as opposed to deviant behavior in this fashion. These authors found that the weekly spelling and arithmetic test scores of the experimental subjects increased significantly compared to the test scores of the control subjects. Subsequent experiments attempted to achieve increases in the underachiever's performance in math, social studies, and general science. These efforts were more successful with the fourth graders than the sixth graders. The fourth grade teacher reported that peers tried to influence the experimental subjects to study and even offered assistance. This type of peer pressure however, was not reported by the sixth grade teacher. It should be pointed out, then, that there may be a number of intervening variables, for example age and particular behavior to be modified, as suggested in this study, which influence the effectiveness or extent of this peer pressure.

Other studies which built in the aid of group pressure via group consequences of individual contingencies are reported by Patterson (1965) in his application of conditioning techniques to control a hyperactive child and Barrish, Saunders and Wolf (1969) who modified disruptive behavior by making the individual's disruptive behavior result in loss of team privileges.

Further evidence that although peers may be extremely potent sources of reinforcement, there are intervening variables which account for their differential effectiveness is provided by Patterson and Anderson (1964). In this study, peers dispensed social reinforcements to condition 33 boys and 32 girls on a simple motor response. They found that older children showed more marked changes in behavior than the younger children. Both boys and girls in second and third grades showed more marked changes in behavior when reinforced by friends than by nonpreferred peers. Thus the investigation provides evidence that both age and degree of preference for peer may be important variables in terms of differential effectiveness of peer influence. It is obvious that a great deal more experimental work in the classroom will need to be done before we will be able to use the very potent reinforcement of peers optimally in the service of behavior change.

Paraprofessionals

One of the most common complaints of teachers who have been implementing behavior modification programs is the amount of time and effort it takes for such activities as recording behavior, giving check marks and dispensing back-up reinforcers aside from the conscious change in their behavior which they must maintain. One of the best ways to deal with this realistic problem is to use paraprofessionals, such as volunteers, teacher aides and other students as ancillary personnel in the program. Available evidence for the feasibility of the use of paraprofessionals is meager but what exists is quite encouraging.

Staats, Minke, Goodwin and Landeen (1968) utilized adult volunteers and high school seniors in their modification of reading behavior of 18 retarded, emotionally disturbed and culturally deprived children. The subjects were given 38.2 hours of training in daily half-hour sessions using the Science Research Associates reading materials. Reinforcement in the form of colored tokens was given by the paraprofessionals for such behaviors as a correct response to a word stimulus, reading the word embedded in a paragraph and correctly answering comprehension questions. The authors report that not only was reading behavior significantly improved but also attention, attendance, cooperation and diligent work behavior were maintained in good strength throughout the study. Staats and Butterfield (1965), as discussed earlier, also report the successful use of a 14-year-old delinquent's probation officer to modify reading behavior.

The use of a fifth grade student as behavioral engineer is reported by Suratt, Ulrich and Hawkins (1969). The subjects were four first grade children who exhibited non-study behavior during individual work time. Lights attached to the four student's desks were associated with the opportunity for reinforcement. The fifth grade student operated a console with a timer which was turned "on" when the student was not working. This in turn turned the student's desk light on or off. The students were reinforced with their favorite activities for a certain percentage of time spent working. Study behavior was increased to a high and stable rate. The student engineer operated the console for less than an hour per day and this was contingent upon his own academic work being above average.

It would be wise for psychologists and others in the future who attempt to set up behavior modification programs in the classroom to pay heed to the amount of time and effort required of the teacher for the operation of the program, and wherever this approaches an unreasonable burden, to think in terms of utilizing paraprofessionals when they are available.

Self-imposed Contingencies

To the writer's knowledge, Lovitt and Curtiss (1969) have made the only attempt to assess the effectiveness of the teacher versus the pupil himself as contingency manager. The target behavior was the academic response rate of a 12-year-old member of a behavior disorders class. In two studies these investigators report that higher response rates occurred when the pupil arranged the contingency requirements than when the teacher specified them. Since the pupil often gave himself more free time for less work than the teacher, a third investigation attempted to manipulate only reinforcement magnitude to see if the amount of reinforcement had interacted with the source of contingency management to produce the increase in response rate. Lovitt and Curtiss concluded from the results that it was indeed the contingency manager rather than the magnitude of reinforcement which accounted for the pupil's performance gain.

If, as Lovitt and Curtiss (1969) point out, our eventual goal in behavior modification is for the student to develop self-management skills as well as to improve his academic or social behaviors, it seems particularly efficient to begin by allowing the student to arrange his own reinforcement contingencies where this is feasible. The possible increase in cost (if tangible reinforcers are involved) or the magnitude of privileges extended may be offset by the value of the learning experience in self-management provided the child as well as increased effectiveness. It is hoped that more and varied experiments in self-management of contingencies will be forthcoming.

Parents

Since this chapter is to be limited to behavior modification techniques which are applicable in the classroom setting, only a few brief comments will be made about the role of parents as behavior modifiers. The problem of generalization has been discussed above as well as the need to treat problems in the environment in which they occur. A child who, as a result of behavior modification techniques is behaving well in the classroom but who is considered by other teachers, parents, neighbors and peers on the playground to be obnoxious, still has a very serious problem which should not be ignored if at all possible. If the child has a motivated and cooperative parent, all attempts should be made to draw this parent into the treatment strategy and thus provide increased probability of generalization of the new appropriate behaviors outside the classroom. In the past few years several investigators have reported success in training mothers as behavior modifiers in the home. Two illustrations will be provided here.

Zeilberger, Sampen and Sloane (1968) trained a mother to modify her 4-year-old boy's aggressive behavior at home. The child's behavior was reported to be under control in the preschool the child attended. This mother was instructed by the experimenter in the use of time-out procedures, the ignoring of undesirable behavior and the rewarding of desirable play. The program was carried out 24 hours per day. At the end of the experimental procedure, the mother reported that her son behaved like a different child.

Hawkins, Peterson, Schweid and Bijou (1966) report the training of a mother as behavior modifier by having an experimenter in the child's home signal the mother when she was to reprimand her son or put him in his room. When the boy was playing in a desirable manner the mother was signaled to give the boy attention and approval. In this way, the mother was trained to recognize appropriate and inappropriate behaviors and how to deal with them. The mother was instructed to behave in her usual way at all other times except during experimental sessions which were carried out for one hour, two to three times per week. These investigators reported successful modification of this child's behavior when the case was followed up 24 days later.

Thus, the situation for training mothers as behavior modifiers at home is very promising. It is hoped that studies reporting the training of fathers as behavior modifiers will also be reported in the literature in the future.

INSTRUCTING TEACHERS TO BE BEHAVIOR MODIFIERS

Any psychologist or educator who has attempted to implement behavior modification in a classroom is aware of the tremendous resistance on the part of many teachers, both young and veteran, even those who are experiencing extreme difficulties in classroom control. Yet the fact remains that if we are going to make any inroads in the field of education utilizing behavior modification techniques, we must attempt to achieve not only the cooperation but also the enthusiasm of teachers, for the success of even the most creative programs depends upon it. The unpleasant truth is that there are simply too many children with problem behaviors and too few professionals to deal with them. School psychologists have traditionally been too overburdened in terms of caseload responsibility to deal effectively with individual children, even if this were shown to be effective, which is hardly the case. The teacher is the perfect person to deal with classroom problems because it is in her best interests as well as the interests of the individual child and class for her to do so. She can no longer rely on the traditional magic hour with the school psychologist to do the job, because it simply doesn't work.

We must examine some of the reasons why teachers resist behavior modification. Some of their reasons, it will be seen, are utterly justified, while others stem from a lack of knowledge and a number of misconceptions. For one, teachers have traditionally felt that children should love learning for its own sake and they should not require tangible rewards. As Becker *et al* (1969) point out, how many teachers would return to work the next day if they were informed that they would no longer be getting paid' for doing so? As Humphrey (1970) eloquently states: "there is clearly something wrong with the critic who expects more dependence on long range, altruistic, socially desirable goals on the part of a child than of an adult." In addition, the fact is that students who have repeatedly experienced failure are simply not going to love learning for its own sake, so we'd better make sure there's something in it for them until some modicum of success takes over.

Another criticism of many teachers is that behavior modification is antihumanistic and manipulative. Bandura (1969) provides substantial evidence that all traditional psychotherapists serve as models for and selective reinforcers of their client's behavior and thus are equally culpable in terms of the extent of control and manipulation of people for whom they are responsible. In addition, teachers themselves may be viewed as quite manipulative in their attempts to teach and control the classroom behavior of children. However, this is generally considered excusable because everyone knows that a child's failure to read or use simple arithmetic would even more greatly restrict his freedom of choice and opportunities for self-direction and actualization. The behavior modifier similarly argues that eliminating behavioral deficits and otherwise improving a child's ability to learn is increasing the child's opportunities for self-determination rather than limiting them as some critics charge.

Many teachers express concern that their students will become dependent on rewards and will not be able to function without them. This simply is not the case in terms of the available evidence although long-term follow-up data is still lacking. A well-designed program includes built-in techniques for "weaning" students from constant reward. In addition, many of the studies reviewed above used successfully only reinforcers which are natural to the school setting and where the schedule for such rewards could gradually be made intermittent.

One very justified criticism made by teachers, according to Lovitt (1968) and Lindsley (1968) is that those who attempt to explain the reinforcement procedures to teachers often use a vocabulary which is foreign to teachers and thus "turns them off." Lindsley suggests several terms for use with teachers, among them the terms "accelerating" and "decelerating consequences" in place of "positive" and "negative reinforcement." If psychologists and other behavior modifiers are made aware of this problem, it is felt that it can be readily corrected.

Much of the evidence psychologists could provide teachers with heretofore concerning the effectiveness of behavior modification has dealt with severe behavior problems studied in laboratory settings (Lovitt, 1969). It is hoped that reviews such as the present one will help to demonstrate to teachers that there is now a great deal of evidence that behavior modification can be very effective in the classroom setting.

Proponents of reinforcement techniques, according to Lovitt (1968) often talk of fancy equipment and the use of personnel which are simply not standard in the classroom setting. It is hoped that this review of the literature will clarify the fact that many successful behavior modification programs have used nothing more than reinforcers natural to the classroom setting and have involved one teacher and an average sized classroom. Here again it is up to the program designer to make sure that, together with the teacher and possibly the parents, they work out an approach which is eminently workable in terms of teacher time and effort and available facilities, and which takes into account the values and attitudes of those who will implement the program.

That beginning teachers can readily be taught to use reinforcement procedures to improve classroom control is illustrated in a study by Hall, Vance, Panyon, Rabon and Broden (1968). Three beginning teachers were given a 15–30 minute explanatory session before each experimental period and daily feedback on the results, in order to provide social reinforcement for the teacher. Hall et al. (1968) urged that teacher preparation instructors begin to teach reinforcement principles to all teacher trainees, a suggestion this writer feels should be considered seriously. Brown, Montgomery, and Barclay (1969) provide evidence that "students with no teaching set are easier to train for a new model of classroom management through social reinforcement" (p. 340). The message is clear—we must train teachers early.

Some interesting work along these lines is taking place at the University of Vermont, where McKenzie, Egner, Knight, Perelman, Schneider and Garvin (1970) report that regular classroom teachers are being trained to function as consulting teachers. These consulting teachers will not only work with individual classroom teachers in setting up behavior modification programs but will also teach courses for teachers at the University of Vermont. It is hoped that these courses and attempts to train teachers will not be placed entirely within the realm of special education but will be available to all classroom teachers.

To the writer's knowledge, only one comprehensive attempt at incorporating the principles of behavior modification into any teaching method has appeared on the scene so far, and this is the focus of the exciting work going on at the University of Kansas Medical Center under the direction of Ogden Lindsley. Johnson (1969) reports on the method developed by Lindsley called "Precision Teaching." Four major procedural steps constitute the method of Precision Teaching. The first is for the teacher to pinpoint the behavior about which she is concerned. The second is concerned with the recording of behavior. The teacher obtains a precise, objective record of the child's performance or of her own behavior via wrist counters, kitchen timers or whatever apparatus can be devised. The child is also set to work recording his own behavior. One way this is done is by having the child make a mark on a piece of masking tape which is stuck to his hand every time he engages in a certain behavior. The number of times the behavior occurred divided by the time in which it had the opportunity to occur allows the teacher to express performance in terms of responses per minute which is then plotted daily on a graph. The child is responsible for plotting his own graphs. The third step involves changing something. The teacher must first decide whether she wants more or less of the behavior. The change may be made in teaching method, curriculum, motivational procedures or classroom environment. The teacher then evaluates by means of her objective record whether the behavior has changed in the desired direction or not. If not, the fourth step is "try again."

The method of Precision Teaching represents a creative attempt to talk the teacher's language. It is also significant in that it is designed to supplement any teaching method. It is not a substitute method, it merely adds precision to whatever teaching method the teacher is currently using. Thus it is just as applicable in a Montessori classroom as it is in a traditional third grade classroom. It is hoped that we will see more attempts in the literature to design techniques incorporating the principles of behavior modification in a way which is so relevant to the educational process.

A final comment here urges behavior modifiers to practice what they preach. When all else fails and resistance is still a problem, remember that teachers have reinforcement hierarchies too! The proper rewards such as consulting fees, graduate course credit and immediate feedback on program progress may provide the teacher with the incentive to give a program a chance. Lindsley reports (1968) that at the Johnny Appleseed School and Training Center, making points for teachers contingent on child improvement caused the number of child behaviors improved to go from 12 before the incentives to 42 after the incentive program was begun. They also went from a success rate of eight percent to thirty percent. The teachers with the most points for the week, month and year receive a number of prizes such as dinner for two, 60 dollars worth of merchandise, and a 500-dollar trip respectively.

SOME COMMENTS ON METHODOLOGY

There are literally dozens of methodological issues of importance with respect to this area of research, however, a thorough discussion of each of these would be beyond the scope of this chapter. There are several issues which will be discussed because of their particular relevance to the classroom situation as opposed to more general theoretical relevance.

The first issue to be taken up here involves the efficacy of the ABAB design which, as discussed previously in this chapter, is the most frequently employed design of experimental investigations of behavior modification programs. As Lovitt (1970) points out, some investigators feel that although this design is experimentally elegant, it is not educationally relevant. There are a number of problems involved in the use of this design although it is unquestionably a very potent method of demonstrating the effects of the particular variable manipulated. For one thing, as O'Leary and Drabman (in press) point out, it may be impossible to effect a precise return to baseline conditions after the experimental program has been in effect. Teachers may be reluctant to return to a previously ineffective procedure or they may simply have forgotten how they behaved before the experimental condition was introduced. In addition, the teacher or school administration may resist such a manipulation on ethical grounds. Unless absolutely necessary, is it proper to cause a child to return to a previously inappropriate or even debilitating manner of behaving, e.g., hyperactivity, dependence, isolation? This writer takes the point of view that there exist suitable methodological alternatives although perhaps not as potent. The multiple baseline procedure is one such alternative. This technique can take two forms: the sequential introduction of variables such as rules, ignoring and praise as used by Becker et al. (1967) and Madsen et al. (1968) or the application of one variable, e.g., attention, to several behaviors, one at a time, as in the McAllister et al. (1969) study. Other suitable alternatives, although somewhat less efficient, are replication studies using other classes and teachers, or the use of carefully matched control groups. The latter is perhaps the most difficult to achieve in behavior modification studies because of the need to control for pre-experimental behavior patterns or target behaviors of the children.

O'Leary and Drabman (in press) indicate another problem with the reversal of procedures in a within-subject design. This is that "demand characteristics" may influence one's data. For example, when a class which has been contingently reinforced with tokens for certain behaviors is suddenly given tokens non-contingently, they may pick up subtle cues that they are now expected to misbehave.

In summary, there are a number of pros and cons to be considered in selecting a design. It is suggested that where resistance by teachers and administrators to a behavior modification program is met in the first place, it might be well to sacrifice elegance and some degree of power and give up the ABAB design in favor of the more palatable multiple baseline technique or one of the other suitable alternatives mentioned.

Another methodological issue to be taken into consideration is the possibility of the "Hawthorne effect" in behavior modification research, that is, the possibility that the attention or novelty involved in setting up a new program may be enough to effect a favorable change in behavior. The Hawthorne effect is most likely to be in operation in short-term studies which do not, obviously, allow for the novelty of the program to wear off. It is felt, consequently, that a good way to make certain that the Hawthorne effect is not a major factor in one's results, is to run the study long enough for any such effect to wear away. Long term measurements will also give us some information about the durability of effects over time, which is sorely needed.

Another methodological issue which most investigators are aware of but which cannot be emphasized enough is the need to control for observer bias. Observers should be totally ignorant of the hypothesis of the study as well as when manipulations have taken place. Another issue related to observers is the need to allow time between the introduction of the observers into the classroom and the beginning of observer recordings unless a one-way mirror is used. This time should be given to allow the children to become used to the observer's presence to insure that baseline recordings are not inflated by show-off behaviors.

One final comment here involves the need for precise definition of dependent variables and the accurate measurement of teacher behavior. Studies need to be replicated in different classrooms with different teachers and observers, so that we may be certain that results are not due to a particular constellation of factors existing in a given classroom. Unless investigators report as accurately as possible in quantitative terms the dependent variable measured as well as teacher behavior, future investigators will find it very difficult to replicate existing studies.

CONCLUSIONS

Lovitt (1970) in an article entitled "Behavior Modification: Where Do We Go From Here?" made some very insightful comments on what the future may look like for behavior modifiers and for education in general. He points out that a new period of optimism was ushered in by the behavior modifiers, who are, by nature of their belief that any behavior can be changed if the appropriate environmental conditions can be arranged, very optimistic souls.

Lovitt foresees that the widespread acceptance of behavior modification could result in a common assessment and training framework. At last educators, psychologists and other school personnel will be talking the same language. Psychologists will talk in educationally relevant terms and there will be no need to translate their messages so that they can be used effectively by the teacher.

Lovitt feels also that behavior modifiers of the future will take measurements without necessarily initiating change. This will be done so that we can get an objective picture of what "normal" behavior in the classroom is in hopes that we can learn to prevent abnormality or at least deal with it in its earliest stages.

The future will hold greater use of reinforcement techniques to teach academic behaviors instead of focusing largely on behavior problems, according to Lovitt. We will also evaluate objectively such variables within the classroom as seating arrangements, room displays and teaching devices. In other words, anything that goes on in the classroom will be potential grist for the behavior modifier's mill.

Lovitt is optimistic that circumstances will be arranged whereby the process of generalization can be successfully measured. This author would add that before it can be measured it must be built into the design of studies and not just expected. It is hoped that studies will be replicated in different environments and with other cues present. Long term measurements are especially needed.

Lovitt discusses the need to look at the parameters or component analysis of teacher and child behaviors. For example, what are the components of teacher attention (facial, vocal, etc.)? These need to be analyzed separately so that we will know which components are the effective ones. Similarly, we should be looking at varying strengths of the same variable as was the case in the O'Leary et al. (1970) study using reprimands.

One of the most exciting of the predictions or wish-fullfillments made by Lovitt is the increased effort he foresees to train pupils to manage their own behaviors. This will help to free teachers and teach children math as well as self-management. Only one study was presented in this chapter which used a child managing his own contingencies (Lovitt and Curtiss, 1969). This is indeed a very fertile field for future research.

There are a number of other concerns which will have to be dealt with in the future of behavior modification. Bucher and Lovaas (1970) suggest that we ought to be more concerned with the detailed assessment of the antecedent conditions which produced the inappropriate target behavior because the choice of the proper behavior modification technique may depend on such knowledge. These authors give the illustration that a child may be an isolate because he lacks the appropriate behavioral repertoire needed for dealing with other children, in which case the best technique to use would probably be to shape the appropriate behaviors. On the other hand, he may be an isolate because peers are noxious stimuli for him, in which case he would first need counterconditioning. This leads to an allied problem for the future which is, as more and more types of procedures for applying reinforcement are developed—and obviously more than one could be appropriate in a particular case—how will we know which one will be the most efficient for a certain type of child with a particular set of behaviors? It seems to this writer that we are going to need to do some research correlating personality, demographic and past history variables with the effectiveness of techniques so that we will eventually be able to "match" the child or class with the optimal technique. Thus the pendulum may swing back just enough to allow us to look in greater detail at individual differences in terms of responsiveness to different techniques, but hopefully individual differences will be taken seriously, not for their own sake but because it will make a real difference to the behavior modifier in how he deals with the child or group of children.

A final point needs to be made here. In just about every study presented in this review, the behavior modification procedures were initiated after things got "out of hand," so to speak. Either classroom control was a problem, children were not producing academically, or an individual child's behavior had proved resistant to change through other methods. It is time now to begin to think of using the wise application of reinforcement principles as a preventive technique. Future teachers should be provided with courses in reinforcement techniques and behavior modification as a matter of course during their preparation so that they can begin to apply these principles from the very first day rather than after things get out of hand. Above all, it will allow them to be consciously aware of the consequences of their own behavior and how it can be used to help children behave appropriately in a classroom and derive pleasure and success in learning.

REFERENCES

Allen, E. K., Hart, B. M., Buell, J. S., Harris, F. R., and Wolf, M. M.: Effects of social reinforcement on isolate behavior of a nursery school child. *Child Development, 35*:511–518, 1964.

Allen, E. K., Henke, L. B., Harris, F. R., Baer, D. M., and Reynolds, J.: Control of hyperactivity by social reinforcement of attending behavior. *Journal of Educational Psychology, 58*:231–237, 1967.

Anderson, R. C.: Educational psychology. In Farnsworth, P. R. (Ed.): *Annual Review of Psychology*, Palo Alto, Calif., *Annual Reviews, 18*:129–164, 1967.

Baer, M. D., Peterson, R. F., and Sherman, J. A.: The development of imitation by reinforcing behavioral similarity to a model. *Journal of Experimental Analysis of Behavior, 10*:405–416, 1967.

Bandura, A.: *Principles of Behavior Modification*. New York, Holt, Rinehart and Winston, 1969.

Barrish, H. H., Saunders, M., and Wolf, M. M.: Good behavior game: Effects of individual contingencies for group consequences on disruptive behavior in a classroom. *Journal of Applied Behavior Analysis, 2*:119–124, 1969.

Becker, W. C., Madsen, Jr., C. H., Arnold, C. R., and Thomas, D. R.: The contingent use of teacher attention and praise in reducing classroom behavior problems. *Journal of Special Education, 1*:287–307, 1967.

Becker, W. C., Thomas, D. R., and Carnine, D.: Reducing behavior problems: An operant conditioning guide for teachers. Educational Resources Information Center Clearinghouse on Early Childhood Education, Illinois, 1969.

Birnbauer, J. S., Wolf, M. M., Kidder, J. D., and Tague, C. E.: Classroom behavior of retarded pupils with token reinforcement. *Journal of Experimental Child Psychology, 2*:219–235, 1965.

Bricker, W. A., and Bricker, D. D.: A program of language training for the severely language handicapped child. *Exceptional Children,* 37:101–110, 1970.

Brown, P., and Elliot, R.: Control of aggression in a nursery school class. *Journal of Experimental Child Psychology,* 2:103–107, 1965.

Brown, J. C., Montgomery, R., and Barclay, J. R.: An example of psychologist management of teacher reinforcement procedures in the elementary classroom. *Psychology in the Schools,* 6:336–340, 1969.

Bucher, B., and Lovaas, O. I.: Operant procedures in behavior modification with children. In Levis, D. J. (Ed.) *Learning Approaches to Therapeutic Behavior Change.* Chicago, Aldine Publishing Co., 1970.

Buell, J., Stoddard, P., Harris, F., and Baer, D. M.: Collateral social development accompanying reinforcement of outdoor play in a preschool child. *Journal of Experimental Behavior Analysis, 1:* 167–173, 1968.

Bushell, Jr., D., Wrobel, P. A., and Michaelis, M. L.: Applying group contingencies to the classroom study behavior of preschool children. *Journal of Applied Behavior Analysis, 1:*55–61, 1968.

Clarizio, H. F., and Yelon, S. L.: Learning theory approaches to classroom management: Rationale and intervention techniques. *Journal of Special Education, 1:*267–274, 1967.

Egeland, B.: The relative effectiveness of tangible reinforcers in teaching reading to culturally deprived children. Paper read at the American Psychological Association Convention, Miami, Florida, 1970.

Evans, G. W., and Oswalt, G. L.: Acceleration of academic progress through the manipulation of peer influence. *Behavior Research and Therapy, 6:*189–195, 1968.

Flanders, J. P.: A review of research on imitative behavior. *Psychological Bulletin, 69:*316–337, 1968.

Hall, R. V., and Broden, M.: Behavior changes in brain injured children through social reinforcement. *Journal of Experimental Child Psychology, 35:*463–479, 1967.

Hall, R. V., Lund, D., and Jackson, D.: Effects of teacher attention on study behavior. *Journal of Applied Behavior Analysis, 1:*1–12, 1968.

Hall, R. V., Vance, P., Panyon, M., Rabon, D., and Broden, M.: Instructing beginning teachers in reinforcement procedures which improve classroom control. *Journal of Applied Behavior Analysis,* *1*:315–322, 1968.

Hammer, T. J.: The relative effectiveness of tangible and social reinforcement during individualized instruction of beginning reading. *Dissertation Abstracts, 29*(10-A):3461, 1969.

Harris, F. R., Johnston, M. K., Kelley, S. C., and Wolf, M. M.: Effects of positive social reinforcement on regressed crawling of a nursery school child. *Journal of Educational Psychology, 55*:35–41, 1964.

Hart, B. M., Allen, E. K., Buell, J. S., Harris, F. R., and Wolf, M. M.: Effects of social reinforcement on operant crying. *Journal of Experimental Child Psychology, 1*:145–153, 1964.

Hart, B. M., Reynolds, N. J., Baer, D. M., Brawley, E. R., and Harris, F. R.: Effect of contingent and non-contingent social reinforcement on the cooperative play of a preschool child. *Journal of Applied Behavior Analysis, 1*:73–76, 1968.

Hawkins, R. P., Peterson, R. F., Schweid, E., and Bijou, S. W.: Behavior therapy in the home: Amelioration of problem parent-child relations with the parent in a therapeutic role. *Journal of Experimental Child Psychology, 4*:99–107, 1966.

Hewett, F. M., Taylor, F. D., and Artuso, A. A.: The Santa Monica Project: Evaluation of an engineered classroom design with emotionally disturbed children. *Exceptional Children, 35*:523–529, 1969.

Homme, L. E., DeBaca, P. C., Devine, J. V., Steinhoist, R., and Rickert, E. J.: Use of the premack principle in controlling the behavior of nursery school children. *Journal of Experimental Analysis of Behavior, 6*:544, 1963.

Homme, L. E.: Human motivation and environment. *Kansas Studies in Education, 16*:30–47, 1966.

Humphreys, L. C.: Functional principles of learning. *Educational Psychologist,* Division of Educational Psychology of the APA, 7, Cornell University, Ithaca, New York, 7, 1970.

Johnson, N.: Precision teaching: A key to the future. Paper presented at the National Society for Programmed Instruction Annual Convention, April 10, 1969.

Kuypers, D. S., Becker, W. C., and O'Leary, K. D.: How to make a token system fail. *Exceptional Children, 35*:101–109, 1968.

Levitt, E. E.: Psychotherapy with children: A further evaluation. *Behavior Research and Therapy, 1*:45–51, 1963.

Lindsley, O. R.: Training parents and teachers to precisely manage children's behavior. Paper presented at the C. S. Mott Foundation Children's Health Center, June 14, 1968.

Lovitt, T. C.: Operant conditioning techniques for children with learning disabilities. *Journal of Special Education,* 2:283–289, 1968.

Lovitt, T.: Behavior modification: The current scene. *Exceptional Children, 37*:85–91, 1970.

Lovitt, T.: Behavior modification: Where do we go from here? *Exceptional Children, 37*:157–167, 1970.

Lovitt, T. C., and Curtiss, K. A.: Academic response rate as a function of teacher and self-imposed contingencies. *Journal of Applied Behavior Analysis, 2*:49–53, 1969.

Madsen, C. H. Jr., Becker, W. C., and Thomas, D. R.: Rules, praise and ignoring: elements of elementary classroom control. *Journal of Applied Behavior Analysis, 1*:139–150, 1968.

Madsen, Jr., C. H., Becker, W. C., Thomas, D. R., Koser, L., and Plager, E.: An analysis of the reinforcing function of "sit-down" commands. In Parker, R. K. (Ed.): *Readings in Educational Psychology.* Boston, Allyn & Bacon, 265–278, 1968.

Martin, G. L., and Powers, R. B.: Attention span: an operant conditioning analysis. *Exceptional Children, 33*:565–570, 1967.

Mayer, G. R., Sulzer, B., and Cody, J. J.: The use of punishment in modifying student behavior. *Journal of Special Education, 2*:323–328, 1968.

McAllister, L. W., Stachowiak, J. G., Baer, D. M., and Conderman, L.: The application of operant conditioning techniques in a secondary school classroom. *Journal of Applied Behavior Analysis, 2*: 277–285, 1969.

McKenzie, H., Clark, M., Wolf, M., Kothera, R., and Benson, C.: Behavior modification of children with learning disabilities using grades as tokens and allowances as back-up reinforcers. *Exceptional Children, 34*:745–752, 1968.

McKenzie, H. S., Egner, A. N., Knight, M. F., Perelman, P. F., Schneider, B. M., and Garvin, J. S.: Training consulting teachers to assist elementary teachers in the management and education of handicapped children. *Exceptional Children, 37*:137–143, 1970.

Nolen, P. A., Kunzelmann, H., and Haring, N. G.: Behavioral modification in a junior high learning disabilities classroom. *Exceptional Children, 34*:163–168, 1967.

O'Connor, R. D.: Modification of social withdrawal through symbolic modeling. *Journal of Applied Behavior Analysis, 2*:15–22, 1969.

O'Leary, D. K., and Drabman, R. S.: Token reinforcement programs in the classroom: A review. *Psychological Bulletin* (in press).

O'Leary, D. K., and Becker, W. C.: Behavior modification of an adjustment class: a token reinforcement program. *Exceptional Children, 33*:637–642, 1967.

O'Leary, D. K., Becker, W. C., Evans, M. B., and Sandargas, R. A.: A token reinforcement program in a public school: a replication and systematic analysis. *Journal of Applied Behavior Analysis, 2*:3–13, 1969.

O'Leary, D. K., Kaufman, K. F., Kass, R. E., and Drabman, R. S.: The effects of loud and soft reprimands on the behavior of disruptive students. *Exceptional Children, 37*:145–155, 1970.

Patterson, G. R.: An application of conditioning techniques to the control of a hyperactive child. In Ullman, L. P. and Krasner, L. (eds.): *Case Studies in Behavior Modification.* New York, Holt, Rinehart and Winston, 370–375, 1965.

Patterson, G. R.: Behavioral techniques based upon social learning. In Franks, C. M. (Ed.): *Behavior Therapy: Appraisal and Status.* New York, McGraw-Hill, 341–374, 1969.

Patterson, G. R., and Anderson, D.: Peers as social reinforcers. *Child Development, 35*:951–960, 1964.

Patterson, G. R., and Brodsky, G. D.: A behavior modification program for a child with multiple problem behaviors. *Journal of Child Psychology and Psychiatry, 7*:277–295, 1966.

Patterson, G. R., Jones, R., Whittier, J., and Wright, M. A.: A behavior modification technique for the hyperactive child. *Behavior Research and Therapy, 2*:217–226, 1965.

Rosenblith, J. F.: Learning by imitation in kindergarten children. *Child Development, 30*:69–80, 1959.

Schmidt, G. W., and Ulrich, R. E.: Effects of group contingent events upon classroom noise. *Journal of Applied Behavior Analysis, 2*: 171–179, 1969.

Sherman, J. A., and Baer, D. M.: Appraisal of operant therapy techniques with children and adults. In Franks, C.: *Behavior Therapy: Appraisal and Status,* New York, McGraw-Hill, 192–219, 1969.

Stevenson, H. W.: Social reinforcement of children's behavior. In Lipsitt, L. P. and Spiker, C. C. (Eds.): *Advances in Child Development and Behavior,* New York, Academic Press, 1965.

Staats, A. W., and Butterfield, W. H.: Treatment of nonreading in a culturally deprived juvenile delinquent: An application of reinforcement principles. *Child Development, 36*:925–942, 1965.

Staats, A. W., Finley, J. R., Minke, K. A., and Wolf, M.: Reinforcement variables in the control of unit reading responses. *Journal of the Experimental Analysis of Behavior,* 7:139–149, 1964.

Staats, A. W., Minke, K. A., Goodwin, W., and Landeen, J.: Cognitive behavior modification: Motivated learning reading treatment with subprofessional therapy-technicians. *Behavior Research and Therapy,* 5:283–299, 1967.

Staats, A. W., Staats, C. K., Schutz, R. E., and Wolf, M.: The conditioning of textual responses using extrinsic reinforcers. *Journal of the Experimental Analysis of Behavior,* 5:33–40, 1962.

Surratt, P. R., Ulrich, R. E., and Hawkins, R. P.: An elementary student as a behavioral engineer. *Journal of Applied Behavior Analysis,* 2:85–91, 1969.

Thomas, D. R., Becker, W. C., and Armstrong, M.: Production and elimination of disruptive classroom behavior by systematically varying teacher's behavior. *Journal of Applied Behavior Analysis,* 1:35–45, 1968.

Thomas, D. A., Nielson, L. J., Kuypers, D. C., and Becker, W. C.: Social reinforcement and remedial instruction in the elimination of a classroom behavior problem. *Journal of Special Education,* 2:291–306, 1968.

Wahler, R. G.: Child-child interactions in free field settings: Some experimental analyses. *Journal of Experimental Child Psychology,* 5:278–293, 1967.

Walker, H. M., and Buckley, N. K.: The use of positive reinforcement in conditioning attending behavior. *Journal of Applied Behavior Analysis,* 1:245–260, 1968.

Walters, R. H., and Parke, R. D.: Influence of response consequences to a social model on resistance to deviation. *Journal of Experimental Child Psychology,* 1:269–280, 1964.

Ward, M. H., and Baker, B. L.: Reinforcement therapy in the classroom. *Journal of Applied Behavior Analysis,* 1:323–328, 1968.

Watson, J. B.: Psychology as the behaviorist views it. *Psychological Review,* 20:158–177, 1913.

Whitlock, C., and Bushell, Jr., D.: Some effects of "Back-up" reinforcers on reading behavior. *Journal of Experimental Child Psychology,* 5:50–57, 1967.

Wolf, M. M., Giles, D. K., and Hall, R. V.: Experiment with token reinforcement in a remedial classroom. *Behavior Research and Therapy,* 6:51–64, 1968.

Wolf, M. M., Hanley, E. L., King, L. A., Lachowicz, J., and Giles, D.

K.: The timer-game: A variable interval contingency for the management of out-of-seat behavior. *Exceptional Children, 37*:113–117, 1970.

Wolpe, J., and Lazarus, A. A.: *Behavior Therapy Techniques: A guide to the treatment of neuroses.* New York, Pergamon Press, 1966.

Yando, R. M., and Kagan, J.: The effect of teacher tempo on the child. *Child Development, 39*:27–34, 1968.

Zeilberger, J., Sampen, S. E., and Sloane, H. N.: Modification of a child's problem behavior in the home with mother as therapist. *Journal of Applied Behavior Analysis, 1*:47–53, 1968.

Zimmerman, E. H., and Zimmerman, J.: The alteration of behavior in a special classroom situation. *Journal of Experimental Analysis of Behavior, 5*:59–60, 1962.

Zimmerman, E. H., Zimmerman, J., and Russell, C. D.: Differential effects of token reinforcement on instruction-following behavior in retarded students instructed as a group. *Journal of Applied Behavior Analysis, 2*:101–112, 1969.

Chapter VIII

WORKSHOPS AND COURSES IN LEARNING DISORDERS OR DISABILITIES

MITCHELL R. BURKOWSKY

At the end of the nineteen sixties, and at the beginning of the nineteen seventies, the areas of learning disabilities—learning disorders achieved high status. Specialists who taught short courses and workshops became "sure sellers" for extension and in-service programs. Elementary and special teachers would travel hundreds of miles to spend their summers studying with a "big name" and, upon completion of the training, return to their communities as the local experts. Undergraduate and graduate colleges and schools of education received and continue to receive an increasing flow of letters asking if the college in question trains specialists in the areas of learning disability, specific learning disability, the interjacent child, learning disorders, minimal brain damage, or even techniques of classroom tutoring. Undergraduates across the country have discovered that tutoring inner city children is relevant, and have brought to the surface many inadequacies in themselves, their college teachers, and teachers in the elementary and secondary classrooms. As one student phrased it: "I did tutoring as a means of learning how to better understand and work with kids. It was a fruitful experience, but I came out of it with more questions than answers."

Regular and special class teachers have evinced a great need for guidance and assistance in dealing with the problems of learning handicapped children. For example, the Syracuse University Bureau of School Services has been requested to provide several workshops and training programs for in-service teachers to acquaint them with how-to-do-it techniques and to provide rationales for working with learning-disordered children. Those who have taken these workshops run the gamut from pre-kindergarten teachers through high school math, English, history, business and counseling personnel. In central New York, a parents' and professionals' organization requested an eight-week course for teachers, other professionals and parents of learning-disabled children. One section was scheduled for a maximum of thirty participants. When the smoke settled, there were nearly fifty in that class, over fifty in another section, and over eighty on the waiting list for the next time that it could be offered.

Why should there be such an almost spontaneous outcry for the satisfaction of a felt need? What are some of the causes of this indication that our schools (and our colleges of Education) don't have all the answers to daily problems?

In December, 1969, at a Ross Laboratories Conference on Pediatric Research, the following information was disclosed:

1. Approximately 5% of children in schools are not promoted each year.
2. To have those children repeat one year costs 1.7 billion dollars.
3. Many children repeat two or more grades (LaVeck, 1971).

If early analysis of a child's learning potential takes place, and if appropriate educational planning is made, unnecessary repetitions of grades may, in part, be eliminated. Children would not have to face a series of failures which might hamper their educational, professional and social development. Unfortunately, at present there are few teachers, psychologists or other child-centered professionals who are capable of going beyond rather rigid disciplinary boundaries, or who can advise other teachers and professionals in a realistic way. What is needed in teacher training is an interdisciplinary approach across several child-centered educational, social service, psychological and medical areas.

Since World War II, many professions have expanded within the field of Education. One of these is Special Education. In this modern age, there has been a great deal of pressure to sub-specialize in educational areas so that even special educators have conformed by super-specializing within the field of Special Education. Therefore we now have teachers of trainable retarded children, of educable retarded children, of children who are slow learners, of children with speech and language problems, of brain-injured children, of aphasic children, of autistic children, of visually handicapped children, of auditorily handicapped children, of emotionally disturbed children, of multiply-handicapped children, of socially-deprived children, of cerebral palsied children, of children with specific learning disabilities, and so on. The striking commonality is that all these specialties deal with children who have—or are supposed to have—some problems in learning and/or adjusting to requirements of society. As the field of medicine has recently discovered, specialists are important and necessary to take care of the great variety of medical problems, but there is a demand for generalists who can take part of the burden from the shoulders of the specialists by deciding who *really* needs to be seen by the specialists. Many cases can be taken care of quite adequately by the generalist who has developed a greater variety of resources than has the specialist. Therefore, there was justified a need for more and better-trained generalists who knew enough about the specialties so that they might refer to and cooperate with the appropriate specialists. As a result of this thinking, and to give more prestige to the general practitioner, the American Board of Family Practice came into being in February, 1969.

In Education we see a similar need. Training in the educational specialties has become deeper and more intensive during the past two decades. State and national certification standards for the qualification of teachers in specialties have required a zeroing in on more and more minute divisions of specific areas of handicap. Six major problems have arisen from this situation:

1. There is a great demand and need for specialists, sometimes fostered by state requirements that school systems hire certain specialists.
2. These specialists may work only with specific types of children.
3. Many school boards feel that their budgets cannot tolerate too many specialists, so, whenever budgetary crises arise the special teachers are among the first to go.
4. Many teachers have been hired to teach a class supposedly

       containing children with only one type of learning problem and discover that their classrooms are dumping grounds for all children with whom nobody else desires to work.

5. Several teachers have been requested or required to teach special classes within their schools when they have not been trained in Special Education.

6. Since there are such things as special teachers, regular class teachers often feel that they are not sufficiently capable of handling unforeseen situations or abnormal child behavior; they therefore try to shunt the child toward other personnel.

In effect, we are lacking generalists in Education who are, or feel, competent to diagnose, remediate, or recommend remediation for children with learning and adjustment problems. In "days of yore" the teacher of the one-room school house took it for granted that she would teach more than one subject on several levels in a typical day. The age range in her room might be twelve years or more. She was, in a way, a generalist in Education, working with children in terms of their capabilities and deficits, doing small group or individual instruction. Today's typical teacher is often restricted to limited curricular guides which in some cases state the page of the text the teacher and class are to be on by a particular date. So many pages are to be done in a given period of time, the curriculum guide inexorably establishing a metronomic pace. Unfortunately, all children do not learn according to the same schedule, and all teachers do not teach the same material with similar ease. Many teachers have told me that they are so busy trying to keep up with the schedule that they have little or no time to help students who can't keep up with it. At the same time, bright students become bored and develop poor attention and study habits.

The one-room school house teacher represented a totality of elementary and junior high regular and special education. Today's teachers have very different self-concepts. Among those I have interviewed, the problem of insecurity in handling both atypical and typical children interacts with their self-concepts. They don't know what to do with certain kinds of children; they don't know how far they should go in helping a child, nor what they are permitted or expected to do. Should they work with the parents? If so, what is their role in working with parents? Should they work with community agencies? What if there are no community agencies? How far can a teacher stick her neck out to help a child without it being chopped off? Can a teacher ask another teacher or administrator for advice concerning a child without losing prestige or making herself appear less competent? If every child in the class doesn't improve, will this be held against the teacher? These are but a few questions and concerns that experienced teachers have presented to me. There are more, not necessarily based on insecurity. A great many teachers sincerely want to be able to do their jobs better, but aren't sure of how to do so. They keep up with their journals and new texts; they buy all the new faddish equipment that they can afford or get their schools to buy; they attend summer sessions, in-service training courses, extension classes and workshops. A recurrent complaint is that they are often told when they do something wrong, but rarely hear approval of their actions, so they are unsure as to when they are doing something right.

I have been involved in a number of training programs and workshops relating to the training of a variety of professionals who work with children. The next several pages will contain a discussion of my interpretation of how I perceived the goals, structures and procedures of those programs. In the chapter following this will be a detailed description of workshop procedures developed by Broadbent, Meehan and Sage as an intensive short-term program for training school personnel in orientations toward children with learning problems.

LEARNING EVALUATION CENTER ORIENTATION

In Spring, 1967, a group of Syracuse University and State University of New York faculty members from the areas of Special Education, Education, Social Work, Psychology and Pediatrics (humorously labelled *Sub-Mensa*) began an informal, unpaid, multidisciplinary-interdisciplinary program. This program grew out of a need to share information and "pick one another's brains" with regard to the most thorough, practical and helpful approaches to the needs of children with learning problems. Ophthalmologists, optometrists and other specialists participated in this program as guest lecturers and discussants. Beginning in the 1968–69 academic year, graduate seminars and workshops were offered to selected students. In 1969, with support from the federal government (approximately $10,000), a Learning Evaluation Center was established at Syracuse University on a temporary basis under the directorship of Dr. Frank Greene. This center was used as a base for clinical training and beginning practical research. These funds were not supplemented by the federal government after June, 1970, and since other funding was not found, the center closed.

At the initiation of the group in 1967, the members, some of whom knew each other—and some who didn't—introduced ourselves and explained what we had considered to be our roles in working with children and with reference to training college students. As we talked we became increasingly aware that our vocabularies prevented accurate transmission of our ideas, and since each of us had previously sent written reports to or had received them from at least one other member of the group, we decided to develop a common frame of reference. Therefore a two and one-half year old boy was selected to be seen by the areas of pediatrics, emotional disturbance, school psychology, speech and language clinic, and social work. This child did the rounds of the clinics and separate reports were written. We then met as a group and discussed the reports. Surprisingly, we were in high agreement with regard to his ability levels, areas of deficit and our inability to determine a prognosis. Representatives of math and reading clinics—who did not see the boy because he was not of an age-level that they would customarily work with, were members of the group and attempted to predict the difficulties that he would have when he became of an age to learn basic academic skills.

Since this was such a successful learning exeprience for our group, we decided to follow-up this child and his family for a few years. An older child with different problems was next seen by our group and by our graduate students. Soon graduate students from one program were spending a semester in the clinics of two or more other programs. For awhile the graduate students worked as a team in the pediatric unit of the Upstate Medical Center, in conjunction with Dr. Theodore Di Buono and his medical and psychological staff. Concurrently, Dr. Frank Greene, Supervisor of the Syracuse University Reading Clinic and sparkplug of our group, arranged for three children and their families from a neighboring city to spend two complete days in Syracuse in order to be "worked up" by the several clinics. This concept was not new at that time, but the innovative factor was that representatives of the school were required to come along for the evaluation and feedback discussions. Another important point of view was that the feedback was given to the child in the presence of the parent and teacher or other school representative, the philosophy being that it is the child's life that is being dealt with. Therefore, the child is expected to know what is done to, for and with him. Using this approach, the child becomes an active *member* of the diagnostic-rehabilitative team rather than merely the *object* of the team. It was astonishing to observe that once the child became actively involved in the solution of the problem his attitude changed and his appearance of intelligence increased. By giving the feedback to the child in the presence of his family and teacher or principal, and then discussing the situation as a group, many breakthroughs were made.

We then evolved a seminar for nearly twenty graduate students. The emphasis was on assessment of literature relevant to children with learning and adjustment problems, with guest lecturers from medical and psychological specialties. The students fairly unanimously felt that this approach was not too good. They wanted to learn from experience, and expressed dissatisfaction with the opinions of the experts. Some wanted to go on to advanced concepts in small group discussion, so the next semester we had two sections—one for the theoretically minded, and one for the practically oriented. The practically oriented group split into two teams to do diagnosis, prognosis and prescription. For a typical child, the team gathered information from home and school, evaluated the paper work, sent out members to observe behavior in home and school environments, discussed implications of the already compiled information, determined the types of further diagnostic procedures needed, and proceeded to obtain the necessary information through formal and informal testing, interviewing, and cross-referral for specialized testing beyond the abilities of the group. As part of the diagnosis dealt with the child's abilities to learn in various subject areas and employ different sensory modalities, diagnostic teaching became important. Could a child learn new skills and concepts? How? How long could these be retained? How could he then apply the skills and concepts to related situations? After he learned something in the clinical situation, could be utilize that information or those techniques in the regular classroom? To answer this last question it became apparent that it would be important for team members to follow-up the child by observing in school and interacting quite closely with the teacher.

At this time we received the small program developmental grant to pay for a secretary, and the School of Education assigned two graduate assistantships to the new Learning Evaluation Center for one year. Faculty time was still contributed, which means that we carried overloads without extra pay. The two doctoral-level graduate assistants and the secretary did an excellent job of coordinating the routine affairs of the clinic and the faculty members ran three diagnostic-prescriptive-follow-up teams pretty much as described in the previous paragraph. During the three years (1967–70) that our group worked together we processed over 100 graduate students through team learning disorders orientations. We also worked with over 100 children. Representative case histories will be found at the end of this chapter.

OFF-CAMPUS PROGRAMS

In 1968, I began teaching extension workshops to in-service teachers. Some of these were semester-long three credit courses taught Saturdays or late afternoons and evenings during the week. Guided by the experience of having worked with the campus teams, I felt most comfortable working with the following format:

First four weeks — Basic concepts of learning and learning disorders.

Breaking-up of class into relatively balanced teams.

Indoctrination with reference to need for long range follow-up.

Teaching of simple diagnostic procedures.

Rest of course — Diagnosis of real children selected from students' schools

Prescription based on diagnosis and diagnostic teaching.

Follow-up in school and at home.

Re-evaluation.

Planning for the child's future.

During the first session, I discuss my orientation to learning problems in children and my preference for the term learning *disorder* rather than *disability*. I feel that the *learning disability* term is artificially restrictive and implies too many different things to too many people. I prefer the *disorder* label because it implies that something is out of order but can be fixed. Perhaps the ideal solution would be to just talk about learning *problems* — but it is difficult to obtain financial support for a program if there is no distinctive label. The outline below is one from which I have lectured in several instances on the first day of class.

1. What is a learning disorder?

   From the literature on learning problems, the following orientations may be noted:

   1.1. It is a neurobiological breakdown or deficit which results in difficulty or inability to adjust educationally, socially, emotionally and, possibly, vocationally.

   1.2. It is primarily a social or emotional problem resulting in poor educational and/or social achievement.

   1.3. It is an overall or partial maturational lag.

   1.4. It may result from a child skipping or missing basic educational concepts prerequisite to the mastery of skills and abilities commonly considered to be of his age level.

   1.5. It may be any combination of the above.

   1.6. Most theorists emphasize problems of the school-age child. Only a few stress the pre-school or pre-academic child. Therefore most practitioners currently work on remediation rather than prevention. This may change soon, in fact, is slowly changing now.

1.7. The newest trend appears to be one wherein *language* is the umbrella which covers all forms of learning. Deficits in various components of language (which encompasses speech, reading, writing, arithmetic, gesture and paralanguage) are evaluated, and remediation may be directed to either weaknesses, strengths, or both.

2. What can be done for children with learning disorders?

2.1. Treat them as human beings first and "cases" as an after-thought.

2.2. As much as possible, discover their self-concepts and goals.

2.3. Discover their parents' and teachers' concepts of them, and, if possible, their expectations for the child.

2.4. If possible, and it is *not* always possible, ascertain the initiating cause or causes of the learning problem and determine which factors have served to continue the problem. Then decide how to cope with the continuing factors.

2.5. Assess the child's strengths and weaknesses in the following areas:

2.51. Social-emotional.

2.52. Physical and perceptual abilities.

2.53. Knowledge and sequential skills already gained.

2.54. Ability to gain new knowledge and skills.

2.55. Ability to relate to himself and others.

2.56. Ability to generalize new concepts to every day life.

2.57. General ability to adapt to new circumstances, environments, etc.

2.58. Ability to teach himself *once he has been taught to do so.*

2.59. Ability to learn to set up goals and discipline for himself.

2.6. The child, the parents, pertinent community agencies and the school must all be part of the diagnostic team and should have the following minimal ground rules:

2.61. Open discussion of the problem, including their

perceptions of, and their reactions to, one another's roles.

2.62. A *genuine* desire to help the child and a willingness to participate above and beyond traditional roles.

2.63. An accurate assessment of how far it is possible to render school, home and individual schedules flexible in order to attempt new procedures so that other team members have a framework within which to work and at which to aim recommendations.

2.64. *Detailed* outlines and explanations of remedial recommendations. Alternative programs should be included in the event that the primary recommendations don't work too well. In order to be more certain as to recommended remediation, several tutorial sessions experimenting with different approaches should precede the final recommendation.

2.65. Liaison between school, home and other participating agencies should be on a steady, on-going basis. No program, once set up, should be considered static. Rather, it should be changed as circumstances dictate.

2.66. Re-evaluation should be built into the program, either on a periodic or felt-need basis.

After the material on the outline is covered I build up developmental educational concepts through lecturing on sensory deficits and their possible results, drawing information from the class to build up a chart such as the one inserted (Table I). Following this I return to an early page in the history of special education with a discussion of a classical case—The Wild Boy of Aveyron—adding to it a fictional case — Tarzan — in order to demonstrate how these cases affected and were affected by developing educational concepts. This discussion leads into a review of language and learning concepts, and is culminated by a case history of a child seen recently in one of the University clinics. It is done something like this:

TABLE I
NEUROLOGICAL ASPECTS OF LEARNING PROBLEMS
POSSIBLE RESULTS OF DEFICITS

CORE AREAS FOR LEARNING	*Functional Disabilities*
I. Sensory Perception	
A. Olfaction (smell)	1. Limited warning system
B. Vision	1. Limited warning system 2. Unable to process visual symbols effectively
C. Audition	1. Limited warning system 2. Unable to process auditory stimuli effectively
D. Balance	1. Lack of physical control 2. Spatial disorientation
E. Gustation (taste)	1. Limited warning system
F. Haptic: Proprioception, including kinesthesia and taction (touch, feelings of movement)	1. Lack of warning (burns, cuts, misjudgment of movements) 2. Visual motor impairment
II. Central Integration	
A. Memory	1. Difficulty in encoding, decoding and processing bits of information
B. Automaticity	1. "
C. Abstraction	1. "
D. Symbolization	1. "
E. Problem solving	1. "
III. Motoric Facilitation (overall neuro-muscular coordination, fine and gross)	
A. Ambulation	1. Limited independence 2. Possible continued physical degeneration
B. Speech	1. Impaired communication
C. Writing	1. Limited ability to communicate effectively for most schools
D. Ocular movements	1. Misjudgment of motions 2. Difficulty in adapting to spatial relationships

Primary Effects	*Learning Problems*
1. Little pleasure in foods or odors	Not significant
1. Poor, distorted or no vision 2. Poor eye-motor coordination	1. Reading 2. Writing 3. Certain physical activities 4. General acquisition of knowledge and emotions
1. Poor, distorted or no hearing	1. Reading 2. Speech 3. General acquisition of knowledge and emotions
1. Poor locomotion 2. Spatial relationship difficulty 3. Vertigo	1. Reading 2. Certain physical activities
1. Little pleasure in food or odors	1. Little
1. Clumsiness 2. Incoordination 3. Poor reflexes	1. Writing 2. Delayed reactions 3. Speech 4. Physical education
1. Much re-doing and re-learning	1. All scholastic areas
1. Doesn't learn well or retain information	1. All scholastic areas 2. Physical education
1. Cannot handle many concepts	1. All scholastic areas 2. Many social areas
1. Cannot handle concepts above concrete level	1. All scholastic areas 2. Many social areas
1. Constant lack of success	1. Math 2. Reading 3. Activities of daily life
1. Restricted life space	1. Variable—from no learning problems through several related to motor deficit (e.g., writing, drawing, arithmetic, etc.)
1. Distorted speech	1. Articulation 2. Voice 3. Expressive language
1. Limited skill in producing letters and numbers	1. Spelling (any form of written language) 2. Math 3. Test writing in any area
1. Poor fixative movements 2. Poor focus	1. Reading 2. Physical education 3. Social interactions

At the beginning of the nineteenth century a young Parisian physician, Jean-Marc-Itard (1775–1838), undertook the training of a savage pre-pubescent boy who had lived naked and alone in a French forest for at least five to seven years. This was the famous "Wild Boy of Aveyron" whom Itard was to train and teach for a five-year period. All of the child's senses seemed inappropriately trained for civilized life. He could quite obviously respond to noises but not learn to discriminate among noises sufficiently to acquire usable speech during the five years Itard worked with him. When he began training ". . . he gave attention to nothing because nothing made any lasting impression upon his senses. His eyes saw without noticing, his ears heard and did not listen; and the organ of touch, restricted to the mechanical operation of grasping objects, had never been used to verify their forms and existence" (Itard, 53–54). For unknown reasons oral communication was more difficult to achieve than visible communication. After much arduous training employing methods developed by Pereira and the Abbé de l'Epée for work with deaf children, Itard was able to teach the boy (whom he named Victor) several nouns, some simple numerical concepts and adjectives such as *big* and *little*. However, all of Victor's vocabulary began with reading; he learned to read and to write simple messages indicating his needs, but other than for the French words for *milk* and *oh, God!*, he spoke only a few random mutterings, nor did he improve beyond this for the remaining thirty-five years of his life. Probably today Victor would have been classified as any or all of the following: aphasic, autistic, psychotic, mentally retarded, maternally deprived, emotionally disturbed, brain-injured, and speech and language delayed.

Victor was not unique in being a wild boy. In 1735, Linnaeus listed ten other children — eight girls and two boys. Wolf children were discovered in India on several occasions in the nineteenth century. Kipling had written one tale about Indian Forestry work concerning a child who had been raised by wolves. Using this as a basis, in 1892 he began a series of short stories which evolved into the *Jungle Books,* whose vogue has scarcely diminished over the years. Avid readers of Kipling will recall that

Mowgli was a toddler when adopted by a pair of wolves. He learned several animal languages and eventually human speech when he lived with people. Kipling endowed him with intelligence, inventiveness and awareness of fine discriminations via all sensory modalities that few civilized individuals possess. Mowgli was quite a different lad from Victor. It is doubtful that Kipling had read Itard's account of Victor, but it is certain that the author of our next wild boy, Tarzan, was familiar with Mowgli. At least Kipling said so in his autobiography when discussing imitators:

> And, if it be in your power, bear serenely with imitators. My *Jungle Books* begat Zoos of them. But the genius of all the genii was one who wrote a series called *Tarzan of the Apes*. I read it, but regret I never saw it on the films, where it rages most successfully. He had 'jazzed' the motif of the *Jungle Books* and, I imagine, had thoroughly enjoyed himself. He was reported to have said that he wanted to find out how bad a book he could write and 'get away with,' which is a legitimate ambition (p. 406, Vol. II of Beecroft, *Kipling: A Selection of his Stories and Poems*).

When carried away from his dead parents by Kala, the she ape, Tarzan was one year old. His real mother, Lady Graystoke, had lost her sanity and could not have been expected to have helped much in developing his abilities. Tarzan lived with the apes until maturity, speaking their language, but unlike Mowgli, he did not learn any other animal languages. However, he did return to the cabin built by his father and discovered picture books and dictionaries for children which Lord Greystoke had brought along for the potential use of children. He taught himself to read and to write between the ages of ten and fifteen. Burroughs' description of the discovery techniques employed by Tarzan is possibly a reflection of the wide-spread publicity of the pedagogical techniques of Maria Montessori whose Casa dei Bambini, for three and one half to six year old children, had opened in 1907. By 1909 several articles concerning Dr. Montessori's success with structuring environments so that children taught themselves had been published in the European and the American Press. *Tarzan of the Apes* was published in 1912. Although Kipling might not have been influenced by Itard, Burroughs was quite probably influenced both by Kipling and by Montessori, and Montessori mentioned several times that she had been heavily influenced both by Itard and by Itard's student, Séguin, both of whom were influenced by Pereira (1715–1780) — an educator of the deaf. Dewey, the American educator, and Piaget, the Swiss child developmentalist, were also influenced by Montessori. Burroughs' several discussions of Tarzan's learning through doing seem not too different from more recent discussions by Dewey, Piaget and a host of their disciples, although it must be admitted that much of the tale of *Tarzan of the Apes* appears unrealistic. For example, Burroughs had Tarzan teach himself to read and write English, but the first human spoken language he learned was French at approximately age twenty. Even this becomes logical upon closer examination, for Tarzan was deliberately taught French by a French naval lieutenant.

Where does this exposition of educational histories of real and fictional wild boys lead? It leads to a realization that the study of concepts of language acquisition is not new and that fertile minds have been actively involved in this area of endeavor for quite awhile. It also affords an opportunity to emphasize that a great many of our modern scientific studies of language and learning in normal children result from interest in abnormal children such as wild boys and deaf and mentally retarded "civilized" children. Montessori, for example, applied deaf education techniques to mentally retarded children and then to normal children. Modern techniques used in learning clinics borrow liberally from Montessori. Even the Fernald and Frostig techniques derive from Montessori and earlier approaches, and such internationally renowned agencies as Merrill-Palmer Institute and the Gesell Institute are concerned with patterns of child development. Sigel and Hooper (*Logical Thinking in Children: Research Based on Piaget's Theory,* 1968) edited a weighty volume which included a series of scientific studies on the development of stages of logical thinking in children. In short, the fields of psychology and education are becoming more and more focused upon developmental patterns and pre-requisites for learning.

Bangs, in her *Language and Learning Disorders of the Pre-*

Academic Child (1968), stresses that *language* is the basis of learning; language "includes the comprehension and usage of gesture, oral and written symbols . . ." (p. 2). When pondering the implications of this definition it becomes apparent that language not only includes gesture, speech, writing and reading, but also arithmetic. Speech, writing, reading and arithmetic are not separate entities. They must be considered, along with gesture, as components of language and communication. All appear to be ordinary, commonplace acts on the surface, but each has as prerequisites at least the following three events: 1) a stimulus, 2) association of the stimulus or stimuli with allied memories, and 3) decision-making. I have indicated only four steps, which is obviously too few, for each of these steps is subdivisible into many others. To confound the problem even more, let's add a few more prerequisites to effective communication:

1. Normal anatomy and physiology
2. Positive environmental stimulation
3. Lack of gross emotional disturbance
4. Need and desire to communicate

West (1957) stresses that language breakdown or lack of development involves inability of the individual in any or all of the areas of automaticity, abstraction and symbolization, which are again subdivisible in terms of the skills employed in speech, writing, reading, arithmetic, music, etc. The use of automaticities implies memory, either short-term or long-term, but primarily long-term. Abstraction implies the ability to go beyond a single reality or event to generalization, for example, from "this chair and this chair are two chairs" to "one and one are two." Symbolization goes beyond abstraction to the point where the letters *o*, *n* and *e,* or a stick-figure line are accepted as the concept of oneness. The spoken phrase "one and one are two" is also on an abstract level, but may employ different forms of memory or inner language than the written phrase, or the drawing of numbers in a formula pattern.

As a means of looking at the communicative process let us recapitulate some high points in the linguistic development of the baby and young child, bearing in mind that interruption of an orderly progression of these stages may lead to delay in one or more forms of communication.

In normal language development the infant hears, sees, feels, smells and tastes stimuli to which he responds first grossly, and then, after the refinement of his neuro-motor coordinations, more subtly. Traditionally he hears what we call speech as a wide spectrum of noises. When these noises are used often enough in combination with other stimuli he begins to associate one set of gross noises with the other accompanying stimuli. This presupposes normal receptive processes and the storage of memories. After several repetitions and some physical maturation he begins to understand the significance of the noises. He may even inadvertently make appropriate physical responses and be rewarded, which reinforces his knowledge of the significance. Eventually specific clusters of noise develop specific meanings to which the infant or young child responds consistently. He becomes capable of differentiating noises which resemble one another very little in their sounds and their meanings. After he has learned to understand several of these grossly different meaningful noises he discovers that two grossly similar words such as *cup* and *come* or *crib* and *bib* are surprisingly different in meaning. This is a crucial step, for if it should not occur early enough in the child's development, many opportunities for decreasing confusion and for increasing learning are lost. The child whose auditory discrimination ability is poor is likely to have difficulties in learning speech, writing, reading, and the subject matter pre-supposing these skills.

Much of this informal auditory and conceptual training occurs within the first few months of life since an average child utters his first meaningful word at approximately twelve months of age. By his first birthday, then, he must learn to listen, to build memories, to experiment with physical movements of the parts of the body involved in speech, to deliberately experiment with sound production, to build up mental associations or inner language in order to determine which sounds he will use and in what combinations, to monitor the sounds auditorily and kinesthetically as part of the selection-rejection procedure, and then to use the selected product in the correct meaningful context in an appropriate physical environment — all this before the age of one year. If a child has not said his first meaningful word by eighteen months or two years many parents fear that he is mentally retarded or deaf. Both are plausible possibilities. As mentioned earlier, additional possibilities include lack of environmental stimulation, emotional disturbance, brain damage or other organic deficit. The presence of long-term or severe childhood diseases may have rendered him too feeble to perform the multiple complex coordinations necessary for speech or for other forms of active learning and exploring the environment, such as pulling himself erect and walking.

Coordination is an important term in this discussion. For a moment let us consider some of the coordinations involved in a baby's saying the word *Hi!* — a relatively easy word. First there must be either an incoming or internal stimulus for him to want to say *Hi!*. In this instance we will assume that his mother has just grinned, waved at him and said "Hi!" The sound waves emitted by the mother go through a series of energy changes or transductions from kinetic to mechanical to hydraulic to electrochemical merely to reach his brain via air displacement, tissue vibration, bone and muscle movement, various fluid agitations and neural excitation. Within the brain the incoming auditory messages from both ears must be fused and coupled with the visual stimuli of the hand wave, the big grin and the open mouth. The visual and auditory messages must then be referred to some as yet unknown storehouse of associated memories so it may be determined whether a response is needed, and if so, which? Since the baby has decided to captivate his immediate world with *Hi!*, he inhales for speech, which requires that several nerves and nervelets slightly alter their normal breathing orders to the muscles which in turn affect bones, viscera and other tissue. The vocal folds remain open in somewhat the same fashion as for breathing — but not *quite*. The mouth is open. A few thoracic muscles and several abdominal muscles contract to expel air from the lungs. The air rushing between the open vocal folds, up the pharynx, curves over the tongue and out of the mouth, producing the /h/ of *hi!* But, even before the /h/ gets a fraction of an inch above the vocal folds, small sets of muscles contract to close the folds so that sub-glottal air pressure may explode them apart in a series of small puffs to produce vibrations necessary to the production of /aI/. Immediately, a pair of very small muscles contract in order to open the folds for normal breathing. Concurrently, several muscles of the face make delicate adjustments to render the production of /aI/ more accurate and recognizable. Each speech sound requires some modification in coordinations from all other speech sounds — and what we may recognize as the same sound repeated twice will often have minutely different coordinations than when the same speaker produced it before. Vision and feeling require similarly complex coordinated interactions and processes.

By the time a child reaches kindergarten he should have mastered hundreds of thousands of coordinations in order to accomplish normal activities of daily life. These coordinations are built up and monitored by all sensory modalities known to man and by X-factors so far only suspected but not entirely proven. The neuromuscular coordinations are relatively easier to see and calculate on developmental scales than are the thought processes. Such scales have long been available to physicians and it is not uncommon to see them posted in pediatricians' offices. Intellectual processes are more difficult to predict and schedule, but the work of Montessori, Piaget and other students of child development is throwing increasing quantities of light upon the subject so that norms are becoming standardized for nearly all developmental aspects. The concepts of motivation and readiness for an activity or concept have spread through the field of Education, although this knowledge has not always been applied as heartily by some educators and parents as by others. In a logical orientation one might conclude that a child feels, hears, and sees, then learns to refine his auditory and visual discriminations (in addition to those of touch and deep muscle movement) to investigate his environment, to develop a mental stockpile of associable information, after which he should be able to undergo more formal education such as the "three r's" and the various subject areas which require reading, writing and arithmetic as bases.

One of Montessori's early accidental discoveries was that some children taught themselves to write before teaching themselves to read. Piaget observed that children had to learn the concept of the conservation of mass, that is, that an object such as a clay ball was still the same clay when flattened, after which they could learn concepts of weight and volume. In the field of reading it is almost axiomatic to state that auditory discrimination, visual discrimination and auditory and visual memory must be established and organized prior to successful reading. In abnormal students, such as the blind, the haptic abilities of touch and deep muscle sensation replace vision, and in the deaf, vision and haptic modalities work harder to compensate for the lack of hearing. The blind and the deaf cannot completely compensate for their handicaps and are therefore usually somewhat slower in their overall acquisition of academic skills.

Let's focus more specifically upon speech, reading and arithmetic interrelations. Many people learn to speak although they cannot read or do arithmetic. Few people learn to read without already having learned to speak unless they have special intensive training, but an autistic male recently graduated from college with a degree in math. Many children who have difficulty learning reading and math also have some form of speech defect, but only a few children with speech defects have difficulty learning to read or to perform mathematic calculations. With our present educational crises — teachers' strikes, desegregation-based school closures, students' strikes, taxpayers' strikes, and partial withdrawal of governmental financial support to education — enough educational programs are being disrupted so that many children, if tested, might prove to be educationally retarded in many ways. One suburban school system in central New York discovered that over one third of the children in the middle elementary grades were reading at least a year and one-half below grade level. Similar studies were not done of their speech or arithmetic so there is no basis for comparison.

In 1968–69, approximately 15% of the children between the ages of 6 and 18 being seen at the Syracuse University Reading Clinic had speech and/or oral language deficiencies. Among children seen at the University Speech Clinic the percentage with reading disorders was negligible. However, in those cases which have both reading and speech problems there may be organic problems alone, organic problems combined with emotional overlay, primarily emotional problems, endogenous or exogenous mental retardation, or insufficient stimulation and motivation for language learning. Each child's remedial training must be planned on an individual basis, with the various clinicians pooling their interdisciplinary resources and information. Emphasis needs to be placed on encouraging the child to apply the needed skills to his own interests. An example would be to have the child dictate a message or story to a clinician who would then type it for him. The child would then learn to read aloud his own story, thus practicing both reading and speaking. The *Language Master* is used in both reading and speech clinics. This is a modified tape recorder which is activated by inserting a card between the playback heads. On the card is a strip of magnetic tape plus a word, sentence, picture, or combination thereof. It is also possible for the instructor to record new practice material on these cards so that the student may work with the machine on his own. The Language Master has proven to be quite helpful in a variety of learning situations, such as with aphasic adults and with foreign students, for it helps to build auditory discrimination and memory. The use of concrete materials, including money, is important in working with basic math concepts.

The following inspirational case history of a fourteen-year-old boy should serve to illustrate several concepts. He was born with a twisted neck and large, floppy ears. There was a strong possibility of at least minimal brain damage. Various diagnoses included: normal intelligence; severely retarded; emotionally disturbed; above average intelligence; idiot savant. Other children and their parents threw stones at him and mocked him. A group of parents signed a petition to have him institutionalized, but the parents refused. In school he became more and more distractable and began to hit other children. After being promoted socially during the first few years of school he was placed in a special class for the mentally retarded, where according to the parents, he learned nothing for three years. He was then evaluated by a team at a large medical center. They recommended permanent institutionalization for severe mental retardation. At this time he was brought to our attention. Despite medical recommendations to the contrary, the parents had cosmetic surgery performed on the ears and neck to normalize his appearance. A laryngologist operated on the excessively large infected tonsils. At the University Clinic we put him on "blitz" therapy — two hours each day during the summer session. Therapy began with calisthenics but consisted mainly of having him read aloud from a book he selected (at home he was required to read aloud to his parents at least one hour daily); he learned speech best kinesthetically, so much emphasis was placed on the physical feelings accompanying speech sounds; for speech muscle stretching he was required to do the reading aloud with several pieces of bubble gum in his mouth. Time was allotted to listening and answering questions based on what he heard. He had to learn to trust people and build up self-confidence.

After one month of training he had increased his reading ability by nearly two years on standardized reading tests. His speech was comprehensible most of the time. He understood most concrete conversation, but was still having difficulty with more abstract speech, especially humor. A conference with school officials in his home town resulted in his being placed in a seventh grade the following fall. Provisions were made for remedial reading and speech therapy. At mid-year he had earned average grades in his courses and his science instructor stated that he would be earning a legitimate B for that marking period. All of his teachers reported that he asked each of them for home work daily, did his work assiduously and handed it in promptly. His parents were surprised but proud to relate that upon returning from school in the afternoon he voluntarily did home work before watching television. On Saturday mornings he would rise at five o'clock to do homework before engaging in other activities. He developed enough self-confidence so that he would go to the neighboring shopping center to do routine family shopping, reading the items correctly from the shopping list. He made friends and has been academically promoted each year since. As of fall, 1972, (five years later) he is a junior in high school. In another age, without parental support and surgical and educational intervention, this child, too, might have become a "wild boy."

AFTER THE FIRST SESSION

In the second meeting, we discuss concepts of diagnosis, presenting formal and informal means of evaluating a child's strengths and weaknesses in all areas previously reviewed. All in-service teachers seem to have at least one formal or informal test in which they have faith. The class members argue the pros and cons of each test, and eventually determine those tests and procedures which they would feel most useful. Usually, there is at least one remedial reading teacher or speech therapist in the group. These two specialists strengthen the composition of the class because their training and experience traditionally include much individual and small-group work with children, and stresses diagnostic teaching or therapy. Tests and techniques which have not been mentioned by the group, but which I consider important, are introduced, explained and demonstrated.

At this time, the teams present reasons for wishing to have certain children evaluated as class projects. Selections are made in such a manner that children with apparently different educational difficulties are scheduled. Case history forms to be filled out by the school and parents are hand-carried to the school and parents by the class member. This person must be closely associated with the child and must promise to ensure follow-up of the child beyond the semester. Permission must be granted by the parents or guardians and the school for the child to be seen. If the parents are reluctant or unco-operative, we do not see the child, a basic concept being that *the child is the parent's property*.

A typical clinical case history form (to be filled out by the parent) is given to each member of the class. We discuss possible implications of each section of the form in terms of those questions that deal with pre-natal, natal and post-natal physical condition of the child and mother, social factors, physical development and other indicators or predictors of maturation. A separate form to be filled out by the teacher or other school personnel asks for information concerning forms of adaptive or maladaptive behavior, specific formal test results given in the school, and teacher impressions of the child. The two forms are intended to help the team determine what other people think of the child. We discuss the need to personally interview the informants who complete the forms in order: 1) to reduce errors in communication; 2) to have an opportunity to evaluate the evaluators, and 3) to gain supplemental information as a normal outgrowth of the interpersonal interaction. I usually recommend that two people interview the informant in order to obtain two subjective reactions.

At this time, members of the class re-form into groups. For ideal group discussion purposes, five to eight participants yield enough backgrounds and personalities to be stimulating. When the groups get larger, it is more difficult for each person to become intensely involved, yet there have been groups as large as fifteen or sixteen which have functioned rather well. By this time team members have submitted names of children who they would like the class to evaluate. These children are tentatively reviewed by each team in terms of whether the description of a specific child's problems appears to be within the scope of the course. First and second priorities are given to the children selected within each group, after which the nominations of all the groups are presented so that variety in types of problems may be seen. Three, four or five children emerge as the choices of the class as a whole, and arrangements are made to schedule them for evaluation.

The third and fourth meetings build on diagnostic concepts presented in previous sessions. General categories of tests and specific tests are demonstrated and discussed. The approach to testing may be enunciated as follows: tests fall into two major categories — *formal* and *informal*. Formal tests are those which have been standardized and for which norms have been established. A certain degree of training in using a formal test is stipulated by the author of the test. Certain tests are presumably not to be used unless the testor has academic or professional credentials which would authorize him to use the test. Other formal tests have norms but no requirement of training other than reading the directions accompanying the test. Representative formal tests include the Stanford Binet, Wechsler Intelligence Scale for Children, Wide-Range Achievement Test, and Illinois Test of Psycholinguistic Abilities. Other commonly-used supposedly formal tests are the Frostig Developmental Test of Visual Perception, The Denver Developmental Screening Test and the Peabody Picture Vocabulary Test. Diagnostic tests of reading difficulty such as those employed in reading clinics are relatively formal and require training to utilize effectively, whereas standardized school-given tests which appear to be formal require little sophistication on the part of the class-room teacher to administer, score and interpret.

Informal tests are those intended to see if certain concepts and abilities are present and may use any available materials. Does a child know his name? Can he count by ones, by twos, by fives? Can be cut with scissors? Which hand does he use? Can he draw with a crayon or pencil? Can he follow simple and complex directions? If he can follow a one-stage command, can he follow two- three- and four-stage commands? Can he run, skip, jump, and perform other complex motor coordinations? Can he read, write and perform simple arithmetic? If he can't, does it appear that he can learn? If he can learn, what seem the best techniques for teaching him? Can he tell stories about pictures? Does he appear to have a good grasp of grammar? Is word choice appropriate? Does he seem to lack basic vocabulary? Can he match a three-dimensional object with its two-dimensional representation (a picture)? Can he feel differences in texture of materials? Can he tell if sounds are similar or different? If given enough information and structure concerning a given chore, can he guess the next sequential step?

In the social-emotional area, how does he react to the testing environment and to the new people involved? Does he enter the situation fearfully, timidly, neutrally, or with enthusiasm? Does he appear to relate better to females or males, or are there certain personality types with whom he seems more comfortable? What appear to be significant parent-child interactions? Does the parent apologize for the child before the child has a chance to perform a task? Does the parent try to "walk the child through" the preliminary instructions? Does the child take the lead while the parent sits helpless and unquestioning? If there is any apparent social structuring, how patterned and formalized does it seem to be?

Informal assessments of a child's personality and abilities often point to a need for formal testing of a special nature. That is why it is perhaps better to observe the child's behavior for awhile before determining the formal tests to be done. Some clinics have a battery of formal tests to be used on all children seen there. It is neither good nor bad to do this; building test batteries forces the evaluators to look at many components of learning and adjustment mechanisms, but many children may perform poorly on an exhaustive battery due to fatigue, confusion and negative emotional factors. For those clinics which have research functions, changing staffs and detailed periodic reports, there may be envisioned a need for less individualization in diagnosis.

A live child is seen during the fifth session. By this time the team has assigned itself to observe the child in school and at home, and has begun interviews with the parent(s) in the home environment. Information from the school and other pertinent agencies has been received by the team. The team members all have specific and general chores to do during the diagnostic period. Some will test motor development, others cognitive and perceptual aspects. The preponderance, if not all, of the testing will be done in full view of the class. Surprisingly, children tolerate this kind of situation very well. An examiner will usually start below the child's presumed level in an area and work upward, attempting to discover patterns of strengths and weaknesses, of skills wholly or partially learned, of lack of prerequisites for advanced stages. For example, a fifth-grade boy who was having difficulty with arithmetic could convert from base ten to base five. The examiner, a fifth-grade teacher, was ready to move him on to a higher stage, and then double-checked skills supposedly learned at a lower level. She discovered that he had never learned automatic multiplication beyond three times three. Therefore, he had resorted to laborious addition devices to replace multiplication, and due to the lack of multiplication abilities, was deficient in division since division beyond a very simple level requires skill in multiplication.

Concurrently, more intensive parent interviewing is going on, and after the interview, the parent(s) and interviewers join the large group observing the child. By this time the child is likely to be so immersed in the required tasks that he barely notices the interruption caused by the returning parents and interviewers. It is common for a parent to be surprised at how well the child is performing some tasks, and conversely, to realize for perhaps the first time where deficiencies lie. If school representatives such as the classroom teacher, counsellor or remedial teacher are present, they may add further information and insight to the outcome of the diagnosis.

After the team has completed the planned evaluation, the parent and child are excused for awhile so that findings up to that point may be summarized and analysed. Further testing or investigation may be necessary, but in many instances definite pictures may have emerged, revealing psychoeducational paths to be taken. Depending upon the outcome of this conference, the results are fed back *to the child* in the presence of the parents and school personnel, and implications and alternatives are discussed with him. As much as possible, the child feeds his own perceptions and interpretations into the final decision-making, and planning begins. Children often have important clues to contribute if they are questioned in a supportive manner. Sometimes they can specify why they have difficulty learning; at other times they give fairly accurate estimates of how they compare with their classmates. By second grade they know who are the smart and not-so-smart kids in their classes, and are aware of their own relative status. I have asked one question of each child I have interviewed during these workshops: "How old do you feel you are?" This question, if built on a discussion of how sometimes we feel older or younger than we are, depending upon what we do, may yield answers that correspond with test results. A nine-year-old boy who tested on the six-to-seven year levels physically and intellectually, said that he felt about seven years old. Conversely, the ten-year-old who could do base five arithmetic but hadn't learned multiplication felt like a ten-year-old.

As part of this session the team schedules conferences with the parents, school and child as needed, and sets up long-term and short-term goals. Each succeeding week team members report on progress and necessary alterations of plans.

Subsequent sessions revolve around diagnosis, placement and recommended teaching and other habilitative strategies for individual children. At the next-to-last meeting of the workshop, threads are pulled together so that an overall pattern of learning and adjustment emerges in terms of children who have become a part of the lives of members of the class. Guided selection of the children studied allows for inclusion of at least one child with neurological deficit, at least one child who is the victim of social-emotional pressures, and at least one child with developmental delay. Where possible, means of solving parent-school conflicts are investigated and solved. Team members develop increased self-confidence as well as confidence in other members of the team, and often begin their own school-centered mini-clinics. One workshop member, a principal, even published an article in an administrator's journal on establishing school-based mini-clinics (Chadwick, 1969).

A recommended list of projects at the beginning of the workshop may bear useful fruit. Ten members of one team developed a manual of perceptual motor activities for the teaching of academic subjects. Another team is following up children seen in the workshop as a function of their parents and professionals learning disabilities association. Several teams undertook the task of compiling lists of services for children within their own geographic areas. These listings are in terms of the services the agencies advertise, but point out what they *really do*—which may or may not be what they advertise. The major comment that is made by workshop participants at the end of the course is that it ends too soon.

One workshop participant, a principal, was so impressed with the results of his colleagues' work that he published a short article on the establishment of small school-based clinics. This article by Mr. Dale Chadwick is reprinted in entirety from the 1969 Fall Edition of *The Elementary Principal:*

WHY NOT A MINI-CLINIC IN YOUR SCHOOL?

The ordinary structure of services in the elementary schools as regards reading help, psychological services, health services, and corrective physical education is usually too little, too late and disjointed at best. Despite the principal's best efforts at the team approach, access to needed services is limited and often spread over a period of time because of schedules and other priorities.

Why not organize the staff we do have at hand so that their talents can be brought to bear on the problems of the child with learning difficulties? The mystique of the "specialist" is an impediment to providing immediate, constructive help to those children and their classroom teachers. In a workshop series recently, I was very much impressed by the talents and capabilities of a group of "ordinary school people." They were teachers of reading, classroom teachers, teachers of retarded, nurse-teachers, parents, and one administrator. By pooling their recommendations and skills in a team approach to several cases, they were able to pinpoint the problems and offer realistic, constructive, usable techniques and direction for improving the achievement of the youngsters presented.

To organize a mini-clinic within a school, the following staff considerations need to be made:

1. Which teacher or teachers is the best in teaching reading? Hers will be a pivotal position.
2. What specialists do you have on call: the speech correctionist, the nurse-teacher, the physical education teacher?
3. Is there someone who can handle interview situations: the principal, an assistant, another teacher?
4. Is there clerical help available to type reports, etc.?

With this small staff you are ready to go. Each member should be encouraged to brush up on the testing techniques peculiar to his field and review his special bag of tricks which might be appropriate to children with learning problems. The school staff needs to be briefed on the operation of the clinic and a referral procedure established.

In practice, the child is referred to the "clinic" for help by his teacher. As a member of the team, she then presents the case to the clinic using the material from the child's academic and health folders, and anecdotals from the daily classroom situation. Based on this information, the team determines what additional information is required and members are assigned to do the testing and report back.

An interview is set up with the parents and they are requested to complete a questionnaire which should delve more deeply into the matters of health, home training, and the child's habits and development. A summary of this material is given the team and any further testing indicated is undertaken.

When all the tests and evaluations are in, the team pools ideas and prepares a report which recommends procedures for home and school, outside referrals which need to be made and gives a summary of the probable potential, the problems, and the prognosis. Copies of this report are given to the teacher and the contents shared with both the parents and the child, too, if deemed advisable.

What are the merits of such a program?—most importantly, the benefits for the youngsters, of course; the staff involvement in a problem-solving situation; the realism of a "by teacher-for-teacher" approach; and finally the wide open opportunity for professional growth by your staff. Why not implement this little gem with your staff?

SHORT WORKSHOPS

I have also participated in half-day or one-day workshops. Half-day workshops are usually intended to inform a group of teachers of basic concepts of learning problems as a whole or of a sub-area, such as perceptual dysfunctions. A presentation varying in length from one to two hours is followed by group discussion. If questions are submitted to the speaker or speakers before the formal presentation, answers can be integrated into the planned part. If none are presented in advance, questions will be based on outgrowths of the lecture. In one half-day workshop I presented material for an hour and one-half, answered questions for half an hour, and the assembled elementary, junior high and high school teachers for that school system broke up into several groups with group leaders who conducted discussions on applications of the topic to the participants' needs within the schools.

In one full-day workshop, Dr. DiBuono (a professor of Pediatrics), Dr. Egeland (a professor of School Psychology) and I each presented our points of view for roughly forty-five minutes and then fielded questions as a panel. After lunch the elementary and junior high teachers from that school system divided into three groups, and each of us spent approximately twenty minutes with one group after another. This procedure was chosen to reduce the formality by decreasing the size of the groups so that discussion was encouraged. As guest lecturers changed groups, different participants advanced ideas and questions that did not seem appropriate to ask of previous lecturers. Also, as one lecturer left after having answered a question one way, his replacement might be asked *his* point of view on the same question without having heard his colleague's response. In this fashion, the workshop participants could double check one guest's opinions with another's, producing lively interchanges.

Half-day and one-day workshops can be mandatory boredom for the in-service teachers or they can be highlights of the week. Since school systems often require all teachers in certain grades (plus special teachers) to attend the workshop, there is customarily a wide range of academic specialties represented, from kindergarten through shop mechanics and classical language teachers. It therefore behooves the lecturers and discussion leaders to keep in mind the need for presenting information and examples in such a manner that the majority present may sense some relevancy in the topic for the day. In one instance the school administrator in charge of the workshop made available to each of the schools two films dealing with the topic. The teachers were encouraged to see the films during the month before the workshop. By the time the workshop took place nearly all of the teachers had seen the films and had discussed them, thus establishing a frame of reference for the workshop. This pre-planning set a tone of high interest and anticipation. Several workshop participants who had had problems with individual children had solved those problems as a result of having discussed the films with other teachers and administrators.

RESULTS OF WORKSHOPS

Short-term workshops of one day or less tend to be informational. Terminology is explained, concepts of normal ranges are advanced, and selected case histories and their implications are explored in moderate detail. Interdisciplinary action is stressed. Among reactions received after such short sessions were those indicating that many teachers were relieved to know that there were other reasons for children failing in school besides being "dumb" or in the classes of poor teachers. They were generally more eager to seek consultation from other teachers and administrators with regard to classroom problems. There was more of a tendency to handle educational problems in-house rather than blindly refer to diagnostic agencies. When short-term workshops were given to medical groups it was noted that more intelligent referrals were made to the clinics represented in the workshop.

Longer workshops of several weeks duration had not only the above results, but several more personal effects. As mentioned earlier, some school-based clinical teams or mini-clinics evolved from the course. In one city the workshop became action-orientated toward fulfillment of laws which were not being heeded in the area of education of the educationally handicapped. Several students developed their own tests from basic concepts discussed in the course or in collateral reading. Strong friendships developed among members of the several groups, and many teachers became more self-confident of their abilities in classroom management and peer interaction. When two or more members of the same school were in a workshop they become valuable resources to the school administrators for they could represent a variety of views with a degree of conviction. Several times it was commented that teachers began to respect and like one another as people and co-professionals when there had been a previous condition of dislike and mistrust. In one workshop composed of teachers, administrators and parents of children with learning problems, two mothers who were hostile toward the school system became compassionate when the workshop revealed the constraints under which the teachers and administrators worked. Instead of vilifying the school personnel they both expressed appreciation of the amount of time, energy and personal frustration the teachers and administrators experienced with their children.

Adminstrators verbalized that this was the first opportunity that they had had to truly understand the combined frustrations of parents and teachers. Teachers of specialty subjects gained greater acceptance by many regular class teachers who were not completely aware of their capabilities and functions. Above all, the concept of diagnostic teaching seemed to give personal status to many teachers who had previously not dared to diagnose children's educational problems. Once they were encouraged to develop their own diagnostic devices there was an awesome display of inventiveness and ingenuity. In diagnostic sessions a pattern soon emerged: at the beginning of the first diagnostic case team members appeared apprehensive until the child, parents and school representatives arrived, but by the end of the first half-hour calm interest prevailed. By the end of the session, several members of the team seemed almost cocky. The other teams functioned as observers and developed their own diagnostic structures either independently or based on their reactions to how they thought the previous team's structure had worked.

CASE HISTORIES

Case histories varied somewhat in format from workshop to workshop, but in general contained vital statistics, medical, educational and social-emotional information, results of tests, the group's evaluation of the child, recommendations for the future, and follow-up information. A short summary of the combined information preceded the detailed section. The following case histories were selected as representative of children seen at the Syracuse University Learning Evaluation Center.

Report Summary on Alex (9 years, 5 months)

Reason for Referral

Parents requested testing to assess Alex's potential abilities relative to a more extensive educational program. He presently attends sessions at the local Association for Retarded Children Center.

Principal Findings

Alex was generally successful in completing representative tasks of the Denver Developmental Scale. He also demonstrated abilities as tested in non-standardized tests of language comprehension, number comprehension and visual decoding function. Although some motor abilities still reflect a general developmental lag, these are not felt to be a hindrance to learning. He has limited expressive-oral language but shows a good potential for acquiring knowledge auditorily and especially visually. We feel that he is ready for a full-time academic program and that he should continue in speech and language therapy. In general, Alex responded at a much higher level than one would expect based on initial observation and his rather involved medical history.

Recommendations

Alex should be placed in a full-time academic situation aimed at teaching reading and general perceptual motor skills. Use of his good visual abilities should aid in his acquisition of all subject matter. Home programs should be set up to support his school work as well as speech and language therapy, which should be continued. Alex responds well to behavior modification procedures; these should be used to control distractibility and to increase attention span. A physical instruction program involving swimming and exercise would be helpful in improving coordination and fine motor responses.

Medical History

Child delivered after a normal full-term pregnancy. Congenital anomalies noted at birth: complete cleft of palate not including alveolar ridge, repaired at 6 years of age; congenital bilateral inguinal herniorophy, repaired at 6 months. Subsequently it was observed that this child retained an interventricular septal defect with pulmonary hypertension (to have open heart surgery when planned.) Gastrostomy tube was placed at 6 months and removed between 2½–3 years old. There is a history of chronic upper respiratory infection and otitis media (controlled). Medication: lanoxin, daily; no limitation on activity relative to septal defect.

Developmental History

Developmental lag in acquisition of motor behavior; sat by self 9 mos.; walked 2½ years.; said "ma ma" at 6 yrs., probably due to feeding problems. Since the gastrostomy tube was main mode of feeding, oral activities of chewing, sucking and swallowing were minimized from 6 mos. to 2½–3 yrs. At 3 yrs. child began on pureed and junior foods and recently has attempted adult foods. He can dress himself but cannot tie shoes. Bladder and bowel control are generally consistent. He demonstrates little oral-expressive language but seems to understand well.

Family History

Father and mother are both in good health. There is one younger sibling, Jane, demonstrating good academic success.

Educational History

At 7 yrs., Alex started to attend the Association for Retarded Children for ½ a day, twice a week. Recently he went ½ a day, 5 times a week. He has been attending the Speech and Hearing Clinic at Syracuse University Department of Special Education from Feb. 1967 to the present, where he has been receiving language and speech therapy. Recently a home-bound teacher has been assigned to Alex pending educational placement.

Relevant Test Results

Intelligence, physiological-neurological, and perceptual-motor testing were attempted at Upstate Medical Center Pediatric Clinic See folder Re. med. report, 10/20/69.

Denver Developmental Test: Only a selected few of the highest level tasks (6 year old level) from the four major areas of test were tested. Results: He was successful in a) balance on 1 foot, 5 secs. b) catches bounced ball, c) backward heel-toe. These were gross motor tasks. Relative to fine motor-adaptive tasks, he was successful in a) copying cross, circle and square, b) picking the longer line. He was essentially successful in all tasks he was asked to perform. However, it was felt that he would not have been able to do the draw-a-man aspects of this section and was not tested on them. (These had been attempted just prior to the testing in another evaluation center; Alex was unsuccessful.) Under the Language section of this test, Alex was successful in a) comprehending 3 prepositions, b) recognizing 3 colors, c) composition of 3 materials. These were tested through his ability to understand language since his expressive oral language is essentially nonexistent. Under Personal-Social tasks, he demonstrated his ability to dress without supervision for the most part, and this subsumes the other tasks in this section.

Along with the Denver test, other tests of a non-specific nature were used and will be discussed below.

Test Interpretation

All specific and non-specific tests used with this child were given to assess his intellectual adaptability and his adaptability to learning situations. Along with the Denver test, other tests were administered to help assess the child's receptive and expressive language abilities, his visual encoding abilities, his understanding of mathematical concepts and his attention span. From the test results, it appears that Alex is still a little retarded in some gross and many fine motor abilities. However, his limitations in these areas do not restrict his general learning ability. In testing for auditory and receptive-language ability, Alex demonstrated his comprehension of motion concepts, tool use, spatial relations and composition of materials. He was also able to follow a three-part command which involved his finding a specific page in a book. His expressive language is limited to gestures and a few words. His physiological support for speech is poor and he had difficulty in imitating the tester's lip, tongue and jaw movements. He does, however, have very good rhythm and prosody in his imitations of words although their articulation is unclear. Relative to visual decoding, Alex has an excellent ability to recognize and learn new words in a few trials. The tester was able to teach the child 10 words in a short time. When presented with an alphabet, he was able to spell a few words by pointing to the letters in succession. It must be remembered that this is a child who has never had any formal education. However, he demonstrated an ability to understand number concepts when the task did not require verbalization or fine motor abilities. He could match the appropriate number of objects to a written number, he could add objects and subtract objects to get a required number.

Alex's attention span is adequate for successful teaching and can be greatly increased by using a positive reinforcer and setting up appropriate contingencies. Firmness and constant reminding usually resulted in recapturing his attention whenever he became distracted. By his overall performance on all the tasks, Alex demonstrated a readiness for the acquisition of academic subjects.

Specific Recommendations

1) Alex could benefit from a full time academic program aimed at teaching reading and perceptual motor skills.

2) He needs specific language and speech therapy and should continue at the Speech and Hearing Clinic.

3) Therapy using behavior modification principles has proved successful and could be applied to his general academic regimen.

4) A home program of chewing, sucking and swallowing to strengthen speech organs is needed. Also a home program in programmed reading instruction would, perhaps, help the child to acquire reading skills faster.

5) He could also benefit from some physical instruction to bring along the lag in his gross and fine motor abilities. A swimming program would be suitable.

6) Although auditory perception is good, it is felt that Alex has an excellent visual memory and decoding ability and, perhaps, this could be used extensively in all teaching situations.

Follow-up Reports

1. After conference with Dr. K_____ of the Syracuse Public School System, tutoring with a Home-Bound Teacher was arranged for Alex until a Special Class in the city schools could be found with a suitable teacher and with room for one more.

2. Alex now attends _____ Elementary School and is a member of Miss K_____'s Special Class.

3. Alex was operated in the summer of 1971 for the heart defect. Since then he has had a substantial weight gain and has become more active physically.

Report Summary on Bella (10 years, 3 months)

Reason for Referral

Bella has difficulty with basic first grade skills even though she is ten years old and in the third grade. She has already repeated a grade. Her main problem is reading. She tries, but can't seem to learn. She sometimes writes backwards.

Principal Findings

It was observed that although Bella concentrates on tasks given to her, she does not attend to all parts of a task. For instance, when she looks at a word, she seems only to be aware of the first letter. When her attention is focused on the entire word, as in the Fernald technique, Bella is able to learn that word. Bella's tendency to make reversals, both in reading and writing, shows a need for developing a more consistent frame of reference in spatial orientation. That is, Bella should be able to distinguish left from right, and also be able to consistently begin reading activities going from left to right.

Recommendations

1. To help Bella look at all the important cues in tasks such as reading, techniques that focus her attention upon all the necessary parts would be valuable. This would include such techniques as tracing and following reading lines with her finger. Other suggestions include presenting work assignments so that a smaller amount of material is on the page. This way, Bella might not be confused by having too much to attend to at once.

2. Activities that help establish a more consistant frame of reference for spatial orientation may also be valuable. Possible activities to be included here would be games of instructions to move in certain directions, drawing circles and writing letters consistently in one direction, and following a line from left to right. It is expected that Bella will improve in her ability to read and write without reversing the position of the letters.

Medical History

Bella had pneumonia twice as a young infant.

Family History

Bella is the oldest of six children, three boys and three girls. She has been living with her mother since she was seven years old. Previously, Bella lived with her maternal grandparents, her own parents having separated before her birth. Her mother now feels that Bella was frequently kept out of school by the grandparents for what she believes were feigned illnesses.

Education History

This is the third school she has attended. She failed third grade last year in another school. She is now in a regular third grade.

Before Bella visited the Learning Evaluation Center, she was observed in her classroom working attentively on the assigned task (11/26/69). She was then given some informal diagnostic tasks to perform outside of the class. They included exercises in following directions, reading and writing. It was found that Bella could follow a series of three instructions, but had difficulty distinguishing her left from her right.

The reading tasks included knowledge of the alphabet, phonics and sight vocabulary. On the alphabet, Bella could identify all the letters in the upper case and confused only b and d in the lower case. She could write all the letters, reversing only the z.

In the area of phonics, Bella could easily identify both initial and final consonant sounds, also writing down the appropriate letter. It was when the letters were present visually and Bella was required to sound them out that she had difficulty. The shoulds for b and d were interchanged.

On the sight vocabulary, Bella knew 120 out of 220 common sight words. It was observed that some words were reversed when read, e.g. *saw-was, no-on.*

Goodenough Draw-A-Person Test (12/2/69): On her drawing, Bella omitted both hands and feet, reflecting an early stage of development in the ability to perceive important parts of the body and include them in her drawing. Her age equivalent score was 6.3.

Bender Visual Motor Gestalt Test: On this test where Bella was required to copy forms, she scored 9 errors (Koppitz system). This is significantly poorer than the expected error score of 1.5 for her age. Upon re-examination, Bella scored 7 errors, also significantly poorer than her expected score for her age. Her errors included misshapen angles in figures 1, 7, and 8; integration in figure 7; and rotation in figure 5.

Frostig Developmental Test of Visual Perception: On the first subtest, *eye-motor coordination,* Bella performed adequately. On the remaining four subtests she performed below the level expected for her age. On *figure-ground,* where one is required to distinguish a shape among other shapes, Bella's age equivalent score was 6.0. On *form constancy,* where one must outline all of the same shapes, Bella's age equivalent score was 6.9. On *position in space,* where on one part, one must select the drawing that is in a different position from the rest, and on the other part where one must select the drawing in the same position as the model, Bella's age equivalent score was 5.6. On *spatial relations,* where one has to copy designs from one side of the page to the other, Bella's age equivalent score was 6.0.

Visual Tracking p. 25 (12/10/69): On this test page, where the letters *a* through *z*, imbedded within a "text" must be circled consecutively, Bella had difficulty locating the letters. She seemed to overlook the correct letter as she was scanning the page. The time it took to complete two paragraphs was 7 minutes 40 seconds, and 8 minutes. Administered again (12/17/69), Bella's time improved to 6 minutes 5 seconds, still a poor performance.

It was also observed during this test that Bella did not draw her circles in a consistent manner, a factor which might reduce her efficiency in writing letters and which can be viewed as rather primitive behavior since consistancy in forming circles is usually achieved well before 10 years of age.

Keystone Visual Survey Test: Using the telebinocular, no problem was found with fusion of images.

Identifying Pictures with Names — buildings and animals dressed to represent various professions. Scarry, Richard; *Best Word Book Ever,* Golden Press, New York: Bella was very attentive to the task of naming the pictures. It appeared that she was looking at both the picture and the word. Bella could name, or at least talk about those buildings and professions relevant to her immediate environment. Although Bella's recall was poor, she was attending to some relevant cues and could make approximations to the correct names of pictures.

Fernald Technique: Bella was first taught three words by the Fernald (Visual, Auditory, Kinesthetic, Tactile) Technique. She learned all three words as seen on immediate recall and also on later retention. Six more words were learned later. She knew all nine words on recall. Retention later was still good. In the word tracing, Bella had difficulty following the line of the letters, occasionally leaving out parts.

Physical Examination (12/2/69): Except for poor gross motor coordination, Bella's exam was normal.

Test Interpretation

Although Bella attends to working on tasks as a whole, she has difficulty in singling out the important parts that would insure her success. This was evident in both word recognition, where

Bella used only the first letter of each word as a cue, and visual tracking, where Bella overlooked the correct letter several times. Other instances include her omission of both hands and feet on her figure drawing, her incomplete outlining of shapes in the figure-ground subtest of the Frostig, and her difficulty following the line of the letters in the word tracing of the Fernald. However, the tracing did help Bella focus her attention upon the entire word to a greater degree than having her only look at the word. Another additional cue that helped Bella was the use of pictures in recalling names of buildings.

It was found that when the total number of objects or cues from which she has to choose increases, Bella's ability to attend decreases. This is what happened in the spatial relations subtest of the Frostig: as the number of dots and lines increased, Bella's accuracy in copying decreased.

Related to ability to pick out the important parts from others is Bella's apparent lack of a consistent frame of reference in space. This becomes evident in her reversal of letters and words, the rotation of a drawing copied from a Bender card, and her poor performance on the position in space subtest of the Frostig. Other indications include her confusion between left and right, and her inconsistent drawing of circles on the Visual Tracking Test.

Specific Recommendations

1. Bella needs help in focusing her attention on the important aspects of the task she is working with.

    a. Use of the Frostig training sheets in figure-ground may give Bella practice in picking out the important cue. She should improve in her ability to outline the shapes when they are imbedded within other shapes.

    b. Use of the Visual Tracking will aid Bella in her ability to process a single element at a time, a letter of the alphabet. Bella will learn to attend to all the letters as she is searching for one in particular. Working for ten to fifteen minutes each day on two or three passages is sufficient. Gradually the time to complete the task will decrease. A graphing page is provided in the book where the time is to be recorded. This way, Bella can see her improvement as she progresses.

    c. In reading, using the finger as a pointer may serve to focus attention on each part, so that Bella doesn't overlook letters as she reads.

d. A card with a slit cut out may serve to focus attention on each individual word as she reads. This may result in less confusion than when Bella views an entire page at once.

e. The Fernald technique is suggested as a means of helping Bella focus on the shape of each letter by using tactile and kinesthetic senses in addition to the visual and auditory. With the Fernald, she traces with her finger the words written with crayon on paper over a wire screen. As Bella traces the word, she says it aloud. It is also said before and after the word is traced. When Bella is asked to recognize a word that she has already learned, she is permitted to retrace it if she cannot recognize it at first.

After the words are learned, they may be written. With the help of the "language master" Bella can check herself. The machine would be programmed to say the word (the word would be written on the back of the card). Then Bella writes the word and checks the back to see if she is correct.

All new words may be compiled using paper strips (4½ x 11) so that they may be kept in a shoe box in alphabetical order. Groups of words could then be reviewed, relearning them if necessary. Words that may be used include the remainder of the sight vocabulary words on the Dolch list as well as spelling words.

With this technique, Bella should be able to eventually identify the words on sight, tracing them occasionally when she is doubtful.

f. To insure that all the lines of the letters are traced over, Bella could trace using a thin pen or pencil over the thicker line of a marking pen. Here Bella would be able to see whether or not she omitted any lines by checking to see if the finer line showed anywhere.

2. Bella also needs help in establishing a more consistent frame of reference for herself. This may have an effect on her ability to read and write without reversing.

a. Help in general spatial orientation can be provided through playing such games as following directions on tile floors. For instance, instructions on slips of paper would read "go two squares left, then one square right." If the correct square was landed on, a paper there would read "yes." Gradually, Bella should become more sure of herself in moving about.

b. To help Bella better identify her left from her right, a ring was purchased for her to wear on one hand consistently. When asked, Bella should be able to identify her left and right with less hesitation.

c. Practice in drawing circles consistently in one direction may have considerable value for Bella in that writing would become easier for her. It would also be much smoother, making it easier for her to read herself.

3. As Bella is capable of learning, she should be expected to participate in those activities where she possesses the skills.

4. Arrangements can be made to help further those working with Bella through the supervisor of the Reading Clinic.

Report Summary on Carmen (14 years)

Reason for Referral

Concern about Carmen's mental ability and low achievement in school. Carmen repeated fourth grade. At the time of this referral he was failing 3 of 4 major subjects in the eighth grade. As the junior high classes continued to move along at a rapid pace, Carmen was falling farther behind.

Principal Findings

Carmen suffers from no physical or neurological impairments. Although he is of below average intelligence, he clearly has the ability to perform well when tasks are at an appropriate level. Carmen is able to form comparisons and reason by analogy. He thinks slowly and occasionally needs concrete aids in dealing with abstract relationships. Carmen appears to be happy and emotionally well adjusted. At present he is trying very hard to survive in family and school settings where others can out-think him.

Recommendations

Carmen should be allowed to remain in the slow learner class, which leads to the work-study program in high school. While concentrating on aiding Carmen to work up to his academic potential in the class, he should also be involved in a strong vocational guidance program which will expose him to many types of jobs. This program may be supplemented by the parents exposing Carmen to other activities as they come up.

Medical History

During childhood Carmen suffered from violent trembling at frightening experiences and only this past year has gotten over feeling almost ill when facing new experiences. He has been very apathetic in an active family and lies down instead of sitting, whenever possible. Carmen displays little energy or interest in doing much physically, but this year has begun skiing and playing touch football.

Family History

Carmen's father is a college professor and his mother is a music teacher. There are five other children in the family. All of the older children were outgoing, talented, and good students. When Carmen was three, another brother eight years older than Carmen had open heart surgery, and two years later this brother died during an operation. During both of these operations Carmen stayed with his grandparents. During these crises the parents tried to conceal their concern and emotional upset from the other children.

Educational History

Carmen's difficulties in learning were first noted during the first grade, and his failures have become more pronounced each year. After repeating the fourth grade, he received special reading help in the fifth grade and also saw a psychologist once a week for talks, which he seemed to enjoy. Carmen was seen at the Arithmetic Clinic during 1967–68. Throughout his past school years, his biggest problems have been immaturity and lack of initiative. This year Carmen was failing three of his four major subjects. Teachers have noted his deficiencies in preparation for tests and assignments and efficient use of study time. They have indicated his needs to improve attention and study habits and to seek help from teachers. During the first school week in January 1970, Carmen was placed in a slow learner class.

Relevant Test Results (all tests administered this center this date, unless otherwise specified)

Intelligence Testing: 1. *Raven's Standard Progressive Matrices — Sets A, B, C, D, E:* 42 of 60 items correct. According to Raven's norms Carmen is in the "intellectually average" range for 14 year olds. 2. *Goldstein-Scheerer Cube Test:* On design 7 needed aids of enlargement and lineal division. On design 10 needed aid of enlargement. He was slow and deliberate in working on most of the 12 designs.

Physical Testing: (12-11-69) 1. Physical exam — normal. 2. Neurological exam — minor difficulties with gross motor coordination.

Informal Interview: When asked what he would wish for if he could have one wish, Carmen said, "No school." At school he dislikes work and likes gym. When asked for three wishes, Carmen wanted to be rich, have no work to do, and tour. He said that in the regular junior high classes others treated him as if he weren't there and the boys made fun of his short hair while in the slow learner class to which he had just been moved he was treated like he was really somebody. The work is easier in the new class and Carmen prefers less work. Carmen recognized that he would have to obtain skills in reading, writing, and mathematics while in school. Carmen's athletic interests include skiing with his family and playing touch football with some of his friends.

Throughout this interview Carmen displayed "flat affect"; he spoke softly and slowly, smiled frequently, and took time to think before talking. He only showed some energy and initiative when allowed to ask the interviewers questions of his own choosing.

Test Interpretation

The results of the physical and neurological exams indicate no impairment in these areas. The Raven's Progressive Matrices are a test of observation and clear thinking. Carmen's score in the average range indicates that he is able to form comparisons and reason by analogy. The Goldstein-Scheerer Cube Test is a measure of abstract behavior. Although Carmen thinks slowly, he is able to benefit from more concrete aids and thus learn to use them to supplement his abstract thinking ability. Carmen needed concrete aids in only two of the twelve designs, indicating good ability to deal with abstract relationships involved in reproducing printed designs with colored blocks.

During the interview many of the things Carmen said were the reflections of socially acceptable statements or opinions of others. In school, home, and the interview Carmen outwardly appears to be quite happy and rarely expresses displeasure vocally, emotionally, or physically. Carmen is trying very hard to survive in a family and school where others can out-think him.

Carmen can benefit most from his placement in the slow learner class, which will lead to the work-study program in high school. He should become strongly involved in a vocational guidance program which will expose him to many types of jobs. However, the main immediate goal is continuing to aid Carmen in working up to his academic potential in the classroom. Carmen's exposure to vocational areas of interest may be enhanced by his parents working with him in exploring new activities.

Report Summary on Damon (10 years, 7 months)

Reason for Referral

Damon was referred to this clinic to evaluate his specific learning disabilities, to determine his strengths and to check the possibility of an emotional overlay as it relates to the blocking of the acquisition of new material.

Principal Findings

The results of the battery of tests support the presence of an organically based cerebral disfunction. Damon's profile of abilities demonstrated both strengths and weaknesses. This profile is not flat and is not typical of endogenously mentally retarded children. Damon appears to be a child who has had difficulty with perception, integration and manipulation of incoming stimuli (especially auditory stimuli) rather than a mentally retarded child. This inability to structure incoming stimuli has probably led to frustration and a stifling of motivation which appears as an emotional negativism to the acquisition of new material. Damon's expressive speech and language abilities are presently retarded but seem to be emerging along the normal developmental sequence although at a very slow rate.

It was found that Damon is able to learn through visual presentation and visual-auditory association through the use of positive reinforcement in an environment controlled for distracting stimuli. Much of the problem of acquisition of material seems to be due to inattentiveness and poor motivation. He responded well in a one-to-one relationship when his attention was redirected to the task through constant reminders and tangible reward for tasks successfully completed. Damon also responded well to stimulation of speech sounds and he appears to be ready for formal language and speech therapy.

Recommendations

It is recommended that Damon remain in the trainable class and that stress should be placed on the principles of socialization, tool use and academic subjects. Toward the end of this year he should be tried in the educable class for an hour or two a day working on his best subject. All subject matter should be presented through a highly structured programmed-instruction approach using social and tangible rewards to build attention span and to remove the blocks to his natural motivation to learn. Damon should be taught through the visual presentation of materials and visual-auditory association. While he is taught new material through his strong channels, remediation should be aimed at his weak channels. Some program for perceptual motor abilities should be used in conjunction with a basic reading readiness program.

Damon's development should be followed medically. The possibility of increasing head size *should be checked frequently*. Some program for physical fitness should be incorporated into his schedule to aid in the remediation of his motor and coordination problems.

Therapy for expressive language and speech should begin immediately. This should utilize techniques both at home and in the school to *gradually* increase sentence length and complexity and to demonstrate the value of good oral-communication abilities. Rhythm and articulation should be worked on as expressive language unfolds. Damon's needs should not be anticipated by his family or teachers, thereby forcing him to communicate his desires through the use of better speech and language. The total environment should be structured to maximize success experiences and minimize failures. If a careful step-by-step procedure is followed in all his instruction, Damon should develop more desire to learn.

It is not recommended that Damon be seen again at this clinic until he has gone through some of the recommended programs. In this way any reassessment will be a more valid indication of the appropriateness of the recommended programs and our assessment of his educational potential.

Medical History

Damon was born 5/30/59, the third of his parents' four children. His mother reported that during the relatively normal pregnancy she became somewhat toxic toward the end which was associated with slightly swollen ankles, itching and blisters on her legs. It was also reported that some x-rays may have been taken during the pregnancy but the actual time was not clearly recalled. The delivery was normal and performed under a local anesthetic. The child's skin was reported to be pale at birth but there were no other items reported about neonatal problems. Damon's development is indicative of a maturational lag in all areas and especially in oral-communicative abilities. At about age three, skull x-rays, E.E.G. and pneumoencephalogram were done in the Children's Hospital at Utopia, but the results of these tests have never been received by this clinic. On November 11, 1969, a neurological examination done at this clinic revealed: motor impersistence, perseveration, right-left confusion, coordination problems, and increasing head size. To check the possibility of active hydrocephaly, expanding head size, or expanding intracranial lesion, skull films were taken. The results of these tests were essentially negative although some degree of assymmetry was noted. Damon's mother reported that previous workups showed unilateral cerebral atrophy. (The supporting records were never received from Utopia).

Damon is a generally healthy child with a good appetite and has received the common immunizations for childhood diseases.

Family History

Not significant

Relevant Test Results

WISC	Scaled Score	IQ
Verbal Scale	5	45
Performance Scale	28	69
Full Scale	33	51

Verbal Tests	Raw Score	Scaled Score
Information	3	1
Comprehension	0	0
Arithmetic	3	2
Similarities	1	2
Vocabulary	0	0
(Digit Span)	0	0
	Sum of Verbal Tests	5

Performance Tests		
Picture Completion	9	8
Picture Arrangement	6	4
Block Design	11	8
Object Assembly	14	6
Coding	9	2
	Sum of Performance Tests	28

Bender Gestalt: Errors

1. a Square or circle misshapen
2. Rotation
3. Integration
10. Distortion of shape (open circles)
11. Rotation
21. b Either hexagon misshapen, extra and missing angles
22. Rotation
24. Distortion of shape

Articulation and language evaluation: (see attached form.)

Visual memory and recall tasks: Damon did well in most of the test areas, especially those that did not require the recall of abstract symbols which were not familiar to him. Both short term and long term memory seemed good, and increasing the intensity of the stimulus seems to have a positive effect on his retention capability. Damon demonstrated poor motivation during the test.

Neurological exam—summary of findings:

1. Motor impersistence
2. Perseveration
3. Right-left confusion
4. (?) mixed hand dominance
5. Some difficulty with non-equilibratory coordination
6. Large head (? increasing ?) Head circumference is about 98th percentile for age.

Skull Films: essentially negative although some degree of assymmetry noted.

Test Interpretation

The battery of formal and informal tests which were given to Damon reveal a strong possibility of both specific and generalized brain damage. This is supported not only by the neurological exam and the skull x-rays, but also by the discrepancy between the verbal and the performance scores on the WISC. Some of the substitutions which Damon used in the articulation test were so different, relative to place and manner (as well as voicing), that it lends further support to the presence of some perceptual or central integrative dysfunction. His poor performance on this test of oral-communicative ability is probably the reason why he received a zero raw and scaled score on the vocabulary subtest of the WISC. Although speech and language are presently emerging, the developmental lag in this area may be the result of a developmental dysphasia due to cerebral insult or agenesis. This is supported by the present and previous reports of unilateral cerebral atrophy and is manifested by a depression of auditory decoding processing which was more apparent in the past than presently. The better performance on the performance subtests of the WISC is probably due to the dependence on visual decoding which seems to be a better channel through which Damon is able to gain knowledge. However, there does seem to be some problem associated with this area also. It is apparent from the results of the Bender-Gestalt test of perceptual motor ability that Damon is functioning at a very low level relative to his age group. However, this may reflect problems which are associated with performing the test rather than perceptual problems per se. It was reported by the tester that Damon paid very little attention to the designs and his attempts to copy them were executed very rapidly. Moreover, the poor performance on this test could be attributed more to motor encoding problems (as revealed in the neurological exam) than actual perceptual problems. In a test of visual memory and recall, it was found that Damon can learn under conditions of positive reinforcement with the environment relatively free from distracting elements. Materials which "stood out" and were high in stimulus value helped him to attend better.

Damon demonstrates abilities and disabilities indicative of a profile of varying educational potentials. This profile is not flat and it would seem that he will be able to make gains through a structured program incorporating visual presentation of materials and stressing visual-auditory association. The Frostig program for perceptual motor abilities should be used in conjunction with a basic reading readiness program emphasizing page turning, spatial relations and visual tracking. Use of behavior modification principles should result in increased attention span especially if materials are used which are high in stimulus value. The classroom environment should be controlled for distractible stimuli if this is possible.

Recommendations for speech and language development have already been made (See attached articulation test results). Other suggestions would include language therapy based on the Myklebust format as demonstrated by the Hortense Barry program for aphasic children. What is important is to aim therapy at a point just below Damon's present developmental level and bring him gradually along the normal developmental sequence through a highly structured program utilizing positive reinforcement and manipulation of the environment to yield many success experiences. The Peabody Language Program or a program based on the subtests of the I.T.P.A. should accomplish the same results. Articulation therapy is at this point less important than language therapy designed to increase spontaneous oral-communicative behavior. Accept Damon's attempts at expressing himself and gradually shape better articulation by therapy and by varying contingencies of reinforcement so that he must speak better before his listener shows that he understands what Damon is trying to relate. This graduated-contingencies approach must be done very slowly so as not to frustrate Damon and cause him to stop responding. At home, Damon's needs should not be anticipated by his family. Allow him sufficient time to request in meaningful sentences (not necessarily complete and balanced sentences) what he wants or what he observed, etc. Gradually, as suggested above, require him to express these things in longer and more complex sentences and reinforce with repeating and developing what he says along with social and tangible rewards. It may also be helpful, at times, to frustrate Damon slightly so that he learns the value of oral-communication.

It is very important that Damon's head size be followed through the years to check the abnormal growth rate. Damon would appear to resemble more a child with brain damage and concomittant dysphasia, emotional negativism and perceptual motor problems than a classic mentally retarded child. This is not to say that his mental development is not retarded, but it emphasizes that the approach should be adjusted and aimed at these weaknesses. Damon should be taught through his strong channels and remediation should be aimed at his weak channels. Major problems seem to be negativism (emotional overlay) and short attention span. Both of these should improve in a structured program fortified with a great deal of positive (tangible and social) reinforcement.

It is felt by this clinic that another visit would not yield any more information than is presently on hand. After a while a reevaluation may be done to monitor the effects of the recommended programs. Damon would best benefit by remaining in the trainable class with emphasis on social development and tool use. Academic subjects and language-speech therapy should by all means continue. It would be beneficial if Damon, toward the end of this year, could spend an hour or so every day in the educable class working on his best subject. There is the possibility that with concentrated effort in school and at home a good deal of improvement will result. Damon's speech and language do seem to be emerging and he does seem to be able to learn tasks when conditions are right. Much of his poor performance is the result of stifled motivation, short attention span and a general lack of interest. He must truly begin to fend for himself in social and academic concerns and be made aware of the rewards of gaining good communicative ability. His future level of functioning cannot be readily assessed at this point, but it appears that he is able to progress further than his present performance might indicate.

Summary of Speech and Language Assessment for Damon

The Hejna Development Articulation Test was administered. Damon displayed multiple articulation problems characterized by omissions and substitutions:

I. Omissions[1]	Initial	Medial	Final
	–/m	–/g	–/m
	–/p	–/l	–/p
	–/w	–/dʒ	–/b
	–/f	–/s*	–/k
	–/dr	–/th	–/z*
	–/kl		–/sk
	–/bl		–/st
	–/th		
	–/s		
	–/z		
	–/st		
	s–/sl		
	–/sw		
	–p/sp		
	–/th+		
	–/sk*		
	–/sn		

[1] Almost all sounds were stimulable
* Could not stimulate
+ *th* = voiced

II. Substitutions

w/l*	h/k*	sh/f*
h/dz*+	p/f	b/d*
gr/gl	r/d	t/ch
sh/ch	h/sh	sh/th*
	h/ch	
	g/z*	

* Substitutions of different phonetic family relative to place and manner of articulation (and/or voicing)
+ *h* = glottal stop; h = aspiration

Damon omitted some sounds which appear early in speech development and the frequency of omitted sounds increased as the developmental age level increased. Most all sounds which involve the tongue tip were absent. However, an examination of the test results reveals that almost all omitted sounds were stimulable. This is felt to be a good prognostic sign. Damon displayed some typical and some atypical substitutions. Some substitutions were so different relative to place and manner of articulation (as well as voicing) that one may suspect the presence of some perceptual or central integrative dysfunction.

During informal testing Damon displayed adequate auditory memory for non-speech sounds and rhythm patterns. His expressive language is emerging and it has not been formally determined as to the extent of his receptive language ability; superficially it appears to be adequate to enable Damon to learn aurally. Damon speaks in short one or two-word sentences in an arhythmic and clipped-speech pattern.

Recommendations

It is recommended that Damon receive speech and language therapy to stimulate receptive and expressive language. His motor behavior should be accompanied by simple sentences describing what he is doing at that moment (action-language). This is done to give the child language to "think" with. Damon's expressive attempts should be expanded by his listeners (teachers and parents). After some preliminary articulation therapy (moto-kinesthetic method is recommended) and auditory perception and memory training is done, Damon should be stimulated to express his needs in complete sentences. As he does this he should be reminded of the correct articulation and rhythm patterns as they relate to these expressions which he himself initiated.

Specific Recommendations

1) Auditory Training for speech sound discrimination (Wepman minimal pairs i.e., *p*in *b*in etc.)
2) Receptive and expressive language stimulation (role playing, action-language etc.)
3) Articulation therapy (moto-kinesthetic method. Also work on rhythm using phoneme *ah* replacing syllables; ăh áh ah ah ah áh as in The boy went to the store.).

It must be remembered that Damon has only been using speech for 2½ to 3 years. His speech seems to be progressing through the natural sequence of development, although at a very retarded rate. With speech and language therapy, it is felt that Damon can progress much further than his present state.

Report Summary on Eliza (6 years, 2 months)

Reason for Referral

1. Vision problems
   a) Corrective surgery for strabismus
   b) Suppression of right eye
2. Home and school behavior
   a) Unable to adjust to routine and discipline
   b) Demanding individual attention
   c) Stubborn
   d) Short attention span
   e) Hyperactive — on some occasions seems unable to control her own actions
   f) Often very depressed

Principal Findings

Eliza is a healthy, normally intelligent child who responds well in a one-to-one learning situation. On paper and pencil tasks she worked hastily and paid insufficient attention to detail. On one occasion she traced a figure with her fingers before trying to reproduce it. On several occasions she wrote words and numbers backwards but corrected herself when asked to rewrite them. The neurological examination reveals that Eliza has good motor tone and that her fine motor movements are grossly normal. She did have some difficulty undressing herself (undergarments), and experienced difficulty maintaining equilibrium when hopping, toe, and heel walking. The nystagmus on lateral gaze (bilateral) reported is not unusual in a child Eliza's age. She also indicated that she used her left eye to "look with," suppressing the use of her right eye.

Recommendations

1. Medication — 10 mg of Ritalin twice daily (morning and noon). Reports of good initial results have already been received.

2. The eye patch which she doesn't like to wear and which is intended to force her to use her right eye, might be replaced by glasses with the left lens blacked out.

3. Consistent discipline — Firm limits of which Eliza is aware should be established. When she acts up to gain attention she should be told by the adult involved that her game is known and the adult won't play.

4. Allow her to have a quiet corner of the classroom for her own where she can work in isolation without distraction.

5. Increase individual time spent with her in the classroom by
   a) Continuing contact with her
   b) Bringing in an older child to work with her within the present classroom structure, to prod her to complete work and to provide her with a suitable model to imitate.

Test Interpretation

The nystagmus reported is not unusual in a child Eliza's age, but does fit in with her past history of eye problems. The difficulty in maintaining balance may possibly be related to the finding that she is suppressing use of her right eye. No action was taken on the Keystone results for Eliza was seeing an opthalmologist at the time that she was coming to the Learning Evaluation Center. Her behavior while taking the Bender is consistent with classroom reports of short attention span and lack of task completion.

Specific Recommendations

1. Medication — 10 mg of Ritalin twice daily (morning and noon). Reports of good initial results have already been received.

2. The eye patch which she doesn't like to wear and which is intended to force her to use her right eye, might be replaced by glasses with the left lens blacked out.

3. Consistent discipline — Firm limits of which Eliza is aware should be established. When she acts up to gain attention she should be told by the adult involved that her game is known and the adult won't play.

4. If a parent group is formed as an offshoot of the Learning Evaluation Center this coming semester, her parents could be invited to join the group.

5. Allow her to have a quiet corner of the classroom for her own where she can work in isolation without distraction.

6. Increase individual time spent with Eliza in the classroom by
   a) Continuing contact with her
   b) Bringing in an older child to work with her within the present classroom structure, to prod her to complete work and to provide her with a suitable model to imitate.

Medical History

Surgery to correct strabismus — July 1965

Continued vision problems — is now supposed to be wearing left eye patch to overcome suppression of the right eye

Tonsillectomy at 3 years, 10 months.

Family History

Eliza is very devoted to her father who was out of the home for some time. Her mother reports that Eliza is still upset even by his routine absences, (i.e. night classes). Her mother seems overwhelmed by the sheer numbers of Eliza and five siblings, and a social worker from the school is now working with her.

Educational History

Problems in kindergarten resulted in placement in special pre-first grade class. Continued problems in first grade include a) unable to adjust to routine and discipline; b) demanding of individual attention; c) stubbornness; d) short attention span, seldom any task completion; e) hyperactive, wanders around classroom, chats with other students — on some occasions seems unable to control her own actions; f) often very depressed. Eliza is presently receiving adult assistance from Miss J. on a regular basis.

Relevant Test Results

Intelligence Testing — none

Physical Testing — The neurological examination yielded:

1. Nystagmus on lateral gaze — bilateral
2. Difficulty maintaining equilibrium on heel, toe and tandem walking, hopping
3. Difficulty undressing (undergarments)
4. Good motor tone
5. Fine motor movement was grossly normal

Keystone Telebinocular — results indicated need for further eye exam

Bender — Development Bender Score   12
Perceptual Age Level   5.3
Eliza made three comments of the "I can't do it!" nature. She paid insufficient attention to the models and her drawings were hastily done. She traced one design with her fingers before reproducing it.

Emotional Testing — none
Achievement Testing — none

Report Summary on Felix (10 years, 8 months)

Reason for Referral

Lack of consistent academic progress. Although Felix has repeated first grade and is currently repeating third grade, he is still one of the lowest students in the class in all areas. Felix has had a minor speech problem and there has been evidence of possible visual difficulty.

Principal Findings

Felix's hearing, speech, perception (visual-motor), visual tracking and visual discrimination were all normal. Results of the neurological examination indicated no organic impairment. Although Felix's spelling is poor, his ability to learn to spell was clearly demonstrated. Word recognition in reading is also poor. Felix showed interest in Radio Reading and was able to correct some of his reading errors. Felix demonstrated ability to learn. It appears that he has accepted his failing status. This identification with failure needs to be reversed through successful learning experiences.

Recommendations

1. Felix can be expected to listen and to participate in class.

2. Spelling may be improved by using a VAKT procedure.

3. Radio Reading may be used both at home and in school. Felix's reading performance may be improved by his responsibility for adequate transmission of the meaning of what he is reading. Help on a word is given only if Felix asks for it.

4. Other subject areas could be worked on in a similar manner. If Felix cannot read the material or write his answers, someone may do this for him. He can be held accountable for finding and correcting his own errors.

5. Direct feedback of his successful performances seems imperative. Graphs and charts seem a reasonable way to transmit such success information.

Medical History

Felix's mother experienced excessive vomiting while carrying him and his twin, John. She was given blood when the twins were born. John was "in danger" during labor. The mother reported that Felix's development appeared slower than her other children's. She experienced difficulty with his toilet training and his overactivity. When Felix was a toddler, he fell down the stairs and was unconscious for half an hour.

Family History

Felix's father is a 33 year old tenant farmer with an 8th grade education. His mother is 33 and had a 9th grade education. Other siblings are Adam 12, John 10, and Mary 5. Felix has been seen at the Special Evaluation Clinic and at a child guidance center for social and academic problems. Felix and Adam are constantly at odds and often fight each other.

Educational History

Felix has been in school since beginning kindergarten in 1964. Felix repeated first grade and is currently repeating third grade. (John is in fifth.) Felix has received special help in both speech and reading. In second and third grades it was noticed that Felix learned in spurts. At the beginning of this year he was doing very well "until the rest of the class caught up to him." He apparently feels that he is stupid and cannot learn.

Relevant Test Results (all tests administered this center this date, unless otherwise specified)

Physical Testing — Normal hearing on pure tone air conduction audiometric test:

	250	500	1000	2000	4000	8000	Hz
Right Ear	10	15	10	5	5	0	decibel (ISO, 1964)
Left Ear	10	15	10	0	0	10	

Neurogical Examination (October 30, 1969): Negative Findings

Bender Gestalt Test: Koppitz Scoring System Total Score 4 Age Norm 8

Michigan Language Program — Visual Tracking p. 25 (October 30, 1969): The mean time to complete each of two paragraphs was 1 min. 35 sec. — within normal limits.

Betts Visual Discrimination: Excellent performance

V-1 a 14/14   V-1 b 16/16
V-2   30/30
V-3   12/12
V-4   15/15   (not all items given)

Hejna Developmental Articulation Test: Passed all items presented (Through norms for age 8)

Achievement Testing

Informal Spelling Test: Felix was given nine words from his school spelling list as a spelling test. Out of the nine he was able to spell three correctly. Of the six words misspelled, three were taught by a phonics approach and three were taught by VAKT (visual, auditory, kinesthetic, tactile). His immediate recall was seven of the ten words. On retest, he missed one word which he had spelled correctly the first time.

Spache Diagnostic Reading Scales: Second grade word recognition level.

Test Interpretation

The results of the physical testing show that Felix has no problems in this area. The neurological examination resulted in only negative findings, ruling out organic impairment. The pure tone air conduction test revealed normal hearing in all frequencies for the right and left ears. Although Felix's error score on the Bender Gestalt is above his age norm, Felix could recognize his errors when asked if his production were "just like" the Bender plates on which he had made errors. Felix demonstrated perfect visual discrimination on the Betts Visual Discrimination Test. On the visual tracking test, Felix's times were within the norms and indicate adequate performance of this skill. Performance on the Hejna Developmental Articulation Test indicates normal articulation and no specific speech problem.

Felix initially performed poorly on the informal spelling test and on Radio Reading using reading passages from the Spache Diagnostic Reading Scales. To teach the spelling words a Fernald technique was employed. A tactile dimension was added to the spelling words by writing them on paper placed over a metal screen. As Felix traced the word with his finger he slowly said the whole word. Immediate recall on a retest of the same words showed that Felix's performance improved so that he corrected four of the six originally misspelled words.

Performance on Radio Reading indicated only second grade word recognition. This technique places the reader in the role of a radio announcer. He must read a selection well enough so that his listeners are able to adequately understand and describe what he has just read to them. They give him feedback by telling him what they heard. Any inconsistencies or errors in the reading of the material are pointed out to the reader. He must clarify these by rereading the material. If Felix does not know a word he may ask the person working with him what it is. Felix appeared to be interested in this technique and worked on it with a number of different people.

Test results indicate that Felix has the abilities to learn in school. It appears that Felix very early became aware of the fact that his twin brother John is smarter. Felix has learned how to play the role of the "one-down" twin perfectly.

Specific Recommendations

1. Felix can be held accountable for his performance in all areas in school. He can be responsible for his own work and then feel good by achieving some success experiences.

2. Both the Fernald technique and the Language Master could be used to help Felix in spelling. By saying, feeling, hearing, and seeing a word at the same time, Felix can learn a group of letters as a meaningful whole comprising a word. The Language Master can be used to supplement spelling tests given by the teacher. By having the word printed on the back of the card Felix can first test his ability to spell a word and then check his performance by turning the card over. Felix should say the whole word, say it again while writing or tracing it and then say it a final time.

3. On written spelling assignments Felix should be expected to get all words correct before going on to the next group. Mistakes should be simply crossed out and not erased. Felix should be encouraged to find his own errors by only having the number of words misspelled placed on the top of the paper. If he cannot find the incorrect word, it may be pointed out to him. If he then cannot find the correct spelling it may be placed next to the wrong one, but Felix still will have to point out the error.

4. Misspelled words that the teacher must write out for Felix may be saved by him. These words should frequently be reviewed by drawing from them and having Felix spell them.

5. Radio Reading could be used to improve Felix's reading skills. This technique, outlined in the preceding section, may be used in school and at home.

REFERENCES

Bangs, Tina: *Language and Learning Disorders of the Pre-academic Child.* New York, Appleton-Century-Crofts, 1968.

Beecroft, John: *Kipling: A Selection of His Stories and Poems.* New York, Doubleday, 1956.

Burroughs, Edgar Rice: *Tarzan.* Frank A. Munsey Co., 1912.

Chadwick, Dale: Why not a mini-clinic in your school? *The Elementary Principal,* Fall, 1969.

Goda, Sidney: Language therapy for the non-speaking retarded child. *Mental Retardation,* 7, 22–25, 1969.

Itard, Jean-Marc-Gaspard: *The Wild Boy of Aveyron,* translated and edited by George and Muriel Humphrey. New York, Meredith, 1962.

LaFontaine, Louise: *The Idiot Savant: Ten Case Studies.* M.Ed. thesis, Boston University, 1968.

LaVeck, G.: in *Report of the Sixty-First Conference on Pediatric Research.* Columbus, Ohio, Ross Laboratories, 1971.

Masland, Richard, Sarason, Seymour, and Gladwin, Thomas: *Mental Subnormality.* New York, Basic Books, 1958.

Sigel, Irving, and Hooper, Frank. *Logical Thinking in Children.* New York, Holt, Rinehart and Winston, 1968.

Silberstein, Richard, and Irwin, Helen: Jean-Marc-Gaspard Itard and the savage of Aveyron: an unsolved diagnostic problem in child psychiatry. *J. of Amer. Acad. of Child Psychiatry,* 1, 314–322, 1962.

Staats, Arthur: *Learning, Language and Cognition.* New York, Holt, Rinehart and Winston, 1968.

Standing, E. M.: *Maria Montessori.* Fresno, Academy Library Guild, 1959.

West, Robert, Ansberry, Merle and Carr, Anna: *Rehabilitation of Speech,* 3rd ed. New York, Harper, 1957.

Chapter IX

A SIMULATION WORKSHOP ON LEARNING DISABILITIES FOR CLASSROOM TEACHERS

FRANK W. BROADBENT, D. ROGER MEEHAN
and DANIEL D. SAGE

NEED FOR TRAINED CLASSROOM TEACHERS

Recent concern from parents, as well as from federal, state, and local education departments, for children exhibiting learning disabilities has led to an increase in the number of programs designed to aid these children to reach their educational potential. The sophistication of diagnostic instruments and remedial materials has also increased the activity in the general area of learning disabilities.

Recently, the federal government, prompted by concerned, informed parents and educators, passed new legislation dealing with specific learning disabilities. This federal program defines the concept of specific learning disabilities, outlines strategies, and appropriates money for research and program development.

A variety of programs may be employed to provide the best educational environment for the myriad of learning problems of children. Diagnostic teams, special classes, and special teachers are being utilized in an effort to determine the appropriate program for each child.

The Bureau of Education for the Handicapped has estimated that 22,000 teachers and specialists are needed immediately in the field. In a survey conducted by Barsch (1968) of colleges and universities in the country, only 350 teachers trained in the area of learning disabilities go into the field each year. The majority of these teachers enter the field in the form of special class teachers, even though thousands of children have a learning problem which is not severe enough to require the special class environment. Many of these children could benefit from specialized programming, resource rooms, and other supportive assistance. Ultimately, however, it is the regular classroom teacher who must bear the responsibility for early identification of the child with learning problems and for remediating these problems in the classroom. A survey of projects funded by the federal government shows a large segment of these devoted to the area of learning disabilities. A review of the objectives of these projects reveals three major areas of emphasis: establishment of diagnostic centers, establishment of special classes, and assistance to classroom teachers. This last point indicates recognition of the need for training of elementary teachers to identify and prepare instructional programs geared to the special needs of children.

The ramifications for preservice and inservice training are monumental. Changes in the teacher's attitude from the current "he doesn't belong in my class" to "what can I do to help him?" are essential to this educational model. Teacher-training institutions may alter their curricula to better prepare new teachers to adjust their teaching to the individual learning style of each child, but thousands of teachers in the field are now in need of inservice training to effect this change.

Along with this change in attitude, the acquisition of skills is needed, especially in informal diagnostic procedures that would enable teachers to assess the problems of their children and hopefully lead them to seek help in solving these problems. The important aspect of the preservice and inservice training programs would be to attempt to motivate the teacher to search continuously for methods of instruction that will fill a child's needs rather than search for ways to make a child fit a particular curriculum. Effective ways of providing such training for teachers are always in demand.

INSTRUCTIONAL SIMULATION

One approach to personnel training involves the use of the simulated environment. Simulation has been defined and described in a number of different ways. Boocock (1966) indicated that simulation provides a vehicle for the trainee to incorporate his own techniques into decision-making as he seeks to resolve problems he encounters in reality-based situations. Simulation increases the alternatives open to trainees for reinforcement of learning which has taken place under other circumstances (Cohen, 1964). Simulation enables the trainee to gain experience in a number of processes considered essential in future performance of the role for which he is training. This method of learning gives the teacher a chance to refine his skill before he faces similar experiences under real circumstances.

Simulation as an instrument for training and evaluation was first used primarily in the military, business, and industry. The military has used simulation as an instructional technique to train personnel in such combat techniques as infantry planning, radar and sonar operations, pilot training, and naval maneuvers. Simulators have been used in business and industry for a number of years. Many are machines — computer fed and electronically controlled.

Recently, educators have adapted the simulation technique to the teaching process using micro-relationships of interaction to provide learning experience; i.e., micro-teaching. Simulation has been used as an inservice technique to improve instruction of administrators in education (Hemphill, 1962; Culbertson, 1960; Twelker, 1968; Sage, 1968). The development of classroom simulators was prompted, in part, by the numerous problems involved in placement of preservice teachers for field experience. Simulators in the field of teacher preservice training have been developed (Kersh, 1961; Boocock, 1966; Cruickshank and Broadbent, 1968; Bolton, 1967).

Certain aspects of simulation are particularly important in the training of classroom teachers. The use of a simulated instructional technique can provide carefully controlled situations in which a teacher may react to a variety of experiences and be provided feedback to his decision-making behavior. It is thought that simulation, with its requirement of total involvement, can be a means of centering attention, increasing motivation, and bringing about desired changes in the participant. The successful development of a simulation exercise aimed at teacher training and dealing with the area of learning disabilities could provide a valuable tool in this expanding field. Hopefully, it would aid teachers in learning an efficient model of remediation and accommodation for use in the classroom.

Since the teacher is the primary person in identifying children with learning problems, simulation training could be useful in providing carefully contrived situations which would allow the teacher to observe, make judgments, and devise a plan of action. Simulation training could enable the teacher to practice the use of discriminating cues that signal potential problems. Feedback sessions, either pre-programmed materials or discussion periods, could enable the teacher to check observational skills applied in simulated situations.

PROGRAM-ORIENTED REMEDIATION MODEL

The field of learning disabilities may be defined very narrowly; i.e., specific perceptual deficits, neurological impairment, brain injury, etc. It may also be more broadly defined, encompassing a wide variety of etiological factors interfering with the normal learning process. The purpose of the simulation package described here was not to train each classroom teacher to be a skilled diagnostic specialist, but rather to increase awareness, observational skills, willingness to seek ancillary help, and motivation to initiate remedial programs in the classroom. Being aware that the classroom teacher is interested in the learning process rather than etiological labels or descriptions of learning disabilities, it was decided to avoid such labels and stress information and task materials from classroom settings.

The simulation was designed to follow a "funnel-like" pattern, having each stage deal with an increasingly more specific concept of learning disability. This was accomplished by having the participants first identify children having learning problems of a broad nature without requiring them to determine etiology and specific problem areas or to recommend remediation. As each stage of the simulation progresses, the participants would be expected to become more precise in their deductions. The focus on learning disabilities would gradually become more narrow until the final stage would require each participant to plan a program for two children having a specific learning disability in the visual-perceptual area.

The simulation requires the participant to assume the role of a third-grade teacher; consequently, the first stage in the sequence begins with the teacher's awareness of behaviors and activities which occur during the normal school day. The sequence on which this simulation is based begins with the teacher (1) observing the children, (2) keeping anecdotal records, (3) seeking ancillary help, (4) doing informal testing, and (5) planning a program. In each stage of the simulation the teacher is the focal point and all task items are based on his perceptions and decisions.

As the simulation progresses, the participant is asked to make decisions based on increasingly pertinent information. At various steps in this process, the participant is afforded the opportunity to form hypotheses regarding the learning problems of selected children in a simulated classroom.

Although simulation is used as the method by which each participant is to reach the stated objectives, the process by which the teacher is to attain the specified behavioral goals is of major importance in designing the simulation pacakge.

As each piece of material is introduced it initiates an information search process and in some cases leads to feedback the participant may need to confirm or change a decision before proceeding to the next stage. The information process, initiated by the presentation of the simulated materials, is intended to lead the participants to make judgments and decisions. Feedback is provided either by predetermined written responses or a general discussion period strategically placed at the end of each of the four stages. In this manner the participant not only receives information concerning his choice of action, but is given the opportunity to discuss this decision with the instructor and other participants.

DEVELOPMENT OF MATERIALS

Since the objective of this study was to enable teachers to become more aware of the variety of learning problems presented by children in regular grades, eight case studies were developed, each representing a different type of learning problem. Each case was a composite developed from actual cases discussed in the literature, clinical records from a learning evaluation center, classroom observation, and personal experiences of the investigators. In developing the composite cases, samples of information were utilized from psychological reports, excerpts from journals, students' classroom work, physicians' reports, team evaluations, and notes made during observations.

Although labeling was avoided in the actual simulation, the eight children represented certain definable learning problems and are cited here only as a point of reference. These composite case studies were developed from files of children having learning problems due to cultural factors, slow-learner characteristics, emotional handicaps, lack of sequential instruction, hyperactivity, auditory perception, visual-motor factors, and visual-perceptual factors.

Each piece of background information or task item was designed to focus attention on the problems of these eight children. The eight case studies were completed and behavioral descriptions written to describe each child and how he might act in school situations. Procedures were devised to portray these behaviors in an observable medium. It was decided to choose a number of school activities which could act as a setting for videotaping. Each setting was planned to display the learning difficulties of the eight children and at the same time include the normal activities of the other children. Since this was to be a third-grade classroom, the activities revolved around activities of that level.

Scripts were written for each scene to be video-taped. These scripts were devised to fit the general patterns of the scene and then rewritten to include words, actions, or patterns of behavior indicative of the learning problems of the eight children. A class was selected, and individuals were coached and rehearsed to present certain information prior to the videotaping.

Two types of material were developed for participant use in the simulation. One type provided the participant with basic information on the class and was designed to be utilized in the diagnostic procedures. The second type of material presented problem-solving situations and involved the participant in a decision-making process.

The information items developed were: videotaped sequences, cumulative record folders, samples of children's work, psychological reports, class lists, a study guide, and the results of tests.

The action items developed were: recording forms, hypothesis forms, choice-of-action forms, response forms, program-planning forms, and a test booklet.

In order to assist the participants in the final planning stage, it was necessary to provide them with commercially available materials. A number of programs, kits, reference books, and other instructional materials were provided for the teacher to become familiar with and use when designing a program.

The simulation package was designed to encompass approximately six clock hours which could be in a number of time blocks, The total package is divided into four stages which are sequential in nature. Each stage has a definite purpose and involves the introduction of information as well as problem-solving exercises.

PRESENTATION OF WORKSHOP

The simulation package was presented in a workshop format to the total faculty of a small elementary school prior to the opening of school. A total of seventeen persons were involved, including the principal. The participants were given a short introduction pertaining to the general objectives of the workshop as well as a short review of the latest trends in the field of learning disabilities. The participants were then asked to assume the role of a third-grade teacher who has just completed recording test scores and is reflecting on the events of the first half of the year. The participants were given the first set of materials. This folder included a class picture (24 children) with name tags attached, and class lists which included current achievement test scores, reading levels, I.Q. scores, and teacher comments. A class list with similar data was also included from the second-grade teacher for the purpose of assessing progress. Forms were included for recording behaviors and for the initial selection of children.

The participants were given the opportunity to become familiar with the children in the class and their previous work by studying the class data provided. The participants were then informed that they would view a videotape of the children as a means of reflecting through the eyes of the third grade teacher. They were cautioned to be alert to the actions and comments of the children and record these on their observation forms. The participants were then asked to list the children they felt might possibly have a learning problem and include the clues which led them to this selection. The discussion period at this stage is aimed at the children who were chosen and the rationale leading to their inclusion. As the children were listed, all members of the group were encouraged to give the clues they felt aided in identification. In this manner every member of the group had an opportunity to volunteer information and also receive information to strengthen his own perceptions. Additional information on the eight children was distributed in the form of cumulative record folders and students' work.

The participants were given the opportunity to choose the best source from which to obtain further information necessary to aid in the diagnosis. Forms were provided which gave responses to these choices. In this manner the participant selected a source of information, received a response, judged the viability of the response, and sought assistance from another source if the first response was inadequate. When a response promised further help, as from the psychologist, this was supplied. In one instance, the teacher was informed that she would have the opportunity to do informal testing. This was accomplished by distributing and explaining an informal test — the Purdue Perceptual-Motor Survey. Following the explanation of the scoring system, the participants viewed a videotape in which two children performed the required tasks of the test. Each participant scored the children in her test booklet. During this period, additional informal test results were distributed.

The discussion session at this stage focused on the conclusions reached regarding the specific learning disabilities of four of the eight children. Of major concern was the step-by-step process involved in the identification and diagnosis as well as the contributions of ancillary personnel in the process. The participants were encouraged to consider the possibilities for remediation within the framework of the public schools.

The last stage in the simulation package requires the participants to review the information collected on two of the children whose learning is impaired by slightly differing visual-perceptual problems. The participants then consider the practical opportunities available for remedial programs, utilize the available instructional materials, and plan a program for these two children. This stage was of primary importance, as it forced the participants to visualize the two boys in the classroom, consider the school organization, involve other staff members, and devise a program for the children.

A final discussion period followed this last stage. It covered the programs developed by the participating teachers, the problems in adapting the program to their situations, and the availability of specific instructional materials. The instructor stressed the importance of early identification, including the teacher's role in identification, diagnosis, and remediation.

The participants were asked to respond to two evaluation instruments specifically designed for this simulation. One instrument solicited opinions regarding the simulation technique and specific aspects of the total package. The other instrument was designed to assess the participants' ability to identify learning problems and seek proper sources of assistance.

RESULTS OF THE WORKSHOP

Reactions to the exercise were very favorable. An overwhelming majority of the participants rated the workshop as extremely worthwhile. Opinions regarding specific aspects of the simulation were also favorable, with the participants enthusiastic about the printed materials and content of the videotapes. The comments by the participants indicated that they had put in a full working day. The pace of the presentation seemed to leave some participants exhausted, but as one person commented, "this has been the best inservice workshop I've ever attended." Another participant likened the sequential nature of the workshop to a detective mystery in which everyone was an "educational" detective. This feeling was echoed by others during an informal gathering following the workshop. It was the feeling of the instructor that interest was maintained throughout the workshop by injecting the element of curiosity into the total package. The participants seemed to be aware that they needed to concentrate on both audiovisual and written materials in order to "solve the mystery."

The evaluation instrument designed to assess the teachers' ability to identify children with learning problems and seek the proper source of assistance was administered to a control group of teachers having similar backgrounds but not having experienced the simulation workshop. The control group had a mean score of 62 out of a possible 90. The experimental group attained a mean score of 75. The results were statistically significant in favor of those teachers participating in the workshop.

The general conclusions reached through analysis of the results of the evaluation instruments, the comments of the participants, and the observations of the instructor suggest that this type of simulation workshop provides an effective method of inservice training for regular classroom teachers.

REFERENCES

Barsch, R.: Perspectives on learning disabilities: The vectors of a new convergence. *Journal of Learning Disabilities*, Vol. 1, No. 1, January, 1968.

Bolton, D.: *Feedback in a Selection of Teaching Simulation*. Unpublished paper, University of Washington.

Boocock, S. S.: The effects of games with simulated environments upon student learning, Baltimore: Johns Hopkins, Dept. of Social Relations, Unpublished Doctoral Dissertation, 1966.

Cohen, K. J., W. Dill, and A. A. Kuen: *The Carnegie Management Game: An Experiment in Business Education,* Homewood, Illinois, Irwin Inc., 1964.

Cruickshank, D., and F. Broadbent: *The Simulation and Analysis of Problems of Beginning Teachers.* Final Report, Project No. 5-0798 U.S.O.E., 1968.

Culbertson, J. A.: Simulated situations and instruction: A critique, *Simulation in Administrative Training.* The University Council for Educational Administration, Columbus, 1960.

Educational Research Information Center (ERIC), Office of Education

Research Reports, U. S. Government Printing Office, Washington, 1967.

Hemphill, J. K., D. E. Griffiths, and N. Frederiksen: *Administrative Performance and Personality*. New York, Bureau of Publications, Teachers College, Columbia University, 1962.

Kersh, B.: The classroom simulator: An audiovisual environment for practice teaching. *Audiovisual Instruction*, November, 1961.

Sage, D.: *The Development of Simulation Materials for Research and Training in Administration of Special Education*, Project No. 6-2466, U. S. Department of H.E.W., November, 1967.

Twelker, P.: *Simulation: Status of the Field*, presented at the Conference on Simulation for Learning, Boston, Massachusetts, October, 1968.

NAME INDEX

SUBJECT INDEX

285